the things that we lost

the things that we lost

JYOTI PATEL

1 3 5 7 9 10 8 6 4 2

#Merky Books
20 Vauxhall Bridge Road
London SW1V 2SA

#Merky Books is part of the Penguin Random House group of companies whose addresses can be found at global.penguinrandomhouse.com

First published by #Merky Books in 2023

www.penguin.co.uk

A CIP catalogue record for this book is available from the British Library.

ISBN: 9781529186338

Typeset in 13.5/16 pt Garamond MT Std by Jouve (UK), Milton Keynes

Printed and bound in Great Britain by Clays Ltd, Elcograf S.p.A.

The authorised representative in the EEA is Penguin Random House Ireland, Morrison Chambers, 32 Nassau Street, Dublin D02 YH68

www.greenpenguin.co.uk

Penguin Random House is committed to a sustainable future for our business, our readers and our planet. This book is made from Forest Stewardship Council® certified paper.

the things that we lost

Prologue

It was a Friday morning in early October. The year was 1990. Avani sat on the periphery of her university campus, her hand moving across a page in her sketchbook. She often found herself surprised by what appeared on the paper when she let her mind wander out through the tip of a pen. On this occasion, what looked like an asymmetrical diamond was forming before her, its edges uneven. It was the shape of a country, she realised, of India.

She'd just come out of a lecture on algebraic structures, where the student sitting in front of her had turned to survey her several times, their eyes meeting without recognition. At the end of the hour, the student removed one of her shoes and socks and placed her bare foot on Avani's desk. She began to tell Avani all about her summer in Goa, and how she'd loved it so much that she felt compelled to get a tattoo of India scratched into her ankle.

Avani remained seated while a flurry of students moved around her. She stared at this stranger's tattoo in bemused silence, noticing how some of the ink had fallen out, how some had bled. The girl's eyes had a frantic gleam to them; she smelt of patchouli, spoke too fast, and finished by asking Avani when she'd moved to England from the *sacred land*. Avani didn't know how to respond. *I've actually never been to India* didn't feel right, but it was the truth, so she said it anyway. She packed away her books and stood to leave, trying her best to shrug away her new companion, but the girl followed, talking about how she'd spent a wholly transformative month in an ashram beside *the Ganges River.* It sounded so unfamiliar to Avani. She wanted to correct her. *The River Ganga,* she wanted to say. *To me, it's the River Ganga.* And to her parents, the river was *Gangaji*, a goddess. Avani's rendition was a mix of the names, an attempt to blend them together. The girl had still been yammering on when Avani simply turned and walked the other way, splitting their path in two.

She pulled a blue-ink fountain pen from her coat pocket and added a vein to the sketch, hoping that she was getting the shape of the river right, these waters that flowed thousands of miles away. She felt like a fraud, being eighteen and having never visited the place that so much of her identity was attributed to. One day, she hoped, she'd be able to greet India in its entirety, away from the romanticised version of it she so often met in Western art, away too from the sentimentality of the Bollywood films her mother cried into her chundri over. Avani's brother, Chand, had visited for the first time the previous summer. He'd come back with a pair of silver jhaanjhar for Avani, which she'd worn every day since. For a few weeks after his return, he'd been bursting with stories of near-lethal rickshaw rides in Delhi, mornings devouring idli and dosa with coconut chutney in Bangalore, the taste of juicy sitafar and papayu in Baroda. The photos he'd taken were alive with the spirit of the place; women selling garlands of marigolds outside temples, giant banyan trees holding centuries of secrets within their aerial roots, green bananas stacked high on brightly coloured carts, luscious pink bougainvillea curled around doorways as though bestowing good fortune. Avani's favourite had been the photo he'd taken from the window of a Tata-mobile in Jaipur, capturing a man lying horizontal on a parked scooter, his feet hanging off the back of it, his arms wrapped around the handlebars as he caught a quick kip, seemingly undisturbed by rush hour zooming past him. When Avani asked her brother why the majority of the photos he'd taken were of the streets, he'd told her: *People think the best part of India is found in the temples and the food and the valleys, but so much of India unfolds in the journey. When you travel from one state to the next. In the 'in between'.*

A light, playful voice drew Avani from these thoughts: 'What've you got there, Av?'

Avani slammed her sketchbook shut and looked up to see Elliot walking across the green, clutching two orange mugs. He brushed through the lawn towards her, the hem of his jeans growing dark with dew. A blue corduroy shirt Avani had never seen before hung loose on him, the sleeves rolled up, and his chocolate curls were held back from his face by a hairband that she recognised as her own. There had been such a change to him in the three weeks since they left home for university; he was already standing taller, no longer hunched, no longer looking apologetic for just existing, no longer trying to disappear. Having a roof over his head, and not having to hop between friends' sofas, park benches and hostels, had brought so much brightness back to his eyes, his cheeks, his soul. The weight of everything they left back in Harrow seemed to have unfastened itself from his shoulders. She noticed, too, that he'd look at people for longer now, instead of lowering his eyes when he spoke. The rhythm of his being felt slower, calmer, as if he had finally stopped running, as if he were at peace.

'Ah, come on, Av,' he said, sitting on the bench beside her, a grin stretching across his face.

She leafed past a flurry of colour until she landed on the right page. Elliot handed her a mug – which smelt of cardamom and ginger and home – then leaned over to take a look.

'India,' he said.

'Yes.'

'And that's Ganga.' His finger followed the blue line. 'The river you were telling me about? Where the cremations happen?'

'That's right.'

'We'll go and see her one day.' His murmured words were followed by a swift kiss on her temple. It had been more than six months now, but her body still responded with a quiet little thrill as his lips grazed her skin.

'This is great, by the way,' she told him, lifting her mug of chai. 'You've definitely got the hang of it.'

'Learned from the best. When's Chand meeting us?'

Avani glanced at the clock tower across the green. 'Eleven.' It was ten past. She scanned the campus, looking for a figure in her brother's trademark denim jacket and Doc Martens. 'Maya's coming too,' she said, taking another sip. 'I convinced her to skive.'

'Excellent. What're we getting up to?'

'He won't say. It's meant to be a surprise. He's taken the whole day off from work.'

'I bet it's a gig, knowing Chand.'

'At eleven in the morning?'

'Fair point. He left this at my place, by the way,' Elliot said, pulling a Canon F-1 from his backpack.

'When was he at your digs?'

'Couple of days ago.' She narrowed her eyes as he lifted the camera, fiddling with the dial. 'He came by to drop off the new Black Sabbath album.'

'And he didn't think to come and see me? His own sister?'

'We've always known he likes me more than you, eh? Smile.'

'Shan't.' But a grin was growing against her lips.

'Oh, go on, Av. The sun's falling on you. You look gorgeous.' Heat rose to her cheeks and he took the photo just as she succumbed to laughter.

They sat in the autumn sunshine, sipping sweet chai, watching students rushing to their morning lectures. There was something so comforting about being outside of the flurry and in something else, just the two of them, together. They chatted about the classes they had just come from, about the party they'd been to the night before, about the new friendships beginning to take shape, Elliot running a thumb over Avani's knuckles absent-mindedly as he spoke. The music department was round the corner, and the wind began to carry the sound of someone playing the piano, filling the space around their words. They fell silent then, listening for a while, until a car horn broke the spell, whipping through the air in short bursts.

The sound blasted towards them once more, longer this time. A black saloon was parked by the gate marking the edge of campus. Square headlights flashed white. 'What's this guy's problem?' Avani muttered.

Elliot's eyes were also focused in the direction of the car, a crease forming between them. 'Av,' he said, pushing their empty mugs into his backpack, 'I think that's Chand.'

She stood up for a better look. 'Can't be. He doesn't drive.'

The driver's face was obscured by large sunglasses. He wore a dark T-shirt under a denim jacket, and was waving towards them.

'Oh my God,' Avani said, grabbing her bag. 'I think you're right.'

As they hurried over to the car, Chand performed an awkward three-point turn, stalling twice. Maya came into view in the passenger seat, dancing to 'Get a Life'. She whooped when she saw Avani and Elliot approaching.

'No way,' Avani said, pulling Chand's door open. 'Is it yours?'

'I was aiming to get it in time to help you move,' he told her, removing his sunglasses as he stepped out of the car. Avani slid straight into his seat. 'Didn't quite manage to pass my test on the first go, though.'

'Or the second,' Maya murmured, reaching over to hug Avani.

Elliot clapped Chand on the back. 'I didn't even know you were learning, man.'

'It's so cool,' Avani said, her hands taking in the shape of the steering wheel. Avani and Chand's parents didn't drive, so they'd never savoured the freedom of a car. Avani scrambled to the back and Chand fired the ignition, turning into the main road. Maya topped up her eyeliner in the side-view mirror, then passed the kohl over to Avani. 'Where are we heading?' she asked, turning to Chand.

'Let's go to the beach,' Elliot said.

'Oh my God, yes,' Avani said. 'I haven't seen the sea in ages.'

Chand rummaged through the glovebox by Maya's knees then dumped an A–Z on her lap. 'Can you direct me out of London?' He swapped her mixtape for a Guns N' Roses album as he spoke.

'Ugh, come on, Chand. Not this again,' Maya muttered, nodding to the stereo. She leafed through the A-Z, sighing. Avani leaned forward, noticing a key chain hanging from the rear-view mirror. From it, orange, white and green stripes ran across the same shape she'd seen on the stranger's foot, the same shape she'd traced in her sketchbook earlier, the shape of India, quietly with them, always. She reached out to tap it with her index finger before Chand murmured: 'Avani, put your seat belt on.' Then, he adjusted the mirror and said: 'What d'you reckon, Ell?'

In the back, Elliot was staring out of the window, watching the city shoot past, his head tilted back slightly. 'Love it, man. Really suits you.'

'I'll teach you guys to drive in this thing if you like, at the weekends.'

'Yes please,' Maya said.

'Me too?' Elliot asked.

'Of course,' Chand said, glancing at him. 'You're family, bro.'

Avani's gaze flicked back to Elliot. He took a deep, slow breath, as though he were inhaling the words, ones Avani knew would mean the world to him.

The grey of the capital slowly gave way to pockets of green. Maya started to moan about the music again, pleading with Chand for some Soul II Soul. When he finally appeased her, she danced in her seat, Elliot humming along from the back, Chand thrumming his fingers on the steering wheel. Avani, meanwhile, basked in the sun that fell through her window, wondering if it was possible to feel any happier. She was finally away from home, with her best friend in the same digs, her boyfriend studying at the same university, her brother living and working just a few miles down the road. They were still in London, but so exquisitely far from the suburb they all grew up in. She was free, they were all free, finally. With a quick glance towards Chand, she unbuckled her seat belt and leaned against Elliot's torso, pulling his arms around her as she lay back, her head against his chest. She watched the road unfurl before them for a while then closed her eyes, soaking in the moment as they skived off from their new lives for the day, a trail of music in their wake. The wide expanse of life was waiting for them, yet unwritten, and so gloriously full of possibility.

I

July 2017

Nik is searching for his grandfather. He wanders up the hospital corridor, peering into rooms, scanning the faces of dozing patients. Around him, an unusual humidity builds slowly in the morning air. Pools of light stretch over the vinyl floors of the hospital and its scent takes on a new quality in the heat – disinfectant mingled with pollen. It makes Nik wrinkle his nose as he weaves from room to room. His grandfather was moved only yesterday, and Nik cannot seem to recall where his new bed is. The longer he searches, the faster he walks, as though he's racing against some invisible clock whose tick grows quicker, teasing him, telling him today is the day that he'll be just a little too late.

He breathes a sigh of relief when he finally notices his grandfather in a bed at the end of the corridor, still asleep. An untouched breakfast tray hovers a few inches above his stomach. He's clothed in the white gown he's been wearing for weeks now. Nik recognises the patient in the bed directly opposite as the same one who shared a room with his grandfather earlier in the week. He ignores Nik's wave, mutters about visiting hours, and lifts his newspaper higher over his eyes.

Nik sinks into the large chair by his grandfather, digs

out a couple of enamel camping mugs from his backpack and pours two cups of chai from the flask he's brought with him.

'Too bloody hot for tea,' the other patient mutters, turning the page of his newspaper.

'Sure you don't want to try it again?' Nik asks. 'I've gone easy on the ginger today.'

'Not with all those extra spices in there. Scratches the old throat.'

'Well, lemme know if you change your mind.'

Nik looks back at his grandfather to see that he's stirring. His fine white hair is ruffled, his dark eyes tired. 'Fancy seeing you here.' Nik holds out his fist, which his grandfather bumps with a chuckle. It's new, this small greeting, something Nik has been doing to lighten the weight of his grandfather's recent fragility.

'Morning, beta,' his grandfather says, his voice still thick with sleep. 'Su chaale che?'

'All good, Bapu. More importantly –' Nik sinks into the chair by the window – 'how're you?' His phone buzzes in his pocket and he pulls it out to glance at the screen.

'A little better today. Is that lovely Layla who's writing to you?'

Nik looks up to see his grandfather running his fingers through his hair, trying to smooth it into place. 'A little better today' was what he'd said just before that second heart attack struck.

'You need to say if you don't feel good, Bapu, yeah? Has the doctor come and seen you today?'

'Not yet.' He rubs the specks of white growing evenly around his mouth, which Nik knows must feel unfamiliar to him. Nik has never seen him with so much as a hint of stubble before his admission to hospital. Sometimes, he'd shave twice in one day. Nik watches him, worry pulsing through his stomach. He slides his phone back into his jeans and pokes around the breakfast tray.

'You should eat something.' Nik picks up a cooling cup of milky tea – 'This stuff looks rank' – and hands his grandfather one of the enamel camping mugs of chai instead. 'Made you some proper chai and flapjacks, if you're hungry?'

'Oh, go on then,' his grandfather says, sitting up slightly. 'Twist my arm.'

Nik digs further into his backpack and retrieves an old ice-cream tub filled with flapjacks. Dark chocolate spills over the top of each square, still slightly sticky from a morning in the oven.

'Now you're talking,' the other patient calls from across the room.

'So it's not too hot for flapjacks, yeah?' Nik tries to keep a straight face as he gets to his feet.

'Never,' the other patient says, picking out a large slice. 'Ta very much, lad.'

Nik's grandfather doesn't say much but sips his chai and chews on pieces of flapjack, blinking sleepily. They sit together in silence, listening to whirring buses through the open window. Every few minutes a nurse shuffles past the room or the patient opposite mutters and turns the page of his newspaper. When they finish eating, Nik helps himself to a wad of paper hand towels from the nearby sink, the patient opposite watching him closely and grumbling about the NHS being overstretched. Nik bites back a smirk and takes a couple more. He draws the curtain around his grandfather and helps him brush his teeth and shave, using a little grey bowl as a makeshift sink. Nik isn't sure if it's because he's studying his grandfather's face more often now that he's in hospital, or if it's the strain of multiple heart attacks, but he seems to grow older with each passing day. He looks as though he's shrinking into himself. The Gujarati word his mother had used to describe him just the previous night was 'sukaygaylu'. Nik thinks of how he'd translate that into English. The closest word he can find is 'shrivelling'.

His grandfather has always been so laid-back, so pensive, so incredibly warm, with all of his quiet authority emanating from his appearance; his six-foot frame, the way he dresses in a shirt and pressed trousers, the way his rich, velvety voice draws attention to him whenever he speaks. Seeing him horizontal, stripped of his height, his voice hoarse, his eyes tired, makes Nik worry for the first time that he might not make it. That he might be slipping away.

Nik can normally tell how well his grandfather is doing by how chatty he is, how much he uses his hands when he talks, how many questions he asks. So Nik prods him, asking how long he reckons the heatwave will last, what he thinks of Nik's plans to leave London at the end of the summer for university. They have these conversations often, Nik using them to measure how much strength his grandfather holds each day. Today, his answers are short, his questions half-hearted. His voice sounds deeper, as if he has to reach further into himself to retrieve it. It makes discomfort pulse in Nik's stomach. Nik notices that he seems distant, ravelled in contemplations, as though distracted by some quiet thought gaining momentum in his mind. There is a pocket of silence which Nik holds himself back from filling, until eventually it comes.

'When's your mum arriving, beta?' his grandfather asks, stealing a glance at the door.

'Not for a while, I reckon,' Nik says, checking his phone. 'She was still asleep when I left.' He lowers his voice and adds: 'D'you wanna talk about yesterday before she gets here?'

Silence.

'You were telling me about my dad, Bapu, remember?'

'Elliot. Yes –' his grandfather's eyes seem to focus for a moment – 'this afternoon. Don't let me forget.'

Nik nods, his index finger running along the veins of his grandfather's right hand. He doesn't want to wait until later. Since their unfinished conversation the previous day, he's been desperately waiting for this moment. He tries to find a route in. 'Was this what you wanted me to get, Bapu?' He fishes out a silver key from the back pocket of his jeans.

'Ha, beta. That's it. Keep it safe.'

Nik nods, winding it around the chain that holds his house keys. Last night, he'd gone straight from the hospital to his grandfather's home, then up to his study, and pulled his desk from the window. As instructed, Nik had plucked a little silver key from a nail hammered into the back of the desk. His grandfather had told him the key would lead him to something that once belonged to his father. In the hours that have followed, Nik's imagination has jumped and skipped ahead, expecting the key to lead to a box of his father's old things, perhaps some of the poetry he used to write.

'You know, I think I'll go home today,' his grandfather says, looking out of the window.

Nik feels his throat clam up when his grandfather takes his hand. It's a regular occurrence but something feels different today. His grandfather is holding on tighter than usual, and it contrasts with his languid air. It reminds Nik of how, when he was younger, his grandfather's fingers would curl around his hand whenever they approached a pedestrian crossing. Nik grips back. He clears his throat before speaking. 'Not today, Bapu. They still want to keep you for a bit longer.'

'Today, beta.'

Nik doesn't know how to respond to this. Instead, he reaches for his grandfather's other hand. They sit this way, drenched in warm silence, content just to be close to one another, until morning fades.

Avani stands by the banister and peers down the stairs, unsure of what she's looking for. The house smells sweet, like butter and chocolate. Silence greets her.

She yawns, the gentle pull of sleep still clouding her mind. It's later than she would like; her son's already at the hospital. The sound of the front door being locked hours earlier had woken her briefly. She recalls hearing him pad towards her room earlier still that morning, push the door open, then close it after a couple of seconds and shuffle back downstairs. She sensed him watching her in that small moment of stillness and curled herself tighter into her duvet. Now, she rubs her eyes, annoyed with herself for claiming a few extra hours of sleep while her son headed over to the hospital on his own.

The mild headache that arrives as soon as she wakes is beginning to land, the one that only fresh air and food seem to stifle. She knows she should head over to the hospital to take her father an early lunch. But then the conversation they had the previous night floats back into focus, the whispers they exchanged tying her stomach into a knot, her chest tingling with the weight of those words. The mere thought of her father, still unwell, still in hospital, is almost too much for her to bear. She is not yet ready to face another day. She decides that she'll let Nik and her father spend some time alone. She'll go for a quick jog and meet them later. So she throws on her running gear, eats a slice of flapjack that Nik's left in the kitchen, and steps out into the summer air. It's unusually hot; there's only the slightest hint of a breeze and when the clouds move out of the way of the sun it throws light generously across Harrow, casting the hilly streets in a late-morning glow. Avani squints against the sun at first, but then relaxes and turns her face towards it.

Roxeth Hill is quiet at this hour; commuters have tucked into their day's work, the children are all in their classrooms, few cars and even fewer people pass her. There is peace in the air, but she does not hear it. 'Paradise City' bleeds clumsily into 'Return of the Mack' against her ears. Her music is on shuffle and a different rendition of her youth steps forward to greet her with each song that plays.

She ignores the sharp pain growing around her weak

knee and the stiffness that hasn't quite eased in her hips, forcing herself to focus on her surroundings as she passes Nik's college, and then the kitsch tea room on the hill – the one she's promised herself she'll go to one day but still hasn't. She painted it once, decades ago, on a hand-sized canvas with acrylics that were almost dry in their tubes. Across the street, the boys from Harrow School walk up the hill in twos, a navy-blue army complete with straw hats. Their shoulders bump against each other as they walk. They haven't yet broken for summer. One chews on a cereal bar. She thinks of the sweet scent lingering around her home this morning and wonders how early Nik must have woken up to make those flapjacks.

Avani slows when she reaches the street parallel to her father's home, and toys with the idea of taking a little detour to check on it. But the thought of seeing the house empty and locked does something unpleasant to her breathing. She'll skip it. He'll be back soon, she tells herself. Maybe even by the end of next week, in time for his birthday. She forces him out of her mind once more, running a little faster. She knows she should double back now but can't bring herself to do so. Before she's fully aware of it, she's approaching Kingsbury, and finds herself heading towards the road that slices right through the middle of Fryent Park. This is where she allows herself to let go, sprinting with all of her might, the last week rushing out of her, the summer breeze wicking past her skin and lifting everything away.

It is amid this that the conversation she had with her father the night before comes back to her, nudging its way through the quiet of her thoughts. This is what she's running from, she realises, these words that she still hasn't allowed herself to return to or process.

Her father had been picking his way through a box of dhokra that she'd prepared, his eyes on the darkening sky outside the window, when he murmured: *I've been thinking about her a lot recently, chakli.*

Who's that, Puppa?

Your mother. She's been on my mind. And Elliot, too.

Silence. Avani stood up for something to do. *Dad –*

Sit down, beta. The strength in his voice had surprised her. *I must ask for your forgiveness.*

Don't be ridiculous. For what?

You know what.

His gaze had pulled the air from her. Under it, she felt herself reduced to the six-year-old who would hide behind his legs, wondering why she was being shouted at, to the teenager who would climb out of her bedroom window to safety, to the woman who never wanted to go back home, even though home also meant seeing him. It had terrified her, him talking like this, as if he was running out of time, as if this was the end. She didn't want to think of a world without him.

I should have found a way to leave. There was such pain in his eyes.

Puppa, bus. There's nothing to forgive, she said, louder, in a tone she hoped would settle the matter. *And I know you couldn't leave. I know it wasn't an option. You did everything you could. Skipped shifts so I wouldn't be alone with her. Tried so hard to reason with her. I saw all of it.* She spoke the words quickly, wanting to get them out and away from her as fast as possible.

He shook his head, wiped his cheeks. *I should have left. Forgive me.*

She followed her father's gaze to see Nik striding back over to them, throwing a purple bag of chocolate buttons in the air with one hand, then catching it with the other. He paused by the open door to let a nurse through, smiling at her as she passed.

Avani, her father said. *Please.*

Avani ignored the look of desperation on his face. She denied him this one ask. *There's nothing to forgive, Puppa. Nothing at all.*

Now, her vision blurs, clearing with a blink. She runs faster still, as if trying to free herself from the shadow of this memory. It's then that something catches in her chest, crumpling. A piece of her – that's held her taut all of these years – slumps and folds in on itself, like a plant stake in her core. It has broken in her and she's running the fastest she thinks she's ever run, as if she's about to take flight. Her music grows louder; she can almost feel Clare Torry's vocals in the air around her, meeting her, pushing her forward, the crescendo just seconds away. Then, just as she looks over her shoulder to check for turning cars, the song stops. Another sound dances through her headphones. Her phone is ringing. Her trance, broken. She slows down, presses her left earbud and hears her son's worried breath against her ear.

'Mum,' he says, 'it's me.' And in the white space between those three small words, she hears the pain he's holding back, the howl trapped in his throat, the silent cry that tells her it's all over.

*

'What do we do now, Mum?'

Nik presses the front door shut and turns to his mother. They've just arrived home from the hospital for the last time and are standing in the hallway. She brushes past him and takes a seat on their staircase, her arms wrapping around her shins, her hands resting limp by her ankles. It is late evening now, and she is still in her running clothes. Like Nik, she doesn't seem ready to proceed further into their home. Their shoes are still on and the lights are off. Darkness envelops them. The silence of their home grows louder, singing to them, taunting them with its emptiness. Nik's been dreading this moment. To him, it is inconceivable for them to simply go home and pick up where they left off.

'Let's just sit, for a second,' his mother says eventually, her voice muffled against her knees. As her words settle into the air around them, there's a frantic knock on the door. Nik opens it to see his mother's best friend, Maya, staring up at him, her dark eyes already shining with the promise of tears. She embraces him then sits on the staircase beside his mother, taking her hand. His mother succumbs to a tide of emotion, Maya holding her together. Nik bites back tears himself and looks away, but the image of them together presses itself into his mind. They look like children, perched on the staircase. Like sisters. There is a vulnerability to his mother that he doesn't know what to do with. It causes a worry to rise in him that is so rich and heavy and deep that he cannot breathe for it. Now that his grandfather is gone, Nik has suddenly been promoted to a position he never wanted. The only other man in his mother's life is her brother, Chand, whom neither of them is close to. He will be here soon, with his wife and daughters. Nik's cousin sister Rajvi has already called to say they are not far. Before they get here, and now that there is someone with his mother, Nik tries to focus on the thought he's been batting away all afternoon. It's blurry, but when it comes, it takes the shape of a silver key. It's the one Nik showed his grandfather earlier, the one he'd instructed Nik to take from his study just yesterday, without properly explaining what it was for. Nik glances again at his mother. He'll head over to his grandfather's place now to try and figure out what the key is for, before grief digs its nails fully into him and makes the details of yesterday's conversation hazy. But just as he steps outside, a silver Mercedes parks up, blocking his mother's Volvo in. A gaggle of masis emerge from the car, Nik recognising one of them as a distant relative. She waddles towards him, places a cold, dry hand on his cheek, then pushes her way past him into his home.

Over the next few hours, extended family and friends who Nik only sees at weddings and Diwali appear in their masses, each depositing their shoes in the hallway and a bowl of food on the kitchen counter. Nik finds they have more bouquets of lilies than vases. Three bunches end up in a pressure cooker pot filled with water. The next two days blend into one. The fridge that's been almost empty for the past few weeks is suddenly full and their cupboards are bursting with packets of sev mamra and ganthiya. A pot of matar bhaat or pan of bateta nu shak seems to constantly simmer on their stove, spicing the summer air with a pinch of turmeric and rai, its scent weaving happily through their home. A photo of Nik's grandfather appears in a large frame on their mantel. A garland of brownish flowers that Nik can't name is placed over it. When he looks closer, he discovers that what he thought were flowers are actually twirly wood chippings. His mother calls it sandalwood.

Nik's told, by some random kaka who smells of peanuts, that he mustn't shave until thirteen days have passed. He nods but finds himself filled with an unexpected rage when, in the next breath, the man uses the word 'expired' to describe his grandfather, as if he's a furry lump of cheese that's been discovered at the back of their fridge. Nik excuses himself and tries to find a corner of quiet, but the buzz around their home cannot be outrun. His mates Will and Teo come to pay their respects at some point during this time. He takes them up to his room to find a masi he's never met before sitting on his bed, rubbing moisturiser into her feet, as she speaks a quick stream of Gujarati into a tiny mobile phone. She smiles at him, as if to let him know his interruption is forgiven.

The hollow tune of silence during those first few moments at home has now developed into a symphony made up of knocks on the front door, glasses of water clacking as they're placed on slate coasters, Sanskrit prayers being recited in a corner of the lounge which has turned into a makeshift mandir, windows being opened and closed, and even the more frequent flushing of their upstairs loo. Their home has come alive.

In the evenings, Nik hoovers up crumbs, grains of uncooked rice, sequins and petals from their wooden floors, sometimes navigating the head of the vacuum around the saris of lingering bas who, in his opinion, are overstaying their welcome. When they leave, taking the hum of the house with them, Nik retreats to bed, searching eagerly for sleep, willing it to find him, falling into lucid dreams that dance against his mind like ghosts. He greets the rising sun each morning with slow, blinking eyes after just a few hours of rest, his mind already heavy with thought. He is too full of energy to lie in. Instead, he looks for jobs to occupy himself with before the mourners arrive. No matter how many times he loops around their home in the small hours, searching for a task that'll distract him, he always ends up ironing the white salwaar kameez that his mother puts on each morning and throws into the washing machine each night.

Whenever he feels the itch of loss crawling under his skin, he changes direction. He sneaks over to Will's for a quick rollie or to Teo's for some FIFA or retreats to the kitchen to check if there is enough milk for the never-ending stream of chai they seem to be brewing. Even if there is plenty, he walks to the corner shop to pick up another pint, just to keep moving.

Death is something Nik could have sworn he had down; both his father and grandmother died before he was born. But it is only now that the true weight of grief fully settles down on him, pushing its claws deep into his chest. He realises that although he has grown up very aware of the vacant space the grip of death leaves behind, he's never actually experienced loss himself. He hasn't watched death snatch away someone who meant everything to him. In his naivety, he assumed that bereavement was simply an absence. Now, it dawns on him that it is an inescapable presence. This loss of his grandfather is always with him, like something feral has been suddenly thrust upon him. When it isn't howling in the night, it's gently tugging at his sleeve, reminding him it's there, exercising its right to his attention. In the rare moments when he's completely distracted, like when he's able to fall into happy dreams, his grandfather's death hits him sharp in the face, punishment for being occupied by another thought. He wakes, panicked, clutching at empty fistfuls of air, reaching desperately for what was once in its place. It's easier when grief plays the tugging creature, he decides, when it's there constantly – a dull ache sitting behind every movement and breath.

During this kaleidoscope of grief, where normality hangs suspended in mid-air, the only thing that seems to anchor Nik in place is the silver key, the one that he continues to turn over in his hands, feeling the thick weight of it, his fingers tracing its uneven edges, wondering, always wondering.

On the morning of his grandfather's funeral, he finds himself lying awake in bed, doing just this. As the sun rises slowly over the horizon, he replays his visit to the hospital the day before his grandfather died, the hushed conversation they'd had, wondering if there was something in it that he missed.

Look, Nikhu, I know your mum doesn't like talking much about your father. I've always kept quiet to respect her wishes. But you're old enough now, beta. There are some things you need to know.

Like what, Bapu?

They struggled, beta.

What d'you mean, like fought?

They struggled to be together. Your nani came round to it eventually, but it took some work. She cared too much about how it would look. She wanted Avani to marry a Gujarati boy.

But I thought they'd been mates since they were little?

Yes, beta, since they were children. But when they wanted to be together it became tough. Not only for your father but also for Avani. His family were . . . well . . . they were troublesome.

What d'you mean?

He had waved Nik's question away and said, instead: *He had a difficult childhood, beta. A couple of years after they got married, your father, he wasn't very well.*

Was it cancer? Nik asked automatically, having spent the last few weeks walking past hospital posters encouraging him to regularly check his privates for lumps. *I thought he died in a road accident.*

Well . . . yes, it was, his grandfather murmured, his eyes tired.

Nik picked at the skin around his thumb, waiting to see if he would go on. *It was an accident?* he asked, unsure if the confirmation referred to a car crash or cancer. His grandfather pressed his eyes shut. Nik could sense he was just about holding it together. *Bapu, don't worry, we don't have to talk about it*, Nik whispered.

He was a good man, beta, he said, taking Nik's hand. *He very much wanted to have children, but he passed before we found out your mum was pregnant. We thought it was the grief that was making her unwell. We didn't know you were in there until she was almost three months along.*

Nik knew this already but savoured each word

nonetheless. He could almost feel his grandfather turning the words around in his mouth, trying to find the right ones. *Nikhu,* he murmured eventually, taking a deep breath. *Listen. None of this is important, really. It's not what I meant to tell you. I have something of his. I shouldn't have kept it for so long, but I always thought, one day, it could be yours. I've been waiting for the right moment to give it to you. She's not going to be happy with me.* He glanced towards the entrance of the ward again.

What is it?

There's a key in my study. It hangs from a nail at the back of my desk.

There was a bustle at the door.

Go on, Bapu.

Nik's grandfather shook his head slightly, as if to silence him. His eyes were following a figure through the ward, towards them. Nik's mother. Her hair was gathered in a ponytail, a summer dress sweeping around her shins as she moved. She stopped to speak to a doctor.

Ah crap, she's early, Nik muttered.

Tomorrow, Nikhu. Remind me tomorrow. Promise me?

Of course, Bapu.

Don't let me forget.

Nik glanced again at his mother – they only had moments until she was within earshot. Nik's grandfather squeezed his hand, and when Nik looked up at him he saw an urgency in his grandfather's eyes that almost reduced him to tears. As his mother's sandals clacked louder towards them, Nik's grandfather whispered in Gujarati, so quiet that it almost wasn't there at all: *Chand will be able to tell you more than I can.*

2

July 2017

Nik's former stepfather exists only in the form of envelopes to him now, which live in a shoebox under his bed. Nik often wonders how someone who meant so much to him, who was so larger than life, could be reduced to scraps of paper. But it wasn't always that way. After Paul left when Nik was eleven, they would meet once a month, usually for a trip to the cinema, or at the park for a game of football. As the months ticked by their catch-ups became more infrequent, until one day Nik realised it had been almost a whole year since they'd last seen each other. By this point, his stepfather existed in the form of phone calls, four neat letters flashing on the screen of Nik's phone every now and again, but those too became few and far between. By the time Nik was fifteen, the biannual presents, always delivered by the postman, always wrapped in brown paper, were replaced by crisp twenty-pound notes tucked into generic birthday or Christmas cards. As far as Nik knows, his mother and stepfather fully cut ties around the same time that the presents stopped – after an awkward Christmas when, to Nik's delight, he received two identical Arsenal football shirts, one from each of them. Since then, the envelopes landing on Nik's doormat twice a year were all that was left – flat, four-cornered reminders of what once was.

It's therefore a total surprise when Nik spots his former stepfather's neat frame at the back of the funeral service. The sight of him fills Nik with unexpected comfort, flooding a dormant part of him with warm joy. It's Paul, he thinks. He's come back. Nik turns once more to catch a glimpse of the figure, trying to be certain if it's Paul he's seeing. He's older and greyer but it's him. It's actually him. Paul spots Nik staring at him, and gives him a small smile, nodding once. Nik wonders if he has just come in, or if he's been there all along – if he heard Nik's eulogy. The softness in Paul's eyes seems like a response to Nik's unspoken question, as though there is some sort of reverence passing between them. Before Nik can digest this, rows of relatives and friends seated between them begin to rise, blocking his view. Rajvi, Nik's eldest cousin sister, has finished her eulogy and has just instructed everyone to proceed outside. Nik's mother stands up beside him and heads towards the courtyard. Unsure of whether to move against the crowd and towards Paul, or outside towards his mother, Nik dawdles, eventually surrendering to the flow of people piling out into the thick summer air. He tries to fall into step with his mother, but Chand is in the way, as always. He's in a suit that's a size too large, and sports his signature combo of thick black frames with a permanent case of resting-bitch-face.

Nik scratches the collar of his shirt, tugging it away from his neck, hoping for a breeze. The rest of London is still riding a heatwave. To Nik, the last four days have been a blur of mugginess, insomnia and too many phone calls.

Four days, he thinks. It's only been four days. Before now, he'd never paid attention to how quick the turnaround was for Hindu funerals. When Will's nan died a couple of years ago, it took more than a month to bury her.

Though Paul is still bright in his mind, once Nik moves outside, he's overcome by a single thought, so devastating in its intensity that he can almost feel it piercing him: Bapu is gone. All that is left of him is ash.

The thought spins inside him like a hot coin, refusing to settle. It makes him feel nauseous. How has it all happened so quickly? The day after tomorrow, he'll board a plane to India, a country that, until now, has always felt worlds away – unreachable – to pour his grandfather's ashes into the River Ganga. Nik moves to a corner of the courtyard and doubles over, pressing his hands onto his thighs. His head pulses and something acidic rises in his throat. He closes his eyes and finds comfort in the darkness, the silence afforded to him. He feels a sudden detachment from himself, one he's never felt before, as if the space between his pupils and eyelids stretches for miles. As if he's standing at the very edge of something, looking out into a deep, never-ending darkness. There is peace here, in this nothingness. Then, the scent of honeysuckle drifts towards him and a hand caresses the spot between his shoulder blades, bringing him back.

'Come on, Nikhu,' Maya whispers, her breath quiet against his ear.

They stand in the middle of the courtyard as relatives begin to approach in a neat line, embracing them and whispering condolences. They're a sea of black and white; British mourners in their customary black and Hindu mourners in white. Yesterday, Nik's mother told him it signifies purity. Not knowing which to pick, Nik went for a white shirt with his favourite black Nehru jacket on top. It's much too hot to keep it on but he won't let himself remove it.

Maya leans over to Nik and murmurs, 'You okay, honey?'

'Hmm,' he says, nodding. She's in the same cotton salwaar kameez as his mother.

'Listen,' she whispers, 'Paul's here.'

'Yeah, I know,' Nik says, shifting his gaze to look at her properly. He notices her eyes look smaller and redder than usual, free from their usual layers of make-up. 'I just spotted him,' Nik tells her. 'I should warn Mum.' He turns to his mother, but Maya pulls him back.

'It's okay, she invited him. I just wanted to let you know, so it's not a surprise.'

'Mum invited him?'

She sighs. Her slick bob bounces slightly as she nods.

Nik feels an unexpected wave of warmth again when he notices Paul just three spaces away, tight-lipped, hands behind his back, performing awkward little bows as he greets the seven next of kin who he had once considered family. Paul passes Chand, his wife Rukmani and their three daughters. The twins, Sarita and Priya, smile politely but their elder sister Rajvi glares at him. The wave of warmth turns into nausea. Nik feels a part of him shutting down, as though his mind cannot hold both the depth of sadness of losing his grandfather and the giddy joy of seeing Paul at the same time. He finds himself caught in the violent space between the two, like being swept out to sea by a rip current. Nik does not know what to do with the nerves fizzing their way down to his fingertips, the sensation that a large, dry mass is stuck at the back of his throat, and the pins and needles rushing down to his legs. His body is preparing for battle. He's overwhelmed by how this conflict has caused such a physical reaction in him, as though the restlessness that has been simmering silently since his grandfather's death has suddenly boiled over.

He takes a deep breath and looks up to see Paul standing in front of his mother. He cradles her elbows, and Nik recalls how he would greet her that way each day when she was home from work.

'Thank you for coming,' his mother says, not quite meeting Paul's gaze.

'Of course.' Paul rubs the top of her arms before turning to Nik. Everyone is watching them; Rajvi has stepped out of the line to face them, and it's clear now that it is Nik, not his mother, that Paul was most eager to see again. They stare at each other for a long moment, Nik aware of something growing behind Paul's eyes. His former stepfather is unable to contain a smile, and even lets out a tiny, dry chuckle. There it is.

'Kid, you got tall,' he says, putting one hand on Nik's shoulder, which stands a few inches above his own. They're too relaxed, these words. Overfamiliar and stretched out like dough in Paul's American accent. Nik doesn't know what to say. They are caught in an almost-embrace, just two small movements away from falling into a hug, and Nik knows he could simply lift an arm and move a step forward to close the circuit. But he freezes.

Up close, Paul looks different to how Nik remembered him. The beard Paul tried out for size after the break-up is gone. Nik can't get over the fact that Paul is shorter than him now. The Paul that exists in Nik's memory had always been bigger than him, in a permanent and indisputable way. He'd always literally looked up to his stepfather. Even though it's just a couple of inches, this shift reminds Nik of how much time has passed. How much has changed. He opens his mouth to speak. Nothing comes.

The moment folds and slips away.

Paul smiles softly at him, squeezes his shoulder, and disappears into the crowd, taking Nik's gaze with him.

Avani heads towards her son's friends, who are sitting on a low wall on the boundary of the courtyard, deep in conversation.

'Hey, Auntie,' Teo says, getting up to give her a hug. This surprises her, so it takes her a moment longer than it should to return the gesture and wrap her arms lightly around him.

Will slides over so that she can sit between them. They're both dressed in smart dark suits, watching her with concern in their eyes. For the first time, she sees the boys that her son's grown up with as young men.

'Thank you for being here today,' she says, 'for supporting Nikhil.'

'Of course. Rohan was a proper ledge,' Will tells her.

Avani notices that Teo's attention keeps gravitating towards her eldest niece Rajvi, who's standing just a few metres from them. She remembers Nik teasing him once, years ago, about a crush Teo had on her. Curiously, this endears Teo to Avani even more. In the jumble of funeral admin and loss that seems to take up every part of her, it feels refreshing – almost hopeful – for this reminder that, in a world running parallel to hers, life goes on. There is room for more than just grief.

'Well done on finishing your exams, by the way,' she says. 'Big plans for the summer?'

Will tells her about a trip to Zante he has planned with his girlfriend, but Avani is not paying attention because her son is coming back out into the courtyard, his head low. He's looked dazed all day, as though he's only half here. He is about to walk straight into Chand. When he notices this, he turns to go back the way he came. It only takes a moment for Chand to catch up with him. He grabs Nik by the elbow and speaks to him, or at him, it appears. Avani can see her son trying to free himself from the conversation. She makes a note to have a word with her brother and tell him to back off; he's been pushing Nik around more than usual since he arrived from Leicester on the evening of their father's death.

She decides to get to the point with the boys. 'Listen, I don't know if Nikhil mentioned, but we're all heading back to our place for some food in a bit. Though I think it might be good for him to go and do something normal later. Why don't you guys go out this evening, if you like?'

They both stare at her, as though they've misheard. Then, Teo says, 'Uh, yeah, if that's cool?'

Will opens his mouth to speak, but then a look passes between the boys. Teo's jaw is set. They're both watching someone approaching. She can sense a sudden air of protection in their gaze, a sense of animosity for who is coming. She guesses it must be Chand but when she skims the crowd she sees Paul making his way towards them.

'Excuse me for a sec,' she says, a flicker in her chest as her eyes meet Paul's.

'Hello, Avani.' His words are loud and smooth. His smile feels too large for the occasion.

'Yes, hello.' She steers Paul over to a corner of the courtyard where they're hidden from view by a concrete colonnade. His hair is longer than he ever wore it when they were together. It's salt-and-pepper now and slicked back. He wears an expensive-looking suit and an aftershave that's rich with bergamot. The scent grabs her by the throat. It's heavy, holding the day they met, the home they shared, the way it all fell apart, just in one breath.

'How're you doing?' His eyes are fixed on her and she notices just how blue they are in the light. She hadn't been able to acknowledge him properly earlier when he greeted her in front of her family. Now, as she stares up at him, she thinks of how much his eyes look like two perfectly round, dark lakes. She used to tell him this, used to tell him that staring into them made her feel as though she were immersing herself in water.

She shifts her weight so that there is distance between them without having to step back. 'I'm fine, thank you. Just getting on with it,' she says.

'I have to head off, sadly, but wanted to check in before I left.'

She finds his gaze too difficult to meet. It's as though she can feel the pity pouring out of him and ebbing towards her. She looks away and tries to make her voice as flat as possible. 'Yes, well, thank you for coming.'

'Of course.'

Silence. Avani scans the crowd over Paul's shoulder, but she can feel him watching her. Her eyes meet his, reluctantly, and she knows he has more to say.

'What is it, Paul?'

'Av, listen. If you need anythi—'

'Thank you. I'll be fine.'

Paul nods, turns to check what she's fixated on, and then says, 'I was wondering if you'd be okay with me dropping Nik a text at some point. Maybe grabbing a coffee with him.'

Her mind wanders back to Will and Teo and the defensiveness in their glare as Paul approached. That must be rooted in something. He was part of their lives too; she remembers them playing football with him on Sunday mornings, and Paul picking them up from school occasionally before it all ended. She wonders if he recognises them now that they're grown, or if he even remembers them at all.

'Av?'

'He doesn't drink coffee,' she says quickly, trying to make up for the prolonged silence. 'But yes, send him a text. See what he says. His number's still the same.'

Paul nods.

'I hope you know you don't have to ask my permission. Your relationship with Nikhil was, and should always have remained, separate from you and me.'

When he speaks, his words are careful and measured: 'I didn't want to step on anybody's toes.'

Avani's expression hardens slightly as the words sink in. She hears the question folded neatly within the statement, like a little origami dove. How unnecessary. She finds herself trying very hard not to glance down at his left hand, for a piece of metal catching the light. Instead, she thinks of how best to respond without giving too much of herself away.

'He's an adult now, Paul,' she says, adjusting a bangle on her wrist, her voice clipped. Then she excuses herself and moves back towards the safety of the crowd.

Nik opens his eyes to darkness, half of his mind trying to clutch back the dream that he's been plucked from, the other half trying to decipher what woke him. He feels himself slipping back towards a warm, dewy sleep while sitting upright in bed. An aftertaste of the dream lingers in the periphery but reaching for it is like trying to grasp handfuls of smoke.

He looks at his phone and realises he's only been asleep for a couple of hours. He rubs his face and lies back in bed. He got home from the shisha bar at around eleven and had fallen asleep on top of his bed covers with his shorts still on. His T-shirt and socks sit in a cold bundle on the floor. He scrolls through his messages, his breath shallow, checking if Paul has tried to contact him. Nik doesn't have his number saved any more, so can't reach out himself. He is quietly devastated that they didn't get to speak properly, that Paul slipped away from the funeral and out of his life once again so easily. He stares at the blank screen, waiting. It's then that he realises what woke him. Voices. Snapping at each other. Downstairs. He swings out of bed and pushes his door open. A light is on in the hallway.

His mother's hushed voice lingers in the space between a whisper and a murmur: 'His results come out next month.'

Chand isn't keeping his voice down though, his arrogant tone carrying up the stairs. 'But why History? What an utter waste of time. Doesn't he generally do okay at school?'

'He's top of his year. He's smart enough to study whatever he wants.'

'Then why History? What can he do with that? He'll come out of university with a mammoth loan and no job prospects.'

'Rubbish. I know plenty of people who've studied humanities and got decent careers out of it. Do you remember Pau—'

'That's not the point, ben. The world is all about tech now. Tell him to study Computing, or Engineering, or Data Science. That's where the money is. And there are some wonderful graduate schemes specifically for minorities. He's too smart for History.'

Nik leans against the banister that curves over their landing. He glares at the back of Chand's head.

His mother tucks a strand of hair behind her ear, like she does when she's had enough. 'It's not all about money. That's not how I've raised him.'

'Listen, I'm just trying to look out for him. Puppa and Mumma didn't work so hard just to watch their grandkids toss about. Sarita and Priya have only just graduated and they're already earning –'

'That's great for the girls, but Nikhil's got very different priorities and he's not tossing about.'

'Right. Well, that's between you two. I do hope he's on the right path, Avani. I must say, I think it's rather disrespectful to go and get pissed like that after Puppa's funeral. And at a hashish bar too. Honestly. He should have been here.'

'I told him to go, actually,' Nik's mother says, her voice rising to meet her brother's. 'He's worked bloody hard and he hasn't let off any steam at all this summer. And it's called shisha, by the way.'

'Really, Avani? At Puppa's funeral?'

'After Puppa's funeral. Chand, what's this really about? Come on, spit it out.'

'Actually, I'll regret it if I don't say. You might want to tell him to be careful with that girl he's been hanging around with. I saw some pictures of them together on Rajvi's Facebook page and they looked rather cosy.'

Silence. Layla appears in Nik's mind. His stomach turns icy. What an actual prick.

'God. You're unbelievable,' Nik's mother says.

'Excuse me?'

'Do not snoop around my son. We don't –'

'Oh, don't be so difficult, Avani. Now that Puppa is gone I feel I have a duty of –'

'Chand, that's enough.'

Nik holds his breath. He's standing very still, not daring to move.

'Of course I know about her. I've met her. And do you know who else has? Puppa. He'd be appalled with you right now.'

'Avani, you've misunderstood me.'

'No, I think I understand you perfectly. I'm disgusted with you. Stop projecting your own shit onto my son.'

'What on earth does that mean?'

'Would you be saying this if she was Gujarati?'

'Who?'

'Layla. The girl Nikhil's seeing.'

Nik's heard enough. He closes the bedroom door behind him, not bothering to do so quietly, and slips back into bed. He removes his shorts, kicking them onto the floor, and watches a thin strip of light move across his wall from a gap in his curtains.

Chand has always picked apart his decisions, but Nik's never heard him speak so bluntly, so viciously, until now. He lies still, trying to catch snippets of the conversation unfolding downstairs. Their voices rise. Nik can just about make out muffled speech. When his mother finally asks Chand, loudly, what he's here for, Nik hears his uncle say that he can't come to India with them after all. He has a meeting with investors that cannot be rearranged. They'll have to scatter the ashes without him. Good, Nik thinks. It'll be easier without him there, anyway.

He turns over in bed, trying very hard to block out the fact that the memory which rises in his mind when he thinks of his grandfather is no longer the last time he saw him alive, but the image of him in a coffin, grains of rice and flowers placed carefully around him, how cold he felt – like he'd been pulled from a still lake – when Nik rested chokha na ladva in his palms. Nik closes his eyes, trying to draw back his grandfather's warmth, his voice, his smile. He cannot fathom how someone so truly loved could be reduced to literal dust.

Despite sleep inching closer towards him, Nik doesn't allow himself to fully drift off until he hears the front door slam shut, and the sound of his uncle's Jaguar purring its way back into the night.

3

July 2017

Avani stares across the River Ganga, trying her best to put what she's seeing into words. Water. Sky. Trees. Locals. Tourists. Bells. Orange. Green. Blue. This is something she has always struggled with – trying to summon words when she feels overwhelmed.

Years ago, when her husband died, she told her father that she couldn't find the right words simply because there were too many languages in her head: Gujarati, a pinch of Swahili from her parents' time in Kenya, some French from school, English, of course. When she's drained, the words from each language blend together. When distracted, she becomes very literal, referring to the sky as 'upstairs' or the tyres on her car as simply 'feet'. When nervous, the words jump and skip over each other, and she can't immediately tell which language they belong to. She told her father how, when she was sixteen, she kept saying *ndio* instead of *oui* during a French oral exam. *The languages*, she told her father, *they mix and blend. It must be because I think in feelings, not words.* But that was only part of the truth. The other part is that what happened to her words when her husband died wasn't at all the same as when she had exam nerves, nor was it the same as thinking about the sky as upstairs or wheels as feet. The silent truth was that she was paralysed by what had happened, frozen. The guilt she felt slammed shut her right to communicate with others, like a hot, angry gale. The words didn't fall between the gaps of one language and another. They simply disappeared.

Her thoughts ebb towards her son beside her and to the eulogy he gave at her father's cremation back home. It was beautiful and reminded her of how he, unlike her, has always had such a way with words. Hearing her father described through the prism of her son's devotion to him had nudged something inside of her, clearing space for a love that she didn't think could grow any bigger. But today he's barely said a word. There are dark circles around his eyes and the beard she still hasn't got used to grows surprisingly evenly around his face. She worries for him, so deeply that she feels herself shuddering slightly, like an old car on the brink of stalling. More than anything, she worries about how he will face this next chapter of his life, if he will be able to heal from this loss before he leaves home, before he's faced with the project of becoming. She'd had her husband, then just her boyfriend, with her every step of the way through university. Their son, on the other hand, will be walking away from home and into the unknown more alone than he's ever been.

She glances at him once more. He's staring across the river, deep in thought, unblinking. She wants to ask him what he's feeling. What he's thinking. If he's afraid, too. She wants to hold him, tight, in the way she couldn't when he was a newborn. She opens her mouth, but the words do not come. Now is not the time.

It devastates her that this is his first taste of India – the country that they belong to but in which they have no living relatives or friends. She thinks about how it felt coming to India for the first time herself. It wasn't the four-week tour from Kochi to Amritsar that her husband had secretly planned as a celebration for their third wedding anniversary, which she'd only discovered after his death. No, her first time in India, her supposed motherland, was as a shaken, seven-stone, twenty-six-year-old widow, here to pour her husband's ashes in the very river that dances before her now. She remembers her mother telling her not to open her mouth as she haggled with rickshaw drivers on their way to the river, Avani clutching her husband's ashes in a dark blue urn. *They'll hear your accent and charge us more for being foreigners*, her mother had said. Of course, Avani hadn't seen any of the sights her husband had planned for them, not the Golden Temple nor the Taj Mahal nor the elephants and tigers in Bandipur Forest. Instead, India came to her in a warp of humidity, jet lag and grief. She realises, the thought trapped painfully in her throat, that her son is experiencing his first taste of India the same way she did.

She came back sooner than she'd expected after that first visit, just six weeks later, still unaware of the life growing silently inside her, to scatter her mother's ashes in the same spot as her husband's. It was a stroke that claimed her mother, the woman that Avani thought would live forever, a force so strong that nothing could shake her. Avani had asked her brother if they could please go to another part of the river to scatter their mother's ashes, but he wouldn't have it. She didn't want her mother near Elliot. She wanted her husband to rest peacefully. As she'd watched her brother pouring their mother's ashes into the river, there had been a moment when she had felt something that made her skin crawl. It was relief, sitting quietly at the very centre of her grief. A seed from which she could rebuild herself and the things her mother had taken from her.

Earlier today, she broke tradition to stand with her son and scatter her father's ashes in the same spot. She thinks about this – about her husband, her mother, her father, all in the river before her, a river so far from home. The thought of another relative, one she never met, one who may well have already been lain to rest, rises in her. He comes to her, from time to time, the one they tried so hard to find. She doesn't often allow herself to think of him, to sit with the uncertainty of what became of him, so the thought makes her feel cold, despite the humidity of July in India, and she watches the smooth skin on her arms surrender to an army of goose bumps, as though tiny javelins are piercing her. She shivers and brings to mind the people she still has around her – friends, extended family, loved ones – to draw strength from. She closes her eyes, takes a deep breath, and the face that waits for her is Paul's.

She recalls, a wash of heat falling over her, the embarrassment she felt when she had got in touch to inform him of her father's death. He must have recognised her number, or perhaps still had it saved after all this time, because he answered with a jovial: *There she is! It's been years, Av. How are you?*

His warmth had taken Avani aback and she'd found herself frozen, emotion collecting inside her, unable to respond.

Are you there?... Avani?... Hello?

She tried to speak. Nothing came. He hung up.

So she made a cup of peppermint tea, curled up on the sofa for a cry, and tried again half an hour later.

Hey, Av. I think you just pocket-dialled me. Silence. *Avani?*

Then she'd mustered a husky *sorry* and felt the shade of his silence change.

Av. Talk to me. What's happened? Is it Nik?

Dad, was all she could manage.

It had felt healing, even though she hates to admit it, to reconnect with someone who knew her so fully, who saw her so clearly, like her father had. She still can't pin down why she'd asked him to come. It had been an automatic response, almost absent-minded, instinctive, like rubbing an aching temple. But seeing Paul at the cremation left a strange taste in her mouth. He hasn't been in touch since. This surprises her, disappoints her, even. But there is something else underneath the surface of this disappointment, another feeling – one she finds herself turning away from, one she does not hold space for.

'Mum, c'mon.'

Avani opens her eyes and pulls herself back to her surroundings, seated among hundreds on the steps of the river. Her son has risen to his feet, a hand outstretched to help her up. She takes it and notices ripples in the crowd as others stand, like a slow and unsynchronised Mexican wave. There is a call from across the river. It is about to begin. She feels people jostling past her, speaking in Gujarati, Kannada, Punjabi, other dialects she can't even take a guess at. She succumbs to the movement of the crowd, taking comfort in the feeling of shoulders, elbows, occasionally knees, brushing against her.

Everyone is facing forward now, watching the priests prepare for the aarti, except for a little girl with beautiful brown eyes, seated in the dip of her mother's hip, who has swivelled round to face Avani. She has marigolds plaited through her hair and blushes when Avani returns her smile. And then, it starts. The woman in front of them gasps and lifts her chundri over her head. The girl looks back towards the river. The crowd sings. Thousands of tourists tucked between mourners press the record button on their smartphones. Clanging bells move with the beat of tabla – the latter has always reminded Avani of the sound of horseshoes clacking on concrete, like a mix of India and Britain. Men clothed in white stand on the banks of the river and wave divas that dance a metre high towards the heavens. A sea of flowers begins to float gently up the current, divas nestled between them. Avani finds that her lips move along with the aarti she didn't realise she knew. The words come to her and it doesn't bother her that she has no idea what she is singing, no idea what the Sanskrit means.

She is mesmerised by the movement of the flames that defy gravity, roaring up to the sky, and she realises that she has never really appreciated the colour orange until now. Bright. Light. Beautiful. She is totally focused on the movement of those mighty orange flames, dancing in circles to the sound of the aarti and the tabla and the bells and the crowd. But as the aarti flows into its final verse, she blinks away a film of tears to realise that it's not the divas themselves she's most entranced by, but their reflections in the water.

4

July 2017

Nik switches off the small screen in front of him and turns to his mother. She's curled up in her seat in a way that couldn't possibly be comfortable; her head pressed into the window, knees against her chest, her arms wrapped around them. She hasn't moved for hours. Although her appetite has totally gone – she has had to borrow one of Nik's old school belts to keep her jeans up – she is at least able to rest, to fall into a world where funeral admin and grief do not reign. Nik stares into space for a while, thinking about this, then yawns widely and flicks the screen back on to watch the progress of their journey. They are currently flying thirty-nine thousand feet above Turkey. They're just over halfway home yet there is still so far to go.

Part of him had expected to feel an immediate affinity when he stepped into India – some sort of magical ready-made bond with the place that he has always been told makes up such a big part of his identity, like how he feels every time he sees the Harrow-on-the-Hill Tube sign. Instead, he had found himself totally out of place, handling a weight that he didn't know how to bear. He thinks about the image of India he'd pieced together from films and the proper colourful, forever-sunny, vibrant cities he'd seen in marketing emails inviting him to take a gap year to help build orphanages. Smiling children with dark eyes full of hope, thrilled at the sight of a camera. But the India that lay waiting for him fitted more with his grandfather's description of it; muggy, fast-paced, overwhelming. Mad queues on the roads. People everywhere. Heartbreak in the faces of child beggars circling him as he took his first steps out of the airport. Something had burst in him, overflowing, as he watched them, rummaging through his pockets for coins, his vision blurring with tears, their faces rising again with every meal he ate, every warm shower he took, every cold bottle of Thums Up or Limca that was flicked open for him during his short stay.

He recognised images from his grandfather's stories – as if fables he was read as a child had sprung to life – in the scooters with five or six passengers happily piled onto the seat and into crevices that simply didn't exist; in the cows sitting in the middle of busy roads, serving as makeshift roundabouts; in the wonder afforded to him by the schoolchildren that followed him down the street, their book bags clutched between tiny fingers as they hurried to keep up with him.

He thinks about how the colour of his skin, only a touch lighter than his mother's, is tied to a geographical location that he has no real connection with. He is Indian, yes, but he does not know India. It is not his home. How can that be right? Is he doing it wrong? He's never fallen into being Indian in the way that his cousin sisters seem to, with their love of Garba and Hrithik Roshan and discovering new ways to drape saris. Chand had called him a coconut when he was thirteen – just about brown on the outside but so disappointingly white within. Nik hadn't known how to respond. He's Indian in the only way he knows – in his ability to speak Gujarati, badly, in his love of the stories from the *Mahabharat* that his grandfather recited to him on their walks home from school, his addiction to jalebi and rasmalai, or in the box he ticks when he has to fill in a form: *Mixed – White + Asian*, like some reductive equation.

He looks again to his mother and thinks of how she answered with 'London' when the pujari at the river, among others, asked where they were from during their short trip. When she's asked this by a Londoner, she always replies with 'India'. He recognised himself in her answer. It's similar to how he feels when he's asked where he's from by someone who is brown or Black as opposed to someone who is white. The former rings of solidarity, of allyship, while the latter of othering, of suspicion. His identity, he realises, is like a pair of scales; the weight of the answer depending on the intention of the person asking.

He turns back to the map on the screen to count the countries between India and Kenya then Kenya and Britain, his finger tracing the journey his grandparents made in '68, just weeks after Powell's 'Rivers of Blood' speech. His grandfather had only spoken of the kindness and the opportunity Britain brought them, despite Nik's knowledge of the prejudice he faced, the fact he took a job in a picture-frame factory, significantly below his previous role working for the British in Kenya, simply because it was all that was available to him. There is so much Nik still wants to know about that move, about the choice they made; why his grandparents felt more of an affinity to England than India after Kenya's independence. Nik thinks of how his grandfather would always say he was Kenyan when asked where he's from: *It was where I was born, where I grew up, the same way you tell people you're from Britain when you go on holiday, beta. Kenya was my home.* He'd tell Nik about the white sand and turquoise waters of Bamburi beach, about eating from plates made of leaves – patravali – whenever there was a celebration, about the sense of community and warmth and love he'd grown up in. This brings a gentle wave of reassurance to Nik; his grandfather never made him feel as though he had some catching up to do or something to make up for. He can be British and Indian in his own way, in a way that makes sense to him, in the way his grandfather was Kenyan and British and Indian. Chand can piss right off.

But thinking of his grandfather is a painful exercise. The memory of his ashes being poured into the river, just a few days ago, pinches when Nik thinks of it. As he stood on the muddy banks of the dark river, the smell of burning flesh in the air around him, he had to use all his strength to stop himself from reaching out to grasp for a handful of ash, the visceral need to find a way of piecing his grandfather back together clouding his mind.

When it was over, he'd looked at his mother and said: *At least Bapu will be with Nani again.* The word felt cold against his lips when he spoke, birthed into the world by his voice but with no one left to claim it.

And your dad, too.

Nik was taken aback by the ease with which she spoke, as if the pain she bore was lifted now they were here.

I didn't realise, Nik murmured, staring out at the river.

Then she said, in a voice so low Nik wonders now if he imagined it: *When we were your age, he told me that he wanted to be scattered where I would be one day, not buried around strangers.*

When they'd returned that evening for the Ganga Puja, it wasn't his grandfather who sat in Nik's thoughts, but his father. In truth, his father has appeared in his mind much more since his grandfather's death, as though the space left behind – the space his grandfather had done his very best to fill – is now twice as large, twice as empty. The only other person who has ever come close to occupying that space is Paul, who reappeared so abruptly at the funeral before disappearing again, like a mirage.

Nik thinks of the three of them, his father, his grandfather, Paul, the men that made him, his mind resting on the first, the one he holds the most of but knows the least about. Everything Nik's mother told him about his father always felt so deliberately controlled and over-sanitised. When he asked about his father as a child, his mother would always talk vaguely, using many words to say very little. Often, they were grown-up words he didn't yet understand, like 'compassionate', 'humble', 'unfathomably special'. Nik would repeat them like they were a nursery rhyme, oblivious to their meaning. For many years, she'd reduce him down to these three facts: he was born near Manchester, worked as an English teacher and supported Arsenal. The only thing of any value she'd share was that she'd never met anyone else like him. Sometimes, when Nik would ask, this was all she'd say. If he pressed her for more, she would shake her head and grow distant. Pushing for information about his father seemed to make her recede into herself, falling into some dark corner of her mind that could take several days to pull her back from.

When Nik grew older and turned to others in their family, his mother became protective, angry even, as if they were gossiping as opposed to remembering, as if Elliot were only hers to mourn. But whenever anyone else did speak of him, their words formed an image of a man who was exceptionally warm and so deeply loved. Nik's cousin sisters in particular had adored him; they'd always puff up and twitter happily like birds when they spoke about him as kids, their voices rising over each other, keen to demonstrate that they alone knew him best. Through them, Nik learned that his parents had met at primary school and had gone to the same university. 'Inseparable' was the word he'd heard Chand use once, and Nik had held on to that, tight, like a medal; his parents had been *inseparable*. As he grew older, anything like this, anything worth holding on to, anything with actual heart, was only ever discovered in passing comments that always felt like slip-ups – the sort of remarks made by relatives or family friends that preceded averted eyes and long moments of awkward silence pregnant with something that Nik could never put his finger on. But when they did come, Nik would savour those little scraps of information, even though they didn't quite fit together, like pieces of different puzzles: *Elliot would have loved this. Wasn't this Elliot's favourite song? Oh, doesn't he so much look like Elliot?* The hostility that emanated from his mother in those moments was tangible, so much so that by the time

Nik was a teenager no one ever mentioned his father at all, as though he'd been forgotten, removed from their collective memory.

Desperate to know him, Nik spent much of his childhood poring over the photos his grandfather secretly slipped him each year, which blended together in his mind to create a voiceless blur of big bear-like hands, round hazel eyes and a seemingly permanent smile. For two years, Nik slept with his favourite photo under his pillow. Sometimes, he'd wake with it clutched tight in a fist. Then it sat, smoothed out, with thin white lines in the spaces where it had been folded, in a frame on the top shelf of his wardrobe, where his mother wouldn't stumble upon it. It was the last photo that was taken of him, the week before he died, in Kew Gardens. He was grinning at the camera, a hand halfway through his curly brown hair, his wife's frame just visible behind him in a blue dress, walking in the distance. Nik was in the photo too, growing slowly and silently, unknown to them. It had delighted him when he'd figured that out as a child, as he counted on his fingers the months between his birthday and the date printed in yellow numerals at the bottom of the photo. It was, in a way, a photo of the three of them. The only one that existed.

Nik closes his eyes and focuses on the white noise of the plane, the image of his father fading against his mind, giving way to that key, the one which led to nothing. It sits now among those to Nik's home, redundant, and he accepts he may well never find what his grandfather meant him to discover, whatever it was that once belonged to Elliot.

Now that he is on his way back home, back to reality, he thinks instead about the summer he had planned instead of this one, the one where he made it to Teo's birthday, hung out with Layla like he'd hoped to, drove his mother's Volvo to Alton Towers with the boys to celebrate the end of their exams. These things all still happened, just without him, and for a moment, he pictures himself there with his mates, included in the summer of fun he's been watching unfold through Instagram and Snapchat. His phone has remained off for the last couple of days, tucked into a pair of socks in his suitcase, all the messages from his mates left unread.

When he thinks of his future, his results, moving away to university, freshers' week, meeting new people, all he feels is a dull ache in the pit of his stomach. There was a time when these things had filled him with excitement. He can't even think about getting through the next couple of days let alone finding the energy to pack, move hundreds of miles away and start afresh. He doesn't want to go, he realises. He doesn't want to leave London yet. He's exhausted but, unlike his mother, unable to rest. It's too much at once. He wants to just breathe, earn some money, travel a bit, visit his mates at their unis. He can defer.

Beside him, as though she has sensed his decision through some internal motherly radar, his mother stirs, opens her eyes, then reaches down for a water bottle that is bent out of shape from the cabin pressure. Nik's mind circles back to his father, his grandfather, the funeral, Paul. The people they've lost.

'Mum,' he says, turning to her, 'did you invite Paul to the funeral?'

Nik already knows the answer of course, so watches her closely. She frowns slightly before replying, as if she is searching for another question hiding between his words. She doesn't seem to find it, so rubs her eyes and says, 'Yes.'

'How come?' His words are quick; lined up and ready to go.

'Funerals have a weird way about them, don't they? I just thought it would be best to put our feelings aside so he could pay his respects. I don't know what Bapu thought of him, by the time things ended, but they had been close, once.'

'What's he doing now?'

'I'm not sure, Nikhil.' She yawns. 'There wasn't much time for small talk.'

'Yeah, he didn't hang around, did he? Does he still live in London?'

'I think so.'

'I always assumed he'd moved back to the States.' She's struggling to open the water bottle so Nik takes it from her and twists the lid off. 'Do you still chat to him?' he asks carefully, handing it back to her.

'I haven't in years.'

Nik look back at the screen in front of him and begins to scroll through the list of films.

'Why do you ask, Nikhu?'

'No reason.' He shrugs, selects a film at random, and presses play. But he still feels his mother's eyes on him long after he's put his headphones back over his ears.

5

August 2017

Avani looks up from the bundle of fruit she's washing in the kitchen sink and calls to her son, who's lounging in the room next door: 'Let's go to IKEA this afternoon, Nikhil. We can start getting some bits together for uni.'

'I'm not going, Mum.'

Blueberries slip between her fingers, thudding gently as they hit the steel sink. She tries to convince herself he's talking about IKEA and not university.

'Why not, beta?'

'I'll take a year off, then see if a London uni wants me.'

Avani clears her throat before she speaks, willing it to stay even. 'Are you sure that's what you want?'

'Yeah.'

She barely catches his reply over the sound of gushing water. 'Look, I know this summer hasn't exactly gone to plan, but –'

'Nah, it's not that.'

She turns the tap off and sighs. She puts the tip of her little finger into a wet raspberry, noticing how much it looks like a thimble. Her father had warned her this might happen; there had been a hushed conversation the night Nik's exams finished. Her father had told her Nik might not want to head away from London for university if he didn't make it, that Nik wouldn't want to leave Avani on her own.

Avani pops the raspberry off her finger and wipes her hands on the tea towel thrown over her shoulder. 'I knew something was up,' she says, walking into the lounge. 'It's been two days since you got your results and you haven't said a word.'

'There's nothing to say.' Nik pauses to scratch his ear. 'I just can't be bothered with it.'

'But you've worked so hard for this.'

He looks back to his novel. It's a thick paperback Tolstoy, the spine strained. He reads like his father did; with annotations dressing the margins, pages dog-eared to mark a particular turn of phrase he's enjoyed, treating a book as something malleable that moulds itself around his hands. If Avani's mother were alive, she would have scolded her grandson. She would have mistaken this tenderness for sacrilege.

'Nikhil,' Avani says, trying to find his eyes. She perches herself on the arm of the sofa. 'What's going on, beta? You're barely here at the moment.' She's been worried about him since they returned from India. He's seemed withdrawn, staying in his room listening to that Kendrick Lamar on repeat and reading all day long, barely seeing his friends.

Nik runs a finger along the pages of his book. Avani watches the paper cascade down like a fan. 'I'm good. I don't see the point, man. Just allow it, Mum, yeah?'

She tries not to panic. 'Don't be ridiculous. What're you going to do with yourself if you don't go to uni?'

He shrugs and then surprises her by saying, 'What're *you* going to do with yourself if I leave London?'

She feels heat rising to her face. Her father was right. 'Is that why you don't want to go? I'll be totally fine. I've got Maya, and work, and my running club. I'll be busy.'

Avani watches Nik clench his jaw. His gaze is fixed on the book but he's not reading. Avani places a hand on his shoulder. 'We need to keep moving, Nikhu. You should accept the offer, beta. Don't leave them waiting.'

He doesn't respond. She stands up. 'Let's go to IKEA after lunch,' she says, heading back to the kitchen. 'D'you still have that list?'

Nik decides he'll keep the receipts. He'll leave everything boxed and wrapped. He'll come back next week, when his mother's at work, and he'll return it all. They set off just after lunch to the IKEA on the Wembley–Neasden border. Nik hates the drive. It's one of the routes his instructor often took him on when he was still learning. It involves performing a weird loop on the North Circular which always leaves him disorientated. But once they're inside, Nik's surprised at the unexpected relief he feels amid the grey floors and gentle buzz of the building. The windowless walls shelter him from the reality that lies waiting outside. After a while, he feels the shadow that's been following him around for the last month fall away.

They're only halfway through the first floor, their trolley holding some saucepans and three 70p mugs, when Nik notices a familiar figure in the distance, one that makes his breath catch. 'Ah, shit.'

'What?' His mother puts down the salad spinner she's just picked up and looks round.

'Nothing.'

Nik tries to appear engrossed in his phone, but he glances up to see his mother looking over his shoulder. Her gaze dances, then rests on something. 'Oh, isn't that your lovely –'

'Oi, Nikhil!'

Nik turns to see Layla rushing towards them.

'Ah, fuck.'

'Nikhu!' His mother tuts. 'Layla, sweetheart. How are you?'

'Hey, Auntie.' Layla wraps Nik's mother in a hug.

Nik tries to think about the last time they saw each other – it was when he had a group of his college friends over at the start of the summer for that barbecue. His grandfather had been there.

'Doing your uni shopping?' Layla asks him. She's wearing purple lipstick which seems to make her eyes look more chocolatey than usual. A pair of earbuds poke out from the buttons in her polo shirt, hanging limp against her chest. Her smile is so large, her face so warm, that Nik finds himself grinning despite his best efforts to play it cool.

'Yeah. Didn't know you worked here,' he says, scratching his beard.

Nik notices his mother attempting to melt into the background. She picks up a plain white mug from a box next to her and inspects it as though it's the most interesting thing she's ever seen.

'Just for a couple of weeks. Was proper last minute,'

Layla says. 'Saving up before uni. How did your results go?'

'Yeah, all right, y'know. Yours?'

'Just all right? I heard you smashed it.'

'He got four A-stars,' Avani says, putting the mug down. 'Got into his first choice.'

'Mum!'

'Sorry, sorry. I need to go and look at some net curtains. Layla, sweetheart, come for dinner one night before you head off to uni, will you?'

Nik looks away.

'I'd love that. Thanks, Auntie.'

'I'll make khichdi.'

'Aww, I love your khichdi. Could you teach me how to make it before I go to uni?'

'Of course, darling. Do you have a pressure cooker? If not I can teach you with a saucepan, but it takes longer. When are you –'

'Mum, man!'

'You know what, just organise it with Nik,' Avani says, blowing Layla a kiss as she walks away.

Nik's about to speak when Layla says: 'I heard about your grandad. He was so nice.'

'Yeah, I got your messages. Sorry I left you on read, it's been mad.'

'It's calm,' she says, though he knows it really isn't. He's stared at their chat and visited her profile on social media several times in the last month, even typed out a message once or twice, but was never able to send it. He isn't sure why he's ignored her for so long, except that he didn't want her to see this version of him, the one who is still trapped under the weight of grief, whose thoughts still feel numb and who doesn't feel like he ever wants to do anything any more, not even the things that once made him happy.

'How's it all been?' she asks.

'Busy. We went to India for five days to like . . . sort his ashes out and stuff. Had to get the whole thing squared in like thirteen days.' Nik scratches his chin. 'First time I've ever been.'

'What, to India?'

'Yeah. Was proper different. Didn't really get to see any of it,' he says. It felt like being introduced to someone important on a night out, then never speaking to them again. He doesn't tell her this though, instead he says: 'I'll go back at some point.'

'Yeah, you should. Jamaica was different to what I expected when my mum finally took us. But I loved it. So was visiting my dad's fam in Ireland when we were little, to be fair.'

Nik nods, trying to focus on her words. She's tied the bottom of a usually boxy IKEA shirt in a bunch by her waist. It makes the fit tight.

'I saw you got shortlisted for some poetry competition,' he tells her, trying to move the conversation on. 'That's sick.'

She beams. 'It's really no big deal.'

'Sounds like a big deal.'

'I know – I'm low-key gassed, but trying to be modest.' She laughs. 'Are you coming to Carnival next weekend?'

Before Nik can answer, a tall bored-looking man

approaches and asks Layla: 'Excuse me, do you work here? I'm looking for –'

'Nah, sorry,' she says. They both laugh when the man walks away, his neck craning to read the signs hanging above the aisles.

'We should do something soon,' Nik says.

'Yeah, maybe. When do you leave?'

'Not until the end of September.'

'So you accepted your first choice? How're you feeling about leaving London?' She narrows her eyes.

Nik laughs, breaking her into a smile. 'Man, what aren't you telling me? Every time I bring it up you go weird. Because you're going to miss me when I leave, yeah?'

'Yeah, you wish. I already told you, remember? My sister went there for a year. Then transferred to Birmingham.'

'Why?'

'Um . . .' She hesitates, watching him. She twists her torso side to side. 'D'you want the truth, yeah?'

'Shit, is it really that bad?'

'It's like . . . proper white.'

'What?'

'Like, the uni itself was all right, but she said the locals were next-level fruity. People used to love telling her she looked so exotic and asking her where she's "really" from.'

Nik lets out a stifled laugh. 'Nah, come on. That's some archaic shit, man. There can't be people who are that level of dumbass still around.'

'Trust. It's bare old school. Not like Harrow.'

'Good thing I'm extra tanned from India, then. They'll be vibesing over my pigment.'

Layla's laughter does something to Nik's insides. He feels a glimmer of his old self reappearing, fluttering just out of reach. She pulls him into a hug. 'I should get back to work,' she murmurs into his ear. Her hair smells sweet, like the honey and cinnamon candle she burns in her bedroom.

'I'll link you soon, yeah,' he says.

'Mum, man! You can't just invite random girls home for khichdi,' Nik grumbles, when he finally finds his mother half an hour later. She's on the second floor, reading the washing instructions on a packet of tea towels.

'Oh, get over yourself, Nikhil. She's hardly a stranger. I thought the two of you were, you know . . . spending some time together this summer.'

'Well, yeah. We were meant to but obviously that didn't go to plan.'

'I hope you were open and honest with her, beta, about why you weren't around. It's not good to just leave girls waiting on the "blue ticks".' She uses her fingers to signify quote marks. 'We often end up thinking it's something we've done wrong if a boy suddenly disapp—'

'I *know*, Mum.'

'And you need to watch your language, Nikhu, it's getting pretty –'

Nik zones out and runs a hand through his hair. 'C'mon, man. I've still got so much stuff to find and this place is some next maze.'

'Fine,' she says, placing the tea towels in their trolley. 'What's left?'

Nik reaches for his phone to check his list. There's a message from an unknown number waiting for him.

> 14:52 +447234209838: Hey, kiddo. How are you doing? Sorry if I startled you last month at the funeral. Thought it was important to pay my respects. Can we meet for a coffee soon? Would be great to catch up properly.

'Nikhil? What is it?'

Nik tilts his phone towards his mother. Her gaze flicks across the screen and her expression hardens. When her eyes settle on the end of the text, she mouths the name Nik's biting back: Paul.

6

August 2017

'Nikhil. I need the car please, beta. Can you come home?'

Nik swings his legs off the side of the sofa and stands up. He can feel Layla's eyes following him as he walks out into the garden. It's drizzling and the rain that covers the patio presses through his socks, dampening the soles of his feet.

'I'm at Teo's, Mum. What's up?' His mother has spent the last few days packing up her father's home, with the help of Nik, his cousin sister Rajvi and her boyfriend Ade.

'Nothing to worry about, beta. Just at Bapu's place and I've found –'

'Mate, y'all right? Ref's given us a free kick.'

Nik looks up to see Teo leaning out of the patio door. Layla tiptoes to peer over his shoulder. Nik makes a vague gesture to tell them everything's fine. 'Say that again, Mum.'

'I'm getting his things together for probate and, well, it looks as though he was renting out some storage space,' his mother says, trying to sound nonchalant, but Nik can hear nerves fizzing quietly under her words.

'What for?'

His friends erupt into a cheer and Nik turns back to the house to see who scored. Teo has moved inside but Layla is still watching him.

'It doesn't say. I just found all the monthly payments in that binder he left.'

Nik thinks of the file they'd found in his study, 'IN CASE OF DEATH' written in his grandfather's neat blue hand along the spine, page after page of meticulous detail – pension plans, bills, premium bonds, bank statements, all printed out and waiting for them. Nik had flicked through it, a lump in his throat as he leafed past a plastic sleeve with his grandfather's birth certificate and passport tucked inside. It had devastated him, the thought of his grandfather preparing for his own passing in this way. He'd asked his mother if it was normal for people to plan their affairs so scrupulously. Over his shoulder, her eyes were glassy, her voice low as she told Nik about how she wouldn't have expected anything less, how he'd always been an immaculate administrator since his civil servant days in Kenya, how he would have approached this final duty with a sense of pragmatism.

'It's a garage in Kingsbury. I just called the gentleman who owns it and apparently Bapu's been renting it for years.'

'Mad.'

'Yeah. He's been storing something,' his mother says.

A pair of warm arms wind around Nik's torso and he looks down to see Layla standing barefoot beside him, her eyes searching for his. He wraps her in a hug. There is a memory playing around the fringes of his mind, propelling itself forward. One he has half forgotten but it rises now, gaining shape, colour. He tries to focus on it; he knows it is important but pinning it down is like trying to catch ink dancing in water.

'I think we should go and check it out,' his mother says, slightly out of breath. It sounds as though she is climbing a flight of stairs. Nik imagines her walking across the exposed wooden floorboards at his grandfather's house and into his study. 'Do you mind coming with me? I need to get hold of a locksmith too because I can't find a key anywhere and they don't keep a spare –'

Nik zones out of his mother's voice, out of the feeling of Layla's hair tickling his chin, the drizzle speckling their clothes, the hollering inside as his friends watch the football. Then, slowly, gently, it comes into view. He recalls a voice – once beautiful and rich, now strained and tired – telling him about a single key hanging off a nail at the back of a desk.

'You know what, Mum?' Nik says, the hairs on his neck rising, 'I think I might know where it is.'

Nik pulls into the driveway outside his grandfather's old house and spots his mother sitting on the front step in an oversized pink jumper and matching Converse. An open umbrella rests over her shoulder and her jeans are dotted with dark drops of rain. She watches him through the windscreen for a moment, then slips into the passenger seat, bringing the scent of rose petals and cardamom with her. Nik places the key, with its ring, into her open palm. Her fingers coil around it. He feels like a child who has taken something that doesn't belong to him.

'Where did you find this?' she asks, her voice tight.

Nik's gaze reaches for hers, but she stares pointedly out of the window. He feels a chill.

'Bapu mentioned it when he was in hospital, the day before he died.'

'So you knew about the garage?'

'Nah, not at all. He started telling me about some key and then got distracted.'

She purses her lips. He wonders what has caused this spikiness. She takes a letter out of her handbag and points to the address in the corner.

'Head towards Kingsbury, please,' she says. After a while she adds: 'Where was it?'

'In his study. Hanging from a nail at the back of his desk.'

They drive in silence for a few minutes before his mother says: 'So, what, you just took the key and never wondered what it opened?'

'Of course I did. I spent the whole evening before he died stuffing it into random doors, man. Couldn't figure it out.'

'Right.' Then: 'And you didn't think to tell me.'

There is hurt in her voice. Nik turns to her but she's still looking straight ahead. Her jaw is set.

He recalls how his grandfather had stopped talking when his mother walked into the ward that day, how he'd told Nik that she wouldn't be happy with him when she found out he'd kept whatever this key led to. Nik thinks of this, then says: 'There was so much going on.' The words sound even more feeble out loud than they did in his head.

'I can drop you back to Teo's, you know,' she says. 'I'll go and clear this thing out on my own and pick you up on the way back. It's just the car I need, really.'

'It's calm,' Nik says. 'D'you even know what's in the garage?'

'Not a clue. Do you?'

'Course not. Doesn't it say in the document you found?'

'I don't think so. Let me have another read.'

But after just a moment of scanning, Nik interrupts her with: 'There were tan lines.'

'Excuse me?'

'Tan lines on the back of the desk, where this key was hanging. The rest of the wood was proper faded from the sun, apart from the bit just behind this key.'

'What's your point?'

'He obviously hadn't used it in years.'

'Hmm.'

'So maybe it's not even the right one. Maybe it's for something else.'

'Yes, perhaps.'

Nik stops at a set of traffic lights and looks at her. Her eyes are on the document and the keyring has been placed over her finger, where a wedding band would sit. Worry laces around his stomach, tying itself into a tight knot. 'What's up? Why're you being weird, man?'

'I'm not,' his mother says, scowling slightly.

'Yeah, you are. You low-key trippin', fam,' he says.

'Goodness.'

He glances across at his mother to see it has worked – she's smiling now. She folds the paper, crosses her arms and murmurs, 'I just have a bad feeling, beta. Oh, I think this is it here.' She points to a road sign.

Nik swings in and drives to the end of the cul-de-sac until they reach a steel gate.

Dusk is settling across London and the sky is darker now than when they left his grandfather's house fifteen minutes ago. Clouds hang above them like puffs of smoke, just visible against the dark sky, heavy with rain. The drizzle that misted over Nik as he stood in Teo's garden has turned into dollops the size of grapes which land unevenly across the windscreen.

'Do we just go in, yeah?' he asks as they get out of the car.

She looks through the gaps in the fence. 'Guess so. I can't see anyone and the gentleman on the phone said all we need is the key.'

Nik pushes the steel gate and walks through. His mother follows. They venture deeper into the cul-de-sac, past a garage that's no more than five metres wide. There are seven to the left and seven to the right. Rust creeps up the metal doors like a disease, turning green to murky brown. Nik's mother checks the letter as they walk and points to a garage in the far left.

'That one.'

The door is the most rusted of the lot. Nik can only just make out the peeling and faded numbers stuck onto the metal. The corner they stand in is totally enveloped by the shadow of a large sycamore tree which towers over them from an adjacent street.

Nik takes the key from his mother and slots it into the lock. It doesn't turn.

'Fuck,' he says, getting to his knees.

'Here, let me try.' His mother crouches beside him and tries to move the key but it won't budge. 'It's the wrong one.'

'Nah, look,' Nik says. 'It fits. It's just needs some –' He stops, noticing movement over his mother's shoulder. There is a man standing in the middle of the cul-de-sac, watching them. 'Oi, Mum,' Nik whispers, standing up.

'What're you doing there?' the man calls. He is dressed in a trench coat and wellington boots and holds a Tesco's carrier bag in each hand. Nik's mother flinches at the sound of his voice.

'S'all right. No need to be alarmed, m'love,' the man says, his eyes on Nik's mother.

Nik takes a step closer to her and calls, 'We're just clearing out this garage.'

'That one?' The man points to the door they're clearly standing in front of, the carrier bag swinging by his waist.

'Er . . . yeah.'

'You're having me on.'

'Beg your pardon?' Nik's mother asks.

'I'm here every day tinkering with my minis, see. So I know the folk of all these garages. No one's seen anyone at number 14 for years.'

Nik wonders what 'tinkering with my minis' is code for, and if they're better off just leaving the garage and whatever the hell is inside it. It's dark now, and there are no street lights lining the quiet cul-de-sac. His mother left her umbrella in the footwell of the car; Nik's hoodie is soaked through from the rain, and strands of his mother's hair stick to her face. Nik moves, trying to act casual, so that he is standing between his mother and the man with the bags.

'Right,' Nik's mother calls. 'Well, it was my father's but we only just found out about it.'

'Hmm,' the man says, walking across to the garage directly opposite them. He pulls the door open to reveal a fully kitted-out workshop complete with an old vintage Mini Cooper. Floor-to-ceiling shelves line the walls, brimming with clear plastic boxes. Nik's eyes battle against the dark as he tries to read the labels pressed into the centre of each box: *brake fluid & engine oil*, *chargers & jumpers*, *strut compressor parts.*

On a whim, Nik asks: 'You don't have any WD-40 by any chance, mate?'

The man puts his carrier bags down, raises a finger and stoops over a unit of shelves. He rummages for a while, then reappears with a dark blue bottle which he hands to Nik.

'Nice one,' Nik says, giving the bottle a shake.

The man motions for Nik's mother to step into the shelter of his garage. 'Come in, love. Out of the rain.' She ducks in, then unfolds the paper and holds it against the light.

Nik's busy spraying the lock when he hears his mother ask: 'Do you know what might be in there?' He shoots glances back at them while he works.

The man laughs. 'Do I? We've placed bets on it for years,' he says, fishing out a packet of Haribo from one of the carrier bags. He rips the top open and offers one to Nik's mother. 'I'm a diabetic,' he tells her. 'Missus doesn't let me enjoy these at home but they're my guilty pleasure. Anyway, turned into a bit of a myth, that one,' he says, nodding to the rusty door. 'Personally, I want to say a three-eighteen. But I could be wrong. My old man, bless him, used to swear he remembers the chap moving it in,' the man says. In one swift motion he removes his flat cap, runs a hand over his head, then pops the cap back on.

'Moving what in? What chap?'

'Was an old Indian chap,' the man says, 'which would add up, y'know.'

Nik imagines his mum holding back an eye roll. The key moves a few more degrees but then seizes again, so he sprays some more WD-40.

'Sorry, what did you say about this three-eighty?' she asks.

'The three-eighteen,' the man says again. 'At least, I think my old man said it was a three-eighteen. This was yonks ago, though. Dad reckons he was about, watched him do it. Said he really struggled to squeeze it in.'

'Squeeze what in?'

'The three-eighteen,' the man repeats patiently, between fresh mouthfuls of Haribo.

'What the fuck is a three-eighteen?' Nik murmurs to himself as he struggles with the key, desperate to see what's inside now.

'Sorry, how long ago was this?' his mother asks. Nik can hear her voice growing more strained and husky, as though she is running out of air.

'Here, look, it'll be on your paperwork, m'dear. See. Right there. May 1998.'

Nik hears his mother take a sharp breath in. Before he can ask what's going on, he feels the key give way in the lock.

'Mum,' he says, twisting the rusted T-handle to one side, 'I've done it.' The door screeches loudly as he pulls it towards him. The sound rips into Nik, and he grits his teeth as he pushes the door up as far as it will go.

A dark green BMW sits inside, a thin layer of dust lining the entire surface of it. It's parked terribly at an angle, nose first, so both the passenger door and driver-side rear door are almost touching the walls. The floor around it is crunchy with dried leaves and cobwebs, which have collected in little piles by the back tyres.

'Rah, sick.' Nik says, staring at the car. 'Proper old school.'

The man from the other garage is right behind him now and lets out a low whistle. 'Jesus. She's gorgeous.'

Nik looks over to his mother. She's staring at the car, her eyes glazed over, her mouth slightly open.

'Mum, you good?'

She doesn't respond.

'Oi, Mum. You okay?'

'I can't . . . I didn't know he kept it,' she says.

'Looks like a '96 plate,' the man says, inspecting the number plate. He wipes the dust from it with his hand then looks up at Nik. 'Might be worth something, you know.'

'What's your name, mate?' Nik asks.

'Christopher,' he says, holding out a calloused hand.

'Nik.'

Christopher retrieves a packet of cigarettes from his coat and offers one to Nik.

'Better not,' he says, nodding to his mother. She's facing away from them now, staring up at the sycamore tree, rubbing her forehead like she does when she's stressed out.

'Fair enough. You may need a hand getting this out, chap.'

'Yeah, I think I might.' Nik moves forward to inspect the car. The key sits on the only shelf. Nik picks it up and, in its place, lays to rest the key he arrived with.

'Let me have a little dig,' Christopher says. 'I may have some bits you can borrow to tow it.'

Nik manages to squeeze into the driver's seat. The car is spotless. He's surprised to find that, beneath the smell of damp and dust, there's an undertone of lemon. He notices that an old photo has been tucked into a corner of the dashboard so that it sits up against the glass. It shows a young woman, probably around his age, sitting on a bench, an orange mug between her hands. There's a sketchbook on her lap, what looks like the outline of a country just visible on the paper. She's smiling. Her lips look as though they're about to part, as though she is just a small moment away from succumbing to laughter. She looks up at whoever stands behind the camera – the person who has caught her at this most transient of moments. She is so full of joy. She is so full of hope. She is his mother.

'Will it start?' she calls. Nik glances up at the rear-view mirror to see his mother leaning against the wall. She looks pale and cold. Her oversized jumper seems even larger on her now, sagging slightly from the rain it has collected. There is something about the way her shoulders are tensed which makes Nik feel uneasy. For a moment, he can't respond. He's holding his breath, the same way he used to as a child when he'd wake up from a nightmare, unable to move. He knows he has stumbled across something important here but doesn't know what to do with it.

'Nikhil? Can you hear me? Will it start?'

He slides the photo into the back pocket of his jeans, then tries the ignition with no luck. He opens the door slightly and calls over his shoulder: 'No, but the steering wheel is unlocked.'

'Just let the handbrake down. You'll have to push it out.'

Nik does as he's told, then puts an arm over the front passenger seat and moves the steering wheel on full lock to the left. He climbs over the top of the car to the bonnet, leaving large footprints in the dust. When he pushes, he finds, to his surprise, that the car moves easily under his hands.

'Whereabouts are you heading, chap? I don't think it's going to make it very far with those tyres,' Christopher says, reappearing.

Nik ducks to look at the wheels. The back tyres are completely flat.

His mother tucks her hair behind her ears, worry creasing her face. 'Look, let's just get it out of this gated bit and call a recovery service to move it later,' she says.

'Do you want to get in to steer?' Nik offers.

'Certainly bloody not. I'm not getting in that thing,' she snaps. The whip in her voice stops Nik from pressing. The barrels complain loudly under the flat tyres and Nik winces as he hears them.

Christopher hurries over to help. 'I'll steer,' he says, opening the driver door.

'Thanks, man.'

Once the car is released out into the lane, filling the space between Nik and his mother, they both stand and stare at it. When their eyes meet, Nik can see that there is more than just apprehension in his mother's gaze; something inside her has been disturbed, forced out from its safe space. The sound of raindrops landing on the car punctuates their silence. Christopher lights another cigarette and looks between them.

'Well, thanks very much,' his mother tells Christopher.

'Hey, no problem. You'll be fine leaving it out there for the night.'

She nods and walks back to her Volvo.

'I'll be here until the wee hours anyway, so will keep an eye,' Christopher tells Nik.

'Thanks, man. Appreciate your help.'

'Sure, no trouble,' he says, shaking Nik's hand. He walks back towards his garage, humming quietly.

Nik circles the car. The paintwork is spotless, as though it's barely ever been driven. It has what Layla would call 'an old rustic charm' to it. Teo and Will would love it. He bends down and places his fingers against the flat tyres, noticing how the rubber almost feels like tough, weathered skin. He touches his hand to his forehead, a small greeting for the shadow he never knew. Then, he tears himself away from the car with a final glance and sprints across to the Volvo, where his mother is waiting.

They drive in silence, Nik sneaking glimpses of his mother every time he checks the wing mirror beside her. She's slumped towards the window, eyes closed, completely still, but Nik knows she is not asleep. The key to the Beemer sits awkwardly in the pocket of his jeans and the metal pokes into his thigh. It feels cold and heavy. He turns the heating on and selects the nineties neo-soul playlist from Spotify which his mother frequently listens to while cooking.

When he approaches their home, Nik stops in the road for a fox to lead her cubs into a neighbour's hedge. One of the smallest shoots ahead to overtake its siblings, staring right at Nik as it hurries across the road.

'Thank you for driving, beta,' his mother says, as he turns into their driveway.

'That's okay. I'll give our breakdown a ring in a bit . . . see if they can bring it back here.'

'Not on the driveway, tell them to put it somewhere further down the road,' she murmurs, reaching for the door handle. 'I'm going to have a hot bath.'

'Was it Bapu's? I thought he didn't drive.' The words rush out of Nik in a single breath. He knows the answer – he has known it since he found the photo – but he needs to hear her speak the words.

'No,' she says, pushing the door wide open. 'It was your father's.'

7

March 1979

Avani heard a tap on the glass and looked up from her maths homework to see someone watching her through the living-room window. It was the new boy from school – the one whose mother walked too fast and who was always angry with him. A few days before, Maya had nudged her during assembly to say: *he's staring at you again.* They'd both swung round to look at him and his cheeks had bloomed red. Now, he stood before her in a faded grey T-shirt. An old bicycle rested on the lawn by his feet. She opened the window.

'Yes?'

'Hello. I was wondering if you would like to go on a bicycle ride with me.'

She had never heard him speak before and thought there was something strange about how he pronounced his words. He seemed to chew them around in his throat before releasing them and they twisted up at the ends in a way she was unfamiliar with.

'I don't think I'm allowed,' she said, looking over her shoulder. She could feel the heat of her mother's glare, even though only her father was home. 'I have homework to do.'

'But it's a Saturday,' he replied.

Avani heard movement behind her and turned to see her father bringing over a plate of thepla he had prepared for lunch. 'How's it going, chakli?' he asked, noticing her at the window. 'Oh. Now, who's this?'

'He's just joined my school,' Avani said. 'We're not in the same class, though,' she added, unsure if this was an important piece of information or not.

'Well, hello, young man,' her father said, pushing the window open wider. Avani tucked herself into the space under his arm and leaned out for a better look.

'Hello,' the boy said. 'I was wondering if we could go for a bicycle ride together.'

Avani glanced up to her father, who was smiling at the boy. 'But I don't have a bike,' she said.

'What's that, then?' the boy asked, pointing to the red bicycle tied to their gate.

'That's my brother's.'

'I'm sure he wouldn't mind you borrowing it for a bit,' he said, scratching his elbow.

Chand was a whole four and a half years older than Avani and he'd always helped her up on the bike when he let her ride it. Without him she worried she'd need a ladder to reach the saddle. She looked again to her father.

'Go on, beta.'

'But Mumma will be angry,' she whispered. The thought of her mother finding out that she was going on bicycle rides with a boy made her stomach gurgle. She'd be in so much trouble.

'Mumma isn't back until tomorrow,' her father said. 'Here, take some lunch with you.'

She pulled her trainers on while her father wrapped a

couple of thepla in tinfoil. He slid two cartons of apple juice into her backpack.

'Be home by six please for your dinner, beta. And have fun.'

'Okay, Puppa.' She nodded. 'But what do we say if Mumma asks?'

His eyes were sad. 'Don't worry about that, chakli.'

The boy had picked the lock on Chand's bicycle and was kneeling down beside it, fiddling with the gears. When he spotted Avani, he pushed the saddle down so it was level with her hip. She didn't know that was an option.

'Hey, what's that on your hand?' he asked, reaching for her palm.

'Mehndi.'

'Mem-di,' he said, looking at the fading orange pattern that looped from her fingers down to her wrist.

'*Mehndi*.'

'Mennn-dee,' he said, beaming. He held her hand tight, his palm warm against hers.

'Almost.'

'Pretty,' he said, and it made her blush in the only way she knew – by smiling. It felt as though he was really looking at her and not turning away from what he was seeing. Her eyes fell to his trainers, resting on his left foot, where a fluffy grey hole was forming. He wriggled his toe through it, which made her laugh.

'I'm Avani, by the way,' she said.

'I know,' he replied, 'and I'm Elliot.'

8

September 2017

Nik's deliberately running late. He was meant to meet Paul at some hipster cafe in east London twenty minutes ago, but he's only just getting off the train now. Despite commuters moving swiftly around him, keen to get away from the sticky flurry of the Tube, Nik refuses to rush.

Since the funeral, Nik has spent more time than he'd care to admit imagining scenarios where he and the Paul of his childhood spend what's left of this year and those to come hanging out at pubs, beer gardens and football matches. He's imagined what it might feel like to call Paul up one day just for a chat, as they used to. A small, quiet part of him flutters with hope at the thought of this. But, as he walks from the station to the cafe, he finds himself repeatedly stifling that tiny flurry of optimism; he'd been hoping Paul would get in touch after the funeral with so much force that it seems to have boomeranged round and graduated into resentment. He knows where this rage has come from – he has overcooked these hopes, as his grandfather would say. He's let them fester for too long. Paul should have got in touch with him sooner, he shouldn't have left the funeral without saying goodbye. He can wait, now. Nik will take his sweet time. The guy abandoned you, he tells himself. He left when you were eleven and never looked back. Don't let him sneak into your life again as if nothing happened.

Growing up, there had been an odd triangle of guardianship Nik's mother, grandfather and Paul had formed. He thinks back to a couple of summers ago, when he was sixteen and bunked off school to have a very illegal and very boozy barbecue in his local park. His mother had been away for a conference, and the boys had ended up at his afterwards. They'd managed to get hold of a twenty-four pack of Budweiser and a couple of spliffs. Someone had thrown up in the rose bush by their front door. Nik had sprayed a whole can of air freshener around the house and was sure he'd cleared all the beer bottles away, hiding them in his Duke of Edinburgh bag until he could take them to the recycling dump. He must have missed one, because a few days later he traipsed into his bedroom after school to find, on his bedside table, a long white rose. It was sitting in an empty Budweiser bottle. A prickly heat had crawled over him as he closed his door and stared at it, praying he was imagining it. He'd sent a photo of it to his mates immediately, terrified to go downstairs, and thinks now of the conversation that followed:

Teo: Fam. That is peaaaaak

Will: Mate.

Nik: Am I in trouble?

Will: Mate. That's legit some passive aggressive shit right there

Nik: WTF do I do now?

Teo: Good luck, broski

Nik didn't touch alcohol again until he was legal. That was just how they worked. She silently made him aware of what was expected of him. He silently complied. Once, when his English teacher explained what the word 'stoic' meant, Nik thought he'd never heard such an apt description of his mother. Since then, every time she strived on despite clearly being exhausted or opened her mouth to say something but then bit back, Nik would think of that neat, unusual word, and how he had never met a better embodiment of it than his mother.

But Nik also knew another side to her. He learned that she could fluctuate between having everything in control and taking things in her stride to barely speaking for weeks at a time, drawing into herself. Many of the most vivid memories of Nik's childhood were tied to being repeatedly overwhelmed by this sudden fragility, of waiting for the day his arms would be long enough to wrap them all the way around his mother, to hold her together, keep her safe, keep her with him. When her eyes lost their spark, Nik's grandfather would wordlessly appear from his little terrace up the road to take the reins, making sure Nik was going to school and that the house was clean and tidy. He always followed up with Nik on what he was reading and taught him how to pay attention to the cinematography in his favourite films. There was not only no such thing as a stupid question in his grandfather's opinion, but also no such thing as too many. He often asked Nik what he was thinking or feeling, simply, it seemed, to satiate his curiosity of the inner workings of his only grandson. It was he who taught Nik to think deep, he who taught Nik about the history of India, from Gandhi's Salt March to

Dyer and the Jallianwala Bagh Massacre. He encouraged Nik to read the *Guardian* with him on Saturday mornings and asked Nik what he thought of what went on in the world, and most importantly, why he thought it. Nik's grandfather added the substance to the frame that his mother put together.

Meanwhile, Paul was the one who brought a wash of raw energy and excitement to Nik's life. He would play football or rugby with Nik, Teo and Will every Sunday morning. He taught them how to defend properly, as opposed to just chase after someone and act as a human shield, like their PE teacher had encouraged. He introduced the boys to the joys of adding green Tabasco to cheese toasties – which he insisted they refer to as 'grilled cheeses'. He taught them how to change a tyre, install floating shelves, and, one particularly dry summer, how to tile a bathroom.

From the age of eight, Nik decided, without consulting anyone involved, that he'd refer to Paul as his stepfather going ahead. Paul and his mother never married, but 'my mum's boyfriend' didn't quite cut it for Nik. Paul was more than just her boyfriend; he picked Nik up from school and fed him tangerines and cups of tea until his mother got home, he helped him with his homework and occasionally joined his mother on parents' evenings, he showed Nik how to style his hair using products that had the consistency of melted chewing gum. He lived with them. And so, Nik realised, one Saturday afternoon as they drove to the cinema, 'Mum's boyfriend' sounded dangerously impermanent for this particular arrangement, like it might one day drop a syllable and just become 'Mum's friend'. Nik couldn't take that risk. So, when they reached the cinema, he walked in front of his mother and Paul to order three tickets for the latest *Spiderman* film. '*One for me*,' he told the cashier, '*and two adult tickets* –' he took a deep breath – '*for my mum and stepdad*.'

Paul's cheeks grew pink as he handed the cashier his debit card, a smile playing around his lips, while Nik's mother simply ducked to rest her chin on the top of his head, pressing her warm hands into his shoulders. And that had been that. No paperwork. No costly ceremony. Just a promotion of words. Nik thinks of that day and how full he had felt. Having a mother and a stepfather. They had been a three and it had been perfect. It had been everything.

Not long after that day at the cinema, he'd been asked to write an essay at school about his favourite person. Teo had chosen Thierry Henry. Will had chosen Cristiano Ronaldo. Nik had written three hundred words about his newly appointed stepfather. He thinks of that essay, how it had been pinned to the board outside his classroom for months, how he told neither his mother nor Paul about it, and how, now, he can't find even one word to describe the man who had once meant so much to him. It makes something rise inside him that he does not want to confront. It's a quiet, slow anger, building in him like lava. Part of him wants to turn round and get right back on the Tube. It also annoys him – he realises, as he approaches the cafe – that Paul hasn't texted him to ask if he's still coming, or why he's so late. Nik hopes, suddenly, ridiculously, that Paul thinks he's been stood up. But Nik's just a few hundred metres from the cafe now and knows, despite the resentment bubbling inside him, that he doesn't have it in him to bail.

As Nik crosses the road, he spots Paul sitting behind the glass front of the cafe, a Kindle in his hand. He looks totally relaxed, his head tilted slightly, an elbow resting on the chair beside him. Nik realises now that this is why he wanted to be late; he wouldn't have been able to wait patiently if he had got here first. It would have been unbearable to sit, waiting, wondering if Paul would show up.

When Nik walks through the door, Paul gets to his feet and says, 'There he is! How are you, kid?'

'Yeah, good thanks,' Nik mutters, sitting on the wooden chair opposite Paul's. The cafe smells like a shed – it has a woody, ashy scent that makes Nik's chest tighten if he inhales too deeply. Potted plants are arranged on shelves around them, their vines trailing down like veils towards the floor. Blackboards with cursive handwriting cover the walls, encouraging them to opt for the brunch special. Nik recognises the music spilling out of the speakers above them as the score of his favourite Marvel film.

He looks up at Paul and feels something shift slightly, as if the floor is moving beneath him. Several thoughts chase each other around his mind, and he doesn't know which one to focus on. They make the tips of his fingers go numb. The music in the cafe is suddenly harder to hear, as if the speakers are at the other end of a tunnel. Nik has thought about this moment for so long. Now that it's here, he doesn't know what to do with himself.

'How's your mum holding up?' Paul asks, watching Nik closely. Nik's expression seems to be bemusing him.

'Yeah, she's okay,' Nik replies with a shrug, cringing at the Americanisms pressed into Paul's speech. He loved this twist in Paul's idiolect when he was younger. He'd thought it was cool. But now the hybrid of one-part Londoner mixed with two-parts Californian feels like a feeble attempt to remain young, to chase the years down and remind people that he grew up in the States.

Silence hangs between them for a few seconds. Nik looks up to Paul, whose eyes are on the back of a waiter's head. His skin has softened and there are deep wrinkles around his mouth. His lips look thinner than the Paul of Nik's childhood.

'I don't wear red lipstick, buddy,' Paul says to a passing waiter, pointing to the powdery red stain on the glass before him. This makes Nik wish he hadn't come. He wishes the Paul he remembers – the young, full-of-life, happy Paul who would have wiped away the red lipstick with the sleeve of his jumper – could take this one's place. He would have been happy with the Paul who only existed in the white A5 envelopes which landed on his doormat twice a year, or the Paul he personified through the never-spent twenty-pound notes, now carefully preserved in an old shoebox. Any of those Pauls would do. A wave seems to erupt in Nik's chest, crashing over his lungs, his torso, creeping through his limbs, stretching all the way to the tips of his fingers and toes, where it fizzes and doubles back, trapped, unable to move further.

The waiter picks up the glass, takes Nik's order and sweeps to the back of the cafe.

'Where were we?' Paul asks.

Nik watches him for a moment through narrowed

eyes, trying to breathe away the anger. He can't stomach the fact that he's sitting across from someone he once considered a parent. This guy's a total stranger. 'Look, man. I think I'm going to go. I don't feel great.'

'What? You've only just got here. Give me a chance, kid.'

Nik tries to stand up, but his legs are numb.

'Listen, you don't have to say anything, just hear me out,' Paul says, taking a sip of his orange juice straight from the bottle. 'I should have stayed in touch. I just got caught up in my own life and it was easier to focus on that instead of looking back at what I'd lost out on.'

Something snaps in Nik. Heat rises in him. His eyes flash up to Paul's. 'That's bullshit.'

Paul raises his eyebrows ever so slightly.

The rage is simmering over. 'You told me –' he can't contain it – 'you told me you'd see me once a month. That turned into once every two, then three, then six, then never. Same with the phone calls –' Nik's raising his voice now but doesn't care – 'and even your birthday cards turned into generic crap. The last one had an electric guitar on it. Do I look like the sort of person who plays the bloody guitar, man? We don't know each other.'

It is hard for him to say this, to speak of the abandonment that has so filled him with shame. Hearing his words out loud, the raw truth in them, makes him want to hide away. Paul no longer deserves the privilege of knowing these things.

'Nik, listen. I know I cocked up,' Paul whispers. His hushed tone juxtaposes the profanity and makes Nik despise him even more. He doesn't need to lower his voice.

The cafe is empty apart from the two of them. 'I want to fix it. I'd like to know you again.'

'I don't know if I want to know you,' Nik replies without a beat. 'I'm moving away for uni tomorrow anyway, so I won't be around much.'

'That's so good to hear, kid. Tell me all about it.'

Nik gives him the highlights, taking in a round watermark on the table. He's biting back telling Paul to stop calling him 'kid'. He wonders if Paul remembers that he's eighteen – literally an adult.

'Ah, so you'll be by the sea, right? I have a client not far from there.'

Nik doesn't respond. Instead, he unscrews the cap of the glass bottle in front of him. He can't remember what he's ordered, so tilts the bottle to read the label – orange juice.

'What course?'

'History.'

'Same as me. Good choice, kid.'

'What?' Nik's eyes shoot up to meet Paul's before he can stop himself. 'I thought you did some finance thing.'

'My first degree was History.'

'I didn't know that.'

Paul settles back into his seat, as though he's found the missing piece of a particularly troublesome puzzle.

Nik doesn't understand how they've gone from hushed profanities to talking about the new life he hasn't even packed for yet. 'Right,' he says, unsure of how to respond, but glad to see Paul's smile falter. He spends longer than feels comfortable spinning the bottle cap on the wooden table. When he gets bored, he presses it into the centre of the watermark. 'My mum knows I'm here . . . in case you thought I'd kept it from her.'

'No, I assumed so,' Paul says, something shifting in his expression. 'How is she?' he asks for the second time, his gaze following the bottle cap at the mercy of Nik's fingers.

'Fine. Single, if that's what you mean.'

'No, that's not what I mean,' Paul says, though the tightness around his eyes seems to suggest otherwise.

'Are you?'

'What?'

'Single?'

A pause. Then: 'Yes.'

'Is that why you wanted to meet –'

'No, Nik. Christ, is that what you think of me?'

'Then what do you want?'

'Your grandfather just died.'

'Oh, cheers, yeah, hadn't noticed,' Nik spits back.

'I thought you might want to – that you might need me.' The words tumble over each other in the rush to get out and Nik notices Paul's jaw tense as he hears them back.

'Need *you*? For what?'

'I don't know, kid. I raised you for seven years.'

'Yeah, then you fully pulled a Houdini.'

'I – look. I . . . yeah, okay, that's fair. I completely intended on keeping in touch and being in your life.'

It sounds rehearsed to Nik, who shakes his head. A moment passes in silence before the waiter comes back over to them.

'Can I get you anything to eat, chaps?'

'No, thanks,' they both say. Nik's words come just a fraction of a second after Paul's.

When the waiter has retreated to the back of the cafe again, Paul says: 'I know your mum and I weren't technically married, but I saw you as my own son for those seven years. It was hard for me, kid. Being away from you both. But I didn't have a claim to you biologically or legally or whatever, and I didn't want to overstep the mark either. I didn't want to get in the way of Av moving on. The less I saw you, the more you were growing up without me. I stopped knowing what you needed from me.'

'Really? Poor you, man. That's like saying a dog gets skinnier the less you feed it. What did you expect?'

'Not this.'

This isn't what Nik had expected either. That bubble of joy he'd felt when he saw Paul at the funeral has completely gone. It burst the moment Paul had greeted him like an old friend, as though nothing but misfortune and busy lifestyles have kept them apart. He's annoyed with himself for longing for this so much, angry that he allowed himself to hope, that he skipped a morning with his friends to give this proper wasteman another chance. If he leaves now he'll make it back in time to spend most of the day with Will and Teo instead. Nik picks up his phone. 'Thanks for trying, yeah?' he says, before walking out.

Avani sits at the kitchen table – alternating between sipping a cup of chai and wrapping a set of saucepans in newspaper – when she hears the front door open. 'Flavour of the Old School' plays from a speaker perched between jars of spices.

'Nikhu?' she calls over the music.

Her son appears a few moments later, shaking the rain out of his hair. It's the last night that he and his friends are all in the same place before they move into university halls, where a different life awaits. Tomorrow, she will drive him three hours north for university. His life will slice away from hers. She has tried not to over-sentimentalise it, tried not to count down the days when she wakes each morning, but still finds herself holding on to each hour, each meal.

'Hey, Mum.'

He brings the scent of tobacco into the kitchen with him. She thinks of that day earlier in the summer when she had absent-mindedly reached for his bag, sprawled over the hospital windowsill. She'd pushed his Oyster card and a battered paperback novel further inside it so they wouldn't fall to the ground. A bright green packet of Rizla had toppled out. She'd stared at it for a moment, then snuck it into the back pocket of her jeans in one quick move so her father wouldn't see it. When she'd mentioned it, Nik had told her he'd stopped smoking, in fact, that he hadn't even started; he'd just been trying it out.

She watches him move around the kitchen, wondering if she should bring it up again. For now, she simply turns the music down and says: 'How was it, beta?'

'Weird,' he says, pouring himself a cup of chai from the pan on the stove. She doesn't know if he's talking about meeting Paul this morning or saying goodbye to his friends. He removes a piece of chewing gum from his mouth and flicks it into the bin. 'What's the point saying goodbye when we're all going to see each other again in a few weeks, anyway?'

Avani opens her mouth to tell him not to expect his friends to have as much time for each other. How they'll meet new people. How some friendships may fall away. But she decides against it. 'What did you get up to?'

'Had a last-minute house party,' he tells her, stirring three heaped spoons of sugar into his chai. 'At Teo's.'

'Fun. And . . . how was Paul?' She's careful to busy herself with duct tape so she doesn't have to look at him.

'Waste of time, really. Wish I'd skipped it and hung out with the boys instead.'

Avani glances up at him, surprised to find herself relieved. 'Remind me where everyone's going and what they're doing,' she says, placing a frying pan carefully into a cardboard box marked 'Kitchen Bits'.

'Teo's at UCL, Will's at Imperial and both of their girlfriends are going to King's.'

'And what about Layla?'

There is a pause before he says: 'Goldsmiths.' He pulls his phone from his pocket.

'Such a bright bunch. Are they all in halls?'

'Yeah,' he says, 'they'll all probably be running into each other on nights out and stuff.'

'You'll make new friends, Nikhu. You've never struggled with that.'

He doesn't respond. He's leaning against the worktop and staring at his phone, the cup of chai against his chest. Avani pushes the window open slightly and a breeze rushes through, bringing with it the sound of drizzle landing across their patio.

'We'll get you a little car with Bapu's inheritance once you're settled,' she says, 'so you can come home whenever you like without having to faff about on the trains.'

He seems to snap out of his thoughts at this. 'The Beemer's still at Papa Burns's by the way.'

The mention of the car cuts through her like a whip, making her suddenly cold. She assumed he'd taken it to the scrapyard already, as she'd instructed him to. She thought storing it at Will's father's garage was just temporary.

Before she can organise these thoughts, her son is saying: 'I was thinking, me and the boys could fix it up over the next few months. Would be nice having a project to come back to.'

'Certainly not,' she says, trying to keep her voice even. Something seems to be pressing against the back of her throat.

'What? Why?'

'Listen.' She can hear the panic rising behind her voice. She tries to push it down. 'I already told you to scrap it. I think it'll be best to just get rid of it.' The image of the car on her driveway sends her back to an evening she doesn't want to think about almost twenty years ago, an evening that makes something visceral stir in her.

'But it's in really good shape, Mum. Will's dad had a look earlier and it just needs some light –'

'Nikhil. We're not keeping it.'

'But I think it would be really cool if I –'

'I'm not telling you again.'

'But why, man?'

'It's not . . . that car is . . . I don't want to be faced with it every day.' It is hard for her to say these words, to admit this, so when the sounds leave her lips a prickly annoyance crawls over her skin, as though she has been forced to physically expose herself.

'Well, it'll be with me at uni, so you won't have to look at it at all.'

Words fail her. She shakes her head.

'Bapu wanted me to have it. He saved it for me.'

The annoyance grows, blooming into red hot anger. 'Nikhil, if you're not going to do as I say I'll get one of the guys from work to pick it up and just take it to scrap –'

'Ugh! Fine,' he says, raising his voice. He pours his cup of chai back into the saucepan and slams the mug back down on the worktop. She flinches. 'I'll sell the fucking thing, if you're going to be so dramatic.'

'That's mature. Look, let's not row about this; it's our last evening together.'

But her son is not listening, he is taking the stairs two by two, and a moment later his bedroom door slams shut.

Nik turns his speakers up, dumps himself into bed and stares at a spider making its way across his ceiling. '*HUMBLE.*' fills the air around him, the beat of it pulling the rage from him. His room is a mess. Boxes line the walls and an IKEA bag is pushed up against his wardrobe with a few hoodies thrown in. A jumper hangs out from the bottom of the wardrobe, one sleeve half-heartedly dangling towards the bag below. He ignores the chaos around him and instead digs his phone out from the pocket of his jeans.

Layla still hasn't seen his last message; he hadn't been able to find her on his way out of Teo's. He rereads the words he typed as he walked away from the warm house that seemed to throb with music and into the cold patter of rain:

23:15 Nik: I have to cut – still gotta pack (proper left it to the last minute lol). See you soon, yeah? x

He wishes now that he'd found her to say goodbye. She appears online and he watches the two grey ticks turn blue. She wanders back offline without replying. He scrolls past and opens up the chat he has with Teo and Will.

23:42 Nik: Won't let me keep it

23:42 Will: Nooo??? WTF

23:42 Teo: Why tho?

23:43 Nik: Dunno man, she's proper vexed. Is it all right if I store it at your dad's a bit longer Will – just til I can shift it mate?

23:43 Will: Yeh, dw it's calm

23:43 Nik: Thanks man. Teo, does your uncle still wanna buy it?

23:44 Teo: I'll check, but I'm thinking like why don't we fix ting up anyway before you sell it?

23:44 Nik: I'm listening

23:44 Teo: We're both gna be back in Harrow on the weekends anyway. Could be jokes

23:44 Will: Ohhhhh yeh let's do that. More £ that way when you sell mate

23:45 Nik: She'll go mad

23:45 Will: Doesn't have to know . . .

Nik stares at the screen before replying.

23:46 Nik: Fuck it. We move

Nik places his phone on the floor and turns over in bed. Now that he's calmed down slightly, he replays the conversation he's just had with his mother. Her anger, and her overall reaction, seems totally unreasonable. It doesn't add up. One thing's for certain though: that car hasn't been in an accident. It isn't how his father died. Will had thought the same thing when they'd towed the car over to his father's garage. His father, Papa Burns, had given it a quick once-over before he locked up, saying: *It's in good nick. Exhaust needs a change, it's rusted as hell, and the tyres will need replacing. You'll need a thorough oil change and a new battery, but the body, well, it's beautiful,* he'd said, running a hand along the car, *very straight body. No damage, beautiful arches too. Engine's looking solid, though we'll have to see how it runs on the road. It shouldn't be much work, probably a few weekends' worth.*

Once they'd tucked it into a corner of the garage, Nik and Will sat side by side on the kerb with a spliff and Nik murmured, looking up at the darkening sky, *Oi, d'you remember what I told you? About what my grandad said?*

He could feel Will's eyes on him. *Mate, I've been thinking the same thing. But it's spotless. There's no way that car's been in a fatal.*

Nik watches the spider crawl into a crack by the window frame and forces himself to get up. Despite his conversation with the boys, he knows that there's no way he'll sell the car if he manages to get it going. His grandfather saved it for him; he wanted him to have it. Nik decides he'll keep it, and deal with the drama when it comes. He goes back to the group chat, hoping to ask Will and Teo if they'll be back in Harrow next weekend to start on the car, but deletes the message before he sends it. Although he doesn't want to acknowledge it, he hates that he won't see his mates all the time any more, that they'll all still be in London while he goes it alone in a totally new city. He's also annoyed with himself for becoming even closer to Layla over the last few weeks; he finds himself liking her more and more each time he sees her. Now she's yet another person he's leaving behind. But moving away from London hadn't seemed like a big deal when he'd applied, back at a time when relocating to a part of the country where he knows absolutely nobody felt like the most exciting thing in the world. He'd stayed up all night when he got the initial offer, thinking about all the new mates he'd make, all the nights out and fun that was waiting for him. The thought was almost too delicious to devour in one sitting; he was so full of hope and anticipation. But that was before his grandfather had died, before he found himself feeling like he was constantly on the brink of something awful, as though a dark mass that he could not see the shape of was lurking just out of sight, something more tangible, more sinister than simply a shadow. Back then, the world was a wave that he was riding, pushing him towards university, and nothing felt more thrilling. Now, he's under the current, being thrown around, unable to find his feet.

He turns his music up to block out his thoughts and

begins to pull clothes from their hangers. He scrunches them into balls and lobs them into bags and boxes scattered around the room. It is such an imposition, he feels, having to pack his life up and deposit it several hundred miles away. When he moves on to his chest of drawers, he lifts and dumps handfuls of socks, boxers and sportswear into bags, not bothering to sort through them. He tugs open the final drawer and spots a pop of orange – the lid of a battered old Nike shoebox at the very back. He looks over his shoulder to check the door's shut. It's the box containing several years' worth of cards from Paul and the photos of his father. Slowly, he pulls the box towards him and opens the lid. Nudging Paul's cards aside, he flicks through the collection of photos and stops at one he hasn't thought about in a while – it shows his father sitting on a sofa with Nik's cousin sisters perched on his lap. His cheeks are red, like they'd be warm to touch and his long brown curls fall over his eyes. His arms, like the wings of an albatross, wrap around the three girls as he reads from a white book with a yellow spine. *Where is Fifi?* the title asks. Beneath it sits a cartoon of Minnie Mouse cuddling a spaniel. Nik feels a pang of something he can't place when he stares at his cousin sisters' delighted faces. It's not quite jealousy – that they got to meet and know and love the man who Nik never will – but more of a sort of longing mingled with disbelief. Chand's figure is out of focus in the background as he walks from the room. This could be a painting, Nik thinks, or a photo shoot of strangers paid to pretend they belong together. It has, in his mind, no root in his reality; it is a narrative that he was never a part of.

He places the photo to the side and shifts through the rest as if they are a pack of cards, searching for the first one he was given – the one that his grandfather handed him when he was still just a boy, shortly after a trip to Madame Tussauds. It was a photo of his mother and father at their graduation. But he can't find it. He rifles through the birthday cards from Paul and the envelopes of twenty-pound notes. But the photo is not in the box. Nik sits back and rubs a hand over his face. It dawns on him that he hasn't actually seen the photo for years. Perhaps even a decade. Did he imagine it? For a brief moment, he genuinely believes this is the case – that finding the photo in the car of his mother as a young woman combined with the fact he is off to university has resulted in some sort of false memory. But he can remember that day at Madame Tussauds vividly and the hushed conversation with his grandfather that followed later that evening, when his mother was in the shower, which ended with his grandfather handing him the photo. He can see it so clearly in his mind. He remembers it living in a silver frame.

Then, it comes to him: he had used a piece of Blu-Tack to stick the photo to the wall beside his bed a few weeks after his grandfather had handed it to him, and woken up the next morning to find it gone. He'd searched everywhere for it, devastated, peering inside pillowcases and bed sheets, too scared to ask his mother if she'd seen it. He had nothing left to show that it had ever existed, apart from an oily stain, the size of a pea, which had marked his wall where the Blu-Tack had been. He discovered by chance, several months later, that his mother had plucked it from his wall, slipped it into a frame and placed it on her dressing table. No words had been spoken, but the message was very clear: *this is not your pain, it is mine.*

Nik is, for a moment, filled with an anger so strong he can feel the heat of it rushing towards his arms. He hadn't understood her actions when he was a child, but revisiting it again now infuriates him. Part of him wants to storm downstairs and confront her. Shout at her. Ask her outright what her problem is – what his father could have possibly ever done that was so awful that she won't let Nik know him. Instead, he pushes his window open with such force that the handle cracks in his hand. He breathes in the cold air, letting it wash over him, until he can think clearly again. Then, he opens his bedroom door and looks over the banister. He can still hear his mother moving around the kitchen. The spiky scent of jeeru and rai being heated in oil wafts up to him. She seems to be batch-cooking a bunch of his favourite dishes to take with him to university, but this realisation does not cool his rage. He walks across the landing as quietly as he can and swings his mother's bedroom door open. Her dressing table is covered with several bottles of perfume, various skincare products and some make-up items that Nik can't name. The photo isn't there. His mother must have moved it. He checks her bedside tables and the surface on top of her chest of drawers, trying his best not to make too much noise. He is about to give up when he spots something by his reflection.

Four photos have been pressed into the space between his mother's vanity mirror and its frame. One photo is of

Nik's grandfather. The second is of Nik's mother with Maya on a hiking trip in Scotland. The third is of a young Nik smiling widely in his first Arsenal shirt. The final photo is of Nik's mother and father at their graduation. Nik's father is staring straight at the camera, with his arm around her shoulder. Her face is tilted towards his, her eyes on him. There is so much love nestled in the centimetre between his parents' faces that Nik almost feels as though he is trespassing.

He stares at it for a moment, then slides the photo out from the vanity and slips it into his wallet, adjusting the others to cover up the space left behind.

9

September 2005

Nik was full of chips, beans and lemonade. He was strapped into the back seat of his mother's Volvo, his eyes firmly shut, his mind a merry-go-round of the figures he'd spent the day with at Madame Tussauds. He held a red instant camera in his hand – a present from his grandfather to make use of on their day out.

Night was settling down gently across north-west London as Nik's mother drove through Kensal Green, back towards Harrow. 50 Cent invited them to explore his candy shop over the radio. Nik's grandfather changed the station over to Radio 4, where a woman read the evening news. She started talking about the inquiry into the terror attacks that had shaken their summer and Nik's mother turned the radio off completely with a loud sigh.

'Is he asleep?' his grandfather murmured eventually, pulling Nik from the fringes of a nap.

A moment passed. Nik imagined his mother's eyes flashing towards him in the rear-view mirror. 'Ha.'

'Beta –'

'Puppa, please.' Nik knew that tone. 'It'll be too much for him.'

They spoke to each other in the usual mix of Gujarati

and English, weaving out of one language and into the other.

'But, beta, that's exactly why you should be open with him. You should bring Elliot up just in passing. Nikhu, bicharo –'

'He's too young,' his mother whispered. 'It'll upset him if I just randomly throw his dead dad into every conversation.'

'It'll upset him or it'll upset you?'

Avani tutted. 'Let's not do this now, Dad. All right?'

The click of the indicator punctuated their silence before the car swerved left. Nik felt his dinner slosh around in his stomach and he braced himself as he slumped to the right. He was starting to feel unwell and silently tugged at the seat belt that was pressing down on his tummy. There was a tension in the car, a worry, he could feel it. He wondered if he'd caused it; earlier, his grandfather had pointed to some actor in a cowboy hat who Nik couldn't name, saying he looked just like Paul. His mother had agreed and told Nik to take a photo. He did as he was told, then he took her hand and asked: *Which one looks like my puppa?*

His mother opened her mouth, as if she was about to answer him, but then brushed him off, distracting him with the promise of finding a new school bag in the gift shop. When she was paying, his grandfather pulled Nik to one side. He simply ran his hand gently through Nik's hair, the way Nik loved. He didn't need to say anything.

'Avani, beta,' his grandfather said, 'I know it's hard for you, but it's not fair for Nikhil not to know his father. You don't have to talk about the end, but at least –'

'Puppa, rheva de, please. He's *my* son. I'll decide what's best for him. I appreciate your help, but just let me manage this.'

In the back seat, Nik opened his eyes and squinted at the back of his mother's head. He stretched out his hand, trying to grasp the words trapped in the warm air of the car. He hoped, one day, when he was grown, he'd be able to understand what they meant.

'As you wish,' came his grandfather's voice, in a final whisper.

10

October 2017

Avani picks up her glass of wine and walks barefoot through Maya's immaculate flat, which is tucked away in a quiet, leafy corner of Highgate. A pair of Devon Rexes pace in cautious circles outside the bathroom. Avani tries to call the strange-looking creatures, Beatrice and Patricia-Marie, over to her. They respond by glancing at her uninterestedly. Patricia-Marie begins clawing at the door while Beatrice throws in the odd meow for some extra drama. Avani watches them, thinking of how unusual their coats are; they look as though they've endured a stint in the washing machine on a very high heat.

'She'll be out in a minute,' Avani tells them, reaching down to stroke Beatrice, who dodges her hand. Avani tuts and walks over to Maya's bookshelves, which she has always been in awe of. They sweep from ceiling to floor and across two adjacent walls. Maya's rearranged them since Avani's last visit, so that the books are organised by the colour of their spine. Novels, memoirs and cookbooks flow across the shelves from a deep red to a bright purple and back again. Each shelf has a copper Hindu deity at the centre of it: Ganapati, Shiva, Saraswati, Lakshmi, Krishna. Maya uses a collection of palm-sized prints as bookends, encased in frames that are several inches thick. Avani spots one that she hasn't noticed before perched against a volume of the *Ramayan*. It looks like oil on canvas, and has a quasi-Impressionist feel to it, but the brushstrokes feel slightly looser than those in the prints of Monet and Renoir that once hung in her bedroom. There's a sense of lightness to the brushstrokes, which can't be placed alongside the tight, overlapping, almost claustrophobic strokes of the paintings she used to love; dense to a degree that they now leave her feeling as though there is no room to breathe.

The image before her is a simple one. A morning sky, the sun hiding behind an army of billowing clouds. Below, the sea. The two coming together in a perfect square.

Avani takes a step closer and notices what looks like birds speckled between the clouds, their reflection in the sea. She pauses, wondering if the reflections are actually ripples in the water. The longer she compares the two halves of the painting, the louder a thought grows in her mind. It itches at her uncomfortably as it forms until it presents itself: perhaps this isn't a painting of the sky meeting the sea. Perhaps it's a sky that meets a sky. Or a sea that meets a sea. Perhaps the place where one meets the other isn't the horizon at all, but the cold, sharp edge of a mirror.

She places her glass of wine on a bookshelf and reaches for the painting. She brings it closer to her and then rotates it so that it's upside down. It's exactly the same. She scours the corners of the canvas for the artist's mark, to figure out which side is the sea and which the sky. But it isn't signed.

Mary J. Blige begins to sing from Maya's speakers. Avani recognises the album they listened to non-stop in the winter of 1992 and into the spring of '93. By the summer, this music had bled deep into the fabric of her life. It was the summer she graduated, the summer Chand married, the summer she and Elliot moved in together. The opening chords of 'You Remind Me' bring a rush of memories: the evening she and Maya shrugged leather jackets over their saris and snuck off from Chand's vidhi to a party with henna on their hands; the excitement she felt as she and Elliot drove away from university after their exams towards the flat they would rent in Neasden; the way he'd thrown her over his shoulder and yelled with excitement when she got the phone call telling her she'd landed a training contract with a major accountancy firm. Those chords make her feel warm for a fleeting moment that moves along so quickly she almost doubts it was ever there. In its wake lies the shadow of everything she lost. This music makes her think of happiness, of the brightest summer there was, of a time she doesn't want to revisit. It makes her think of her husband.

'Should we eat?' Maya appears in the doorway. Although they've already spent an hour together, Avani finds herself taken aback by how beautiful her oldest friend looks. She's wearing a grey knitted dress that sweeps down to her shins, where a sliver of skin glows above designer slippers. Her chin-length hair, which is usually straightened to an inch of its life, today falls in relaxed waves that ebb around her face. She hasn't embraced its natural curl since they were teenagers. It suits her.

Avani turns back to the painting. 'Is this . . . a trick?'

'I think that's the beauty of it.' Maya takes the painting from Avani's hand and rotates it. 'That either way you rest it, it's the same.'

Avani watches as Maya puts it back on the shelf. She tries to figure out if it's the same way it was when she found it. There's no way to tell. She picks it up again and looks at the back, to see if there's a hook. 'This is madness,' she laughs, when she doesn't find one.

'Isn't all art?' Maya says, her eyes playful. She bends down to stroke Patricia-Marie, who is brushing against Avani's legs. 'In fact, wasn't it you who told me that, back when you fancied yourself a painter?'

'An artist,' Avani corrects, blinking away Maya's question. 'Are those little things birds in the sky, then? Or ripples in the sea? Or a reflection?'

'I think they can be any of the above,' Maya says, inching closer to it. Avani notices her usual honeysuckle perfume has been swapped for a headier oud. The scent brings with it the image of long-stemmed roses burning on a wood fire. Avani doesn't realise Maya is still watching her until she feels a hand on her arm and hears Maya say, 'Let's eat.'

She puts the painting back, picks up her glass, and follows Maya into the kitchen. 'There just . . . there has to be an answer, a right way up,' she finds herself saying, leaning against the door frame as she looks back towards the bookshelf. 'One side must be the sky and one the sea.'

'But I think that's the point,' Maya says, checking the lasagne that's bubbling away in the oven. She pulls it out and places it on the worktop. 'Equivalence.'

The word feels unfamiliar in Avani's mouth as she tastes the shape of it.

Maya motions for Avani to sit down. She cuts the lasagne into neat little squares while Avani slices up a loaf of sourdough.

'So, tell me,' Maya says, taking a seat, 'how's everything? And I want a proper answer this time, not the "totally fine" you gave me when you came in.'

'I'm honestly fine,' Avani says. Maya gives her a look which she pretends not to notice. 'Still adjusting to Dad and Nikhil being gone, but I'm getting there.' She nods to the bread. 'Did you say this is home-made?'

'Yes, but not by myself. Av, how's Nikhil?'

'I think he's all right,' Avani says after a moment, trying to sound casual. 'Things are better now, but we had a bit of a . . . spat as he was leaving.'

'What d'you mean?'

Avani is ready to brush the question away, but instead, she finds herself putting her fork and knife down carefully. 'Remember . . . the car that Elliot bought?' She bounces the words off each other as she speaks, in an attempt to get them out smoothly. She reminds herself she is in a safe space, the safest of spaces, probably the place she feels is next in line to her own home, now that her father's house is in the process of being sold.

Maya doesn't respond. She's staring out of the window, deep in thought. 'Yeah, I do. That big green thing.'

'Yeah, that's it.' Avani picks her cutlery up again and cuts her lasagne up as she speaks. 'It was a fancy BMW. Chand helped him pick it. Bought it outright with the inheritance money that came through from his favourite aunt, the one he used to stay with when things got rough with his parents.'

'I remember. You rowed about it, right? You wanted to save up to redo the house and he surprised you with a new car.'

'Yeah, it was just a couple of months before he died.' She catches Maya's eye and notices a shift in her expression. She waits for Maya to speak but her friend holds back whatever it is that she is thinking. 'We just didn't have room for a second car – and I gave him so much . . .' Words leave her and she tries her best not to cry. 'I really told him off for it, so we were still arguing about it when he –'

'I remember, honey. It's okay. People fight all the time.'

'He loved that thing. He wanted one ever since Chand taught us to drive at uni.'

Maya nods, her eyes sad.

'My dad kept it, all this time.'

'Sorry, what?'

Avani tells Maya about the documents she found, the key hidden behind the desk, the garage. She breaks pieces of sourdough into chunks as she speaks. 'I should have expected it, really,' she says. 'Big or small, there's always a secret in death's wake. I was waiting for something to surface, if I'm honest. But I totally didn't expect it to be this.' She thinks then of her husband, of how – when she eventually summoned the strength to start sorting through his things – she'd searched through his desk for that Moleskine journal he kept. She'd told her father to look out for it when he'd helped pack Elliot's clothes, books and life away. Now, she wonders, not for the first time, if her father had lied; if he'd found it and hid it, as he did the car; if there was something in it he didn't want her to see.

'This is an awful lot,' Maya says, pulling her back. 'Why would he store it like that, for all these years?'

'You know what Dad was like. He would have felt it was such a shame to sell it, when Ell had only just bought it. He was so sentimental about things like that.'

'But Nikhil's selling it?'

Avani nods. 'He said he'd take care of it when I dropped him at uni. Remember little Will? His father has a garage so I expect he'll help shift it.'

'Good.'

'I've told Nikhil to use the money to buy a second-hand Polo.'

'He must be loving university.'

'I think so. Though there's definitely more going on with him. He's not being very forthcoming at the moment. I think losing Dad and then also Paul showing up at the funeral has just shaken everything up for him.'

Maya grimaces at the mention of Paul. 'How was it for you? Seeing him again?'

Avani thinks about this, trying her best to be honest with herself. 'It was nice to see him,' she says, 'but I didn't want it to be.'

Maya sighs and leans back in her chair. She swirls the dregs of wine around in her glass and says, 'He's the other side of London now. South of the river.'

Avani watches her, willing her to go on.

'Single.'

'How do you even –'

'Facebook.' Maya downs the wine.

'Goodness.'

'Don't judge. It keeps me connected when I'm away on cases.'

'He could be seeing someone though and just not have her plastered all over his social media.'

'True,' Maya says, her gaze finding Avani's.

'Discretion is his speciality, remember?' Avani says tightly, wiping her hands unnecessarily on a napkin. 'Anyway I'm bored of talking about myself. What else is new with you? Why've you been so hard to get a hold of?' She thinks of the unanswered calls, the fact she's barely seen or heard from Maya since her father's death, the new hair and perfume, the way the cats won't leave Maya alone, as if they too have been missing her. A thought begins to form at the back of Avani's mind. It makes her nervous. She doesn't like the shape of it, how it's tall, how it looks like a man.

'I'm going to come back to this, just to warn you,' Maya tells her after a pause. She tops up their glasses. 'I'll allow a little intermission for now, since it segues so neatly.'

Avani raises her eyebrows.

'I've met someone, actually.'

There it is. 'What? Where?'

'Online.'

'I knew it.' This is a lie and Avani isn't sure where it came from. She had no idea that Maya had been seeing anyone before just a few moments ago. Or that she was even looking. She's slightly embarrassed that she missed this, and that Maya's waited until now to mention it.

'Tell me everything.'

'It's still early days,' Maya says. She delivers the key facts as though she is presenting evidence, in short sharp sentences. 'He's really great. Baked the sourdough, actually. Lives down the road in Crouch End. Never married. No kids.'

Avani does her best to pay attention as Maya tells her about this software developer, Richard. But after just a few moments she realises that she hasn't heard Maya talk about a man like this in years. She notices how Maya's avoiding making eye contact, switching instead between reaching for her wine and moving the lasagne around on her plate, consuming neither, as if she's bashful about how obvious it is that she likes him. Her smile grows larger and her eyes brighter as she speaks. Avani sips her wine, takes bites of her dinner, which she can't really taste any more, and makes all the right noises. But inside, what she is thinking is this: Maya is her only single friend. She's been like a sister since they were children, and they'd become closer still after things ended with Paul, bonding over how awful dating is in one's late thirties, before they both gave up trying. Now Avani's about to lose her, too.

Avani wonders if she'd feel the same way if her father was still here, and if Nik hadn't left for university. Since her father's death, it feels as though all those closest to her are moving on in their own small way. It's selfish, and extremely premature, but Avani already begins to mourn for what their friendship was, and the empty space that will be left in its wake. Maya has always been her person, the one she could say anything to, the one that was always available. She thinks back to a couple of months after she broke things off with Paul and had just endured a series of appalling blind dates; she left a doctor's waiting room, missing her appointment and driving back home with a bladder infection that was moving its way up to her kidney, all because of the insufferably besotted pregnant couple sitting opposite her. They were unable to keep their hands off each other, and switched between baby talk and discussing their weekend plans at length. To make things even more trite, they had matching Barbour jackets on; with their arms wrapped around each other it was difficult to tell where one started and the other began. The man had a habit of giving his partner a peck on her temple or cheek whenever there was a rare moment of silence. But it was the way they looked at each other which had caused a visceral reaction in Avani. She hadn't been able to stomach the way that the man gazed at his partner, with an expression so full of love and warmth that it had left her in physical pain. She recognised, in it, everything she herself had had snatched from her, and then tried and failed to replicate again with Paul. It had made her feel a deep and inescapable loneliness.

Fuckers, Maya had said, when she turned up at Avani's door with some surplus antibiotics from her own medicine cabinet. *Report them for indecent exposure.*

Maya had been the only one who'd really understood how difficult it was to be around other couples, the only friend who didn't roll her eyes when Avani insisted they watch an action film instead of a romcom. Avani had married Elliot and had Nik several years before their wider friendship group caught up. She'd been the first to marry, the first to have a child, leading the way it seemed.

It was much later, when things ended with Paul, that her friends began disappearing into marriages and babies en masse and she'd found herself alone once more. She'd seen two paths unfold in front of her: the first was sticking to the life she had with her son, the second was attempting yet again to meet someone, and have another chance at a proper family, giving Nik a sort-of father, possibly a sibling. She'd taken the former. Avani and Maya had become the two outliers, each calling the other for support when, at weddings, nosy masis would approach to ask if they would like help with husband hunting. The last time it happened, they'd been at a friend's wedding when a cluster of masis had descended, one pointing to a much older kaka watching Avani from the opposite end of the hall. He had a five o'clock shadow that looked almost green, which framed a heavy, stale-looking moustache. He eyed her sternly as he raised a glass of lassi to his lips, a carpet of wiry dark hairs coating his knuckles, visible even from across the room. Maya had made a gagging sound next to Avani.

I recognise him, Avani told the masi. He was that kaka who was forever staring at them, unperturbed even when they met his gaze with hostility. *Didn't I go to his wedding like ten years ago? What happened to his wife?*

Eh pun off thaigya, the masi had puffed. So she fancied herself a widow matchmaker, did she? Brilliant.

If I have to wake up to something that furry every day, Avani murmured to Maya once the masi had shuffled off, *I'd much rather get a dog. Probably more love and affection and less bakwaas that way, too.*

As the rest of their friends settled into their second and third, sometimes fourth, children, something had happened to the pace of their lives. With Nik much older than her friends' children, and her father just down the road and always ready to help, Avani had been the only one still free to go out for last-minute dinners and hiking trips with Maya without having to find a babysitter or negotiate with partners. Their friends' routines grew into waltzes of babies and husbands and school runs, while Avani and Maya watched from the outside, together, the beat of their lives stuck in mid-tempo.

A clear, dark voice tells Avani that might be about to change. It is not as though Maya has been short of men. Rather the opposite. Maya has dipped in and out of dating, never admitted to so much as fancying a man, seeing it simply as a muscle to exercise, fun to be had when she's in between cases. But they have always been fleeting, never staying long enough to require names. It's not the man Avani's worried about as such, but rather the look on Maya's face when she talks about him – this Richard. The last time Avani saw this look on her face, the one she's wearing now, was when Maya had fallen head over heels in love with a partner at her law firm, Siddarth. They'd been in their early twenties at the time. Avani hadn't seen Maya for four months. She'd disappeared into the folds of love as though it were a book that had swallowed her whole, reappearing dishevelled and depressed only after it ended. The same thing had happened when Maya fell for her first boyfriend at university, Kasun, an optometry student who'd grown up in Galway. She isn't able to balance love and life in equal measures. Avani knows their friendship may soon be forsaken. It has always been Maya's way.

Avani pushes through the rest of the evening with this thought sitting uncomfortably at the pit of her stomach, poking and prodding at her. She tries to drown it out with more wine and lasagne, but her appetite is gone. Maya's perfume seems to have grown more pungent. It draws a headache towards Avani's temples. Her eyes keep gravitating to the snoozing Devon Rexes lounging on Maya's window seat. Perhaps she too should get herself a companion, now that her son is gone and her best friend is lost to the fog of new love. She'll get a poodle, or a Labrador, to mark a new transition, something she can pour her time and love into, something to soften the sting of loneliness.

She is preoccupied, her mind racing with these thoughts, so she doesn't feel as though she is fully present until much later, when, as she is slipping her shoes back on and getting ready to leave, Maya turns to her and says: 'You're doing so well, sweetheart –' Avani feels a pang of irritation that she knows is more to do with the alcohol and late night than the patronage – 'and I know I haven't been around as much but you seem so much stronger than I expected you to be –' annoyance flicks her again, a hot rubber band against her skin – 'and, I don't know if you realise, but today's the first time you've described Ell's death to me as simply him dying.'

The words don't immediately register. 'What?'

'You always allude to the other word, when it's just me and you.'

Avani doesn't know what to say. She is confused for a moment, then angered. Betrayal bubbles under her skin. Maya knows the rules; they only talk about Elliot when Avani brings it up. That's how it's always been. He is not anyone else's to throw into conversations as an anecdote, to bring up without warning like this. The wine has made her mouth dry and she knows it is also making her more impatient than she would otherwise be.

Maya seems to mistake Avani's silence and wraps her in a hug. 'I feel like something's shifting,' she says, 'like you're finally letting go. I'm so proud of you.'

Avani feels herself stiffen. Heat rises to her cheeks. She tucks a strand of hair behind her ear and opens her mouth but Maya gets there first.

'Come out with Richard and me on Friday. He's got a friend who we'd really like you to meet. He's a tremendously handsome archit—'

'Not a chance,' Avani says, shoving her arms into her coat.

'Oh, Avani. Why not? It'll be fun.'

'I'm not interested, Maya.'

'Honestly, you'll love him. He's –'

'Look, don't bring up Elliot like that, all right?' Avani says, unable to stop herself, her forehead creasing. 'Don't talk to me about letting go. You've no idea.'

Maya's bottom lip disappears into her mouth. Her eyes look tired. 'Hey,' she says, her voice soft as Avani reaches for the door, 'it's about time you made some space, Av.'

'What?'

'You weren't the only one who lost him. I grew up with him too.'

She has heard these words before. She thought they'd laid this conversation to rest. 'You didn't know him like I did, Maya. You didn't see all of him,' she says, furious now.

'Absolutely. But you weren't the only one that loved him. We all lost him too. We're all with you in your grief. It's been almost twenty years, Av. You don't need to push us away.'

'Who exactly is "us"?'

Maya shrugs. 'Your dad, me, Chand, Nikhil . . .'

Avani stares at her, incredulous, the image of all of her loved ones standing against her as opposed to beside her. She shakes her head and storms out, letting the door slam shut between them. Rage blossoms in her, maturing to a shame so acute that it freezes her in place. She's aware that she should turn round and make it right. But pride glues her in place. She doesn't leave until she hears Maya's slippers on the other side of the door, padding their way back towards the kitchen.

11

October 2017

Nik isn't one hundred per cent certain what to expect when his new flatmate Melanie knocks on his door on a rainy Sunday morning, not long after he has arrived at university, and asks if he would like to 'go to town'.

'On what?' he asks.

She giggles and tells him to get his coat. It transpires, to his disappointment, 'going to town' means wandering through cobbled streets lined with boutique shops and independent restaurants. His university campus sits in the middle of a heavily pedestrianised medieval city that is nothing like he has ever experienced. The pace of life is slower here. People amble as opposed to rushing like they do in London. Bus drivers seem to have no qualms about idling a few seconds longer when they see someone in the distance signalling at them to wait. Even the air feels fresher. Nik notices stars twinkling above once darkness falls, their shine no longer blurred out by the pollution of the capital. There is a certain charm to the place, he'll admit, but also a sense of claustrophobia. This is heightened when, after a few hours of walking around with his flatmates, he begins to recognise the same faces walking past, as though there are so few people here that they recycle themselves. He soon discovers that 'town' consists of a surplus of pubs and churches arranged around a single shopping centre with all the chain stores crammed into it, hidden away inside concrete walls, as if the locals are too ashamed to admit they have need for Primark and JD Sports and Pizza Hut.

He hadn't noticed this on the open day, when he was so enamoured by the country's best History department, and the fact that the ratio of female to male students was almost 70:30. Now, he notices another ratio, the thought collecting in him slowly before he fully registers it: this little town is much less multicultural than London, just like Layla warned him it would be. When the occasional non-white person does pass him, something interesting occurs. He is queueing for a table at Nando's with his flatmates the first time it happens, when a girl who looks just like Teo's sister passes him. As she walks by, she smiles at him, a smile so wide that it suggests they know each other. He glances over his shoulder sheepishly to check if he is in the way of someone else. But it is him she is looking at. The same thing happens when he stops to buy tobacco at a Tesco Metro – an elderly kaka a few tills down gives him a friendly nod as he leaves. He looks back again to see the man watching him still, warmth in his eyes. It isn't until he is on the bus back to campus, when he takes a seat in front of a family chatting away in Urdu, who greet him as though he is a much-loved nephew that has popped over for lunch, that he understands these nods and smiles are some form of code, a small sign of unity in what is a very white world, one much whiter than he has ever seen growing up in Harrow.

'So hold on,' Nik says, when he and his flatmates are

almost back at campus, 'is that literally it? So like, that's all the shops? They're all in one place?'

Melanie watches him for a moment then says, 'Correct.'

'Well, yeah, obviously.' Simon – a local Geography student – turns from the seat in front of Nik. 'It's a town, mate.' Simon's a foot shorter than Nik and already balding at eighteen. He wears a flatcap, which seems to hold the dual purpose of covering up his hairline and also adding an inch or two to his height.

'It's so tiny though,' Nik says, almost to himself, trying to get his head around it as he prepares a rollie. He no longer has the option of walking to St Anne's in Harrow or driving to Brent Cross or tubing it to Westfield. Here, there is only one option – 'town'.

'Not big enough for the London boy?' Simon asks. Nik doesn't know how to respond. He watches Simon smirk, then twist a gold ring around his pinkie.

'Nik, whereabouts is home again, buddy?' Dan – another flatmate, who Nik shares a few lectures with – asks, filling the awkward silence with his calm, slow words. There is a quality in them that makes Nik think of Teo, of Will, of London, of home.

'Harrow, mate. You're Tottenham, yeah?'

'Yeah. Nice having another Londoner about,' he says, raising his fist for Nik to bump.

Simon's glare follows their hands as he says: 'I'm sure there will be plenty more of you city boys kicking around. Where you actually from though, Nik?'

Nik feels his eyes narrowing slightly. Fuck's sake. Not this shit already. 'Harrow, mate. Like I just said.'

'You know what I mean. Where did your parents grow up?'

Melanie's eyes shoot across to Simon, her face crumpling into a frown.

'Harrow,' Nik says, slower this time. 'Would you like their National Insurance numbers, too?'

Simon puts his hands up and says, 'Fucking hell,' as if trying to reason with someone who is attempting to rob him. 'Only asking. You just don't look like a Nik.'

'What's a "Nik" supposed to look like, pal?' Dan asks, his voice flat.

'Jesus,' Simon mutters, facing the front of the bus again.

'Happy to work on the beard, mate,' Nik says.

Melanie bites away a laugh, turning to give Nik a smile instead. Simon shakes his head and puts a pair of earphones in.

Nik's glad the conversation is over, but the discomfort in his chest hasn't quite eased when Melanie announces: 'I had a Bollywood-themed eighteenth.'

Nik licks the edge of the rollie he is assembling. 'Right.'

'It was so much fun. I wore a sari and a bindi and everything.'

Nik returns her smile through tight lips. He's grown suddenly hot and can feel sweat collecting on his back. He's too confined to remove his jumper so rolls yet another cigarette just for something to do, then offers it to Dan, who tucks it behind his ear, loose pieces of tobacco blending into his brown hair. For the rest of the journey, Nik sits very still, afraid moving will draw too much attention to himself. Layla, warm and comforting, rises in his mind, bringing with her a gentle swooping in his stomach. She was so right. Nik instinctively checks his phone. No messages. Like Will and Teo, she too is busy meeting new people, going to freshers' events, forging new friendships.

He thinks again of Layla's warning, how he'd brushed it off, embarrassed by his naivety. His eyes find Dan's hands, resting on his knees, just inches from Nik's own. They look almost identical in size. Neither bites their nails. Both have long, fine hair creeping out from the sleeve of their jumpers. The only difference is the shade of their skin. He's suddenly so aware of this organ stretching over every inch of him – still darker than usual from five short days under the glow of India's sun – here, away from the comfort of London, defining him.

A couple of weeks later, on a Thursday towards the middle of October, Nik is woken by four quiet knocks on his bedroom door. He opens one eye to see light streaming in through the thin, ill-fitting curtains that dress his window. He had been dreaming of home and something tightens unpleasantly in his core when he registers that he is not waking up in Harrow.

The sound of four gentle knocks comes again. He is so close to sleep, pressed flush against it, even, when he hears the handle of his door move up and down and a deep voice call: 'Hey, mate. You all right in there?' It's Dan.

'Hey, bud.' Nik pushes his head out of the covers and aims at the hallway when he speaks. His voice is thick with sleep.

'We've got Rosenbaum in ten. You gonna make it?' Dan calls.

'Not a chance, bro.'

There's a pause. Then: 'Message me if you want anything from the shop.'

'Cheers, man.'

A van rushes past Nik's open window, and somewhere down the road a baby begins to wail. A dog joins in, its barks bouncing off the concrete and up into Nik's room. Sleep slips further away from him. He clutches at it, pressing his eyes harder together and trying to clear his mind. There's silence for a moment. A beautiful, still silence. He inhales it. Then the sound of a siren fills the street below, screeching its way up to his room. He groans and gets to his feet.

Nik reaches for the glass he placed beside his bed last night and downs the inch of warm water inside it. He grabs his phone. Along with a missed call from his mother, the screen shows a message from an unsaved number:

> 10:54 +44 7234 209838: Hey kid. Happy Diwali. Look, if you don't reply to this, I'll leave you alone. I know you're probably at uni now having a blast, but I just wanted to check in. I'm currently in the Maldives but heading up your way for a meeting next Friday. If you want to see a friendly face over a bite, let me know. Paul

Nik groans as he throws his phone onto the pile of laundry accumulating under his desk. He gets back into bed and pulls the covers over his head. He wakes up to the sound of loud, angry knuckles beating against his door several hours later. They aren't polite like Dan's, but incessant, relentless.

'What?' he shouts, yanking the door open. He has risen much too fast and feels his head spinning. His eyes take a moment to adjust to the fluorescent lights of the hallway.

His friend Alice stands a metre away from him. 'What the hell, Nik? You missed another whole day of lectures.'

Nik makes a noise that even he can't decipher.

'Are you poorly?' she asks. Before he has a chance to respond, she adds: 'It's a Thursday, so you can't have been out last night.'

'I know what day it is,' he grunts, scratching his chest. He looks down to realise that he's wearing nothing but a pair of boxer shorts. She peers over his shoulder. He closes the door an inch. 'What do you want?'

'Well, I was worried about – what on earth is that?' She points to the pile of clothes under his desk.

'Laundry.'

'That looks like something could nest in it. It's disgusting.'

'You're not my mum, man.'

'Pull yourself together and get that down to the launderette. Come on. We'll go together.'

'I'm about to make dinner. I'll do it tomorrow.'

'Do you have any food in?'

Nik pauses and rubs the beard he's sporting, which is still in the itchy phase. He forgot to pack a razor, so hasn't shaved since moving away.

'We'll go to the shop while the clothes are in the wash. C'mon. Hurry up.'

'Nah, I'm good. I don't even know where the bloody launderette is. This campus is like a maze.'

'It's literally round the corner. I need to go to the shops anyway. Come with me.'

'I'm good, man.'

'Great! I'll wait right here.'

Nik mutters darkly as he steps into the faded tracksuit bottoms he's been living in for the past couple of weeks and pushes his arms through a crumpled T-shirt from the pile of laundry. He stuffs the rest of his dirty clothes into a blue IKEA bag.

'Come on then, you bloody pest,' he grumbles, closing his door behind him a minute later.

In that time, Alice has sunk to the floor outside Nik's room, cross-legged, engrossed in her phone. She stands when she sees him, tugging the strap of her tote bag over her shoulder. The words 'De Beauvoir Deli' are etched across it.

'Happy Diwali, by the way,' she says.

'Thanks.'

'Are you celebrating?'

'Clearly.'

'What do you usually do for it?'

Nik considers this, but the image of home stirs something in him that he doesn't want to deal with. He hasn't been back yet since moving away. He does not want to think about Diwali without his grandfather. Best to just pretend the day isn't happening at all. So he shrugs and grunts, hoping Alice will pack it in.

'Is it your first one away from home?'

'Hmm.'

'Wait here,' she says when they reach the stairwell. She sprints up the stairs.

'Where are you –'

'I need to grab my laundry,' she shouts, her voice echoing down to him.

He stands in the grey stairwell, squinting against the fluorescent lights that seem even brighter here than in the hallway. He's unreasonably exhausted for someone who has spent the last few days moving at the pace of a sloth. At first, he thought this feeling was just a prolonged hangover. Then, he assumed it was the inevitable fresher's flu. But when his sudden exhaustion wasn't joined by a cough or fever it began to dawn upon him that it might be something else altogether.

His limbs are almost too heavy to hold up. Without thinking about it, he sinks to the floor. A slow, dreadful numbness ebbs towards him. He feels sweat collecting in the space between his shoulder blades as he presses his back against the cold wall. He forces himself to focus on the walls, noticing what a perfect square the stairwell is. The sense of dread gains pace, creeping over him. It's the same one that came to him for the first time in the days after his grandfather's death. It's the feeling that something awful is just around the corner, that something terrible is coming. The walls grow closer. A sudden, urgent need to go back home shoots through him. This has happened a few times now – this quickening of his breath, the clamminess of his hands, the feeling that he needs to run, to escape back to safety. His body prepares for a battle that doesn't arrive.

The first time it came over him, he was working in

the library beside Melanie. He'd packed his things up and retreated to his room in a blur, sitting in the dark until he'd returned to a normal temperature and his heart had stopped threatening to leap out of his chest. The second time, he was tucking into a Pot Noodle and watching *Stranger Things* with Dan. He thought he was allergic to an ingredient in his dinner and read through the list on the pot until his eyes could no longer focus and he couldn't breathe properly. He'd been mortified to be around someone he barely knew, someone he thought was cool, as his breathing quickened and his T-shirt grew dark with sweat.

Breathe in through your nose, mate, Dan had said. *Out through your mouth.*

I can't, Nik puffed, in between jagged breaths, as he hung out of Dan's window.

Try, Dan told him. *It's harder to hyperventilate if you breathe through your nose.*

Hyperventilate, Nik thought. Finally, a word he could wrap around these episodes, like an ill-fitting, dusty coat.

He wonders if it's possible to become unwell from change. Surely not. Yet every time he wakes, once the reality of his life settles in – the fact that his grandfather is gone, the fact that he's stuck at a university hundreds of miles from home – his fingers go numb and his chest feels as though there's a weight pressing down on it. He's overwhelmed by a sense of disconnect, as if everything familiar and safe has been wiped away. It has been almost a month since he arrived at university, and the plan of going home every weekend hasn't quite worked out; the journey would take four hours door to door. He's annoyed at himself for this, for not fixing the car up before he left. But progress is being made; most of the new parts have now arrived at Papa Burns' garage. He'd texted Nik a few days ago, offering to do the work in between other jobs, but Nik replied telling him he felt he needed to do the car up himself. A part of him had warmed, though, when Papa Burns had replied with a simple: OK. Here if you need. Take care of yourself, son

Nik had stared at those three small letters closing off the text for a very long time, so long that he'd found himself tracing their shape on the screen.

He clears his throat and fishes out his phone from the bag of laundry, with the aim of googling 'Can you get ill from change?' His hands are shaking, and he tries to focus on the trembling screen as he rereads Paul's text and then goes to write one to his mother. When he sees her name in his list of contacts, his finger lingers on the call button, but he knows he can't press it. Hearing her voice today will unravel whatever it is that's barely holding him together. They managed to gloss over the row they had the day before he left, both pretending nothing had happened when they packed the car up the next morning, each politely insisting that the other could choose a Spotify playlist for the drive. In the end, they decided to pick a song each in turns, his mother telling him they were the songs she listened to when she was at university. Mica Paris, Des'ree and Soul II Soul intertwined with Kendrick, Dizzee Rascal and Skepta. Despite the niceties, Nik feels so far away from her, in a way that transcends the physical miles between them. He sees that she's online, so sends her a message instead.

18:04 Nik: Hey, Mum. Happy Diwali. Sorry for missing your call this morning. How's stuff? I'm about to do a load of laundry with Alice, then making dinner x

18:05 Mum: Nikhu! Was just going to try and call again. Happy Diwali, beta. How are lectures? Make sure you wash your jeans separately to your white T-shirts please or else the colour will run. Say hello to Alice from me. What are you making for dinner? I'm planning to make a load of theplas tonight. Not as fun with no one to share. Love, Mum xxx

18:06 Nik: I don't know about dinner yet, probs pasta or something. Will call you tomorrow? x

18:06 Mum: OK, beta. Try to get some veggies in there please. And light a divo this evening if you can. Remember, it's our new year tomorrow. Speak soon. Love, Mum xxx

He opens that chat with Layla. He clicks on the little round circle to look at her deep brown eyes, her smile. Pain swoops through him. She has barely messaged him recently, and when she has, her responses have been shorter than usual. This isn't on her though, he knows that. He's outright ignored her twice when she's asked if he's free to FaceTime. He knows that he's pushing her away, not because he doesn't want to speak to her, but because he's terrified of her seeing him as he is now, this version of him that can't even summon the strength to take a full breath. Last week, she posted about winning that poetry competition she'd been shortlisted for. Her entry – a villanelle about an estranged father and daughter – will soon appear on a billboard at Oxford Circus station. Platform 4, according to a press release Nik read last night.

Since leaving London, Nik's watched her grow brighter and even more beautiful through Snapchat stories of her dancing on nights out, playing drinking games, making new friends. She's having exactly the sort of university experience he'd assumed would be waiting for him too. They made no promises to each other before he left, Nik simply saying that he'd be back most weekends and they'd see if they could meet up. Although home is all he wants right now, he can't bear the idea of his friends, and especially Layla, seeing who he's become.

His breathing hasn't yet steadied, so he closes his eyes and tightens his fists. He tries his best to keep the rising panic away. He opens an eye and stares up the stairwell, willing Alice through the door. She annoys the absolute hell out of him but being around her also makes him feel closer to home. He was so glad to run into her on his first day of lectures – he had been late for a seminar and noticed a head of long blonde hair swivel interestedly in his direction when their tutor asked for his name, ticking it neatly off the list in front of him before continuing without giving Nik any instructions.

Nik slid into the only empty seat at the back of the room, then looked up to see the blonde girl still staring at him. She offered him a smile, which he was too mentally dishevelled to return. Instead, he busied himself by pulling his textbooks from his bag, which he realised were for a completely different module. The girl followed him out of the room and down the pathway to the university bar when they were dismissed.

Nik?

Yeah? Nik had called over his shoulder, stopping when he noticed her rushing towards him.

Nik Harroldson?

It's Harrison.

Ah, that's it. I can't believe it's you. Alice!

Huh?

Alice Lincoln. We went to Elmgrove together.

Nik stared at her and something slotted neatly into place. *Oh, yeah. I remember. You moved away in Year 6, didn't you?*

Yeah, that's right. We moved to east London.

The sound of a door slamming shut slices through Nik's thoughts. He looks up to see Alice rushing down the steps. 'Ready!' she calls.

He gets up and exhales slowly. When she reaches him, she asks: 'Did you, like, run a marathon in the five minutes it took for me to get my laundry?'

'What?'

'Seriously, you look like hell,' she says, her voice low.

'Rah, will you ever stop trying to chirpse me?'

The sound of her laughter makes him feel warmer for a moment. He sneaks a peek at her as they reach the bottom floor. Her hair is tied in a knot on the top of her head, held in place by a coiled pink band that reminds Nik of an old telephone cord.

'What's up with you? Why are you so far away?' she asks, catching his eye. They're outside. Nik hoped being in an open space would help, but the sky is so deeply black it gives him the sensation that a dark blanket has wrapped itself around Earth, drawing in tighter. He can't remember the last time he was outside when it was light.

'I'm totally fine,' he says, hearing his mother's defiance in his voice. They turn a corner and Nik spots the launderette straight ahead. He'd assumed it was on the other side of campus, not a mere couple of minutes from his halls.

'Don't seem it.'

'I said I'm good, man.'

'You know, I think if you try once more, but really say it with some conviction this time, I'll believe you.'

Nik holds the launderette door open for her. She slides neatly under his arm into the stuffy room. Nik follows her and turns his makeshift laundry bag upside down, emptying the contents straight into a washer without bothering to sort through them. He stares into the drum.

'Do you want to talk ab—'

'What did I miss today then, in lectures?' Nik asks.

Alice hands him a capful of detergent and eyes his laundry. 'You can have a copy of my notes if you want. The first was all about the rise of witchcraft in England – super interesting – and then the second one was about the Viking Phenomenon, but you probably didn't read the book, did you?'

Nik throws her an empty stare.

'Yeah, thought so. Right. We've got forty-five minutes till these are done. Let's go to Sainsbury's.'

When they reach the shop, Nik picks up a couple of baskets and trails behind Alice who, it transpires, didn't need to come to the mini supermarket at all. They complete a loop of the store, Nik reaching for packets of instant noodles and pre-cooked rice, and Alice grimacing at each item he deposits in his basket. Remembering his mother's comment about vegetables, Nik throws in a bag of salad as they pass the chilled aisle. After they circle the shop once, Alice stops to scan the newspapers.

'Are you serious?' Nik asks, stifling a yawn. 'Who even reads the papers any more?'

'Please tell me you read the news.'

'Don't be stupid. That's what Twitter's for.'

'You're incredible,' she says.

'I try.'

She rolls her eyes and picks up a copy of the *Guardian*. It makes Nik think of Saturday mornings as a child, when his mother would be at her weekly running club, and Nik would wake up to the smell of cardamom and ginger. He'd find his grandfather sitting at their kitchen table, dipping biscuits into his chai while he read the paper. The memory brings a wave of nostalgia and homesickness that is so strong Nik can feel it pressed against his face, like a wet cloth. He tries to distract himself by looking over Alice's shoulder to the front page. More Brexit news. Something about Merkel. A piece on the future of the NHS. He thinks back to last year when the referendum result was announced. He'd never taken it seriously, hadn't thought for a second that it would actually happen. As the results tipped over, he'd messaged his cousin sisters, who have always been more political than him

Nik: Yo you watching this? What the fuck is happening?

Priya: I literally can't. I have no words

Rajvi: This is some next shit

Sarita: Kalyug, man

The automatic doors to the mini supermarket open again, and a young couple amble in, their arms wrapped around each other's waists. The breeze that follows them makes Nik shiver slightly. He's still refusing to fully unpack, and so is going without a coat. He locks eyes with a man standing further along the magazines and newspapers display, who seems to be waiting for someone. He's short and clean-shaven, sporting a cap, bootleg jeans and a frown. Nik looks back at Alice's paper, but can't get the man's glare out of his head. There was something accusatory in it, as if to say, *watch yourself*. When Nik looks up again, the man's face grows colder still, his eyes skipping between Nik and Alice, who's standing just inches away, her warm body turned towards him. Nik tries to engross himself in Alice's paper. He wonders if the man knows Alice or if he's just some sort of creep. When Nik realises he's read the same paragraph twice without taking in a single word, he glances up once more at the man. He's still staring. Not at Alice, but at Nik. Nik doesn't look away this time, which makes the man's glare grow darker still. Confused, but with an uncomfortable thought washing slowly over him, Nik tugs Alice's elbow: 'Come on, man. We haven't got all day.'

'We've got half an hour, actually,' she tells him, not looking up from the paper.

'Right. Well, I'm paying for this and heading back.'

Nik looks the man straight in the face as he passes. 'There a problem, mate?'

The man seems taken aback by this confrontation. He dawdles but doesn't respond. Instead, he looks at Alice, who has put the paper back. 'Y'all right, love, yeah? He bothering you?' A dirty, thick finger pointing at Nik.

'No . . . not at all,' she says, staring between them, 'we're together.'

Disgust colours the man's face. His friend joins him now from the till, a packet of cigarettes and a can of Monster in his hand. He too stares pointedly at Nik, before leaving. Nik and Alice carry on over to the tills. Alice helps Nik bag his items, glancing towards the two men through the window.

'What a couple of total fucking knobs,' she whispers.

'Yeah,' is all Nik can manage. He tries to steady his hands as he pays for his shopping, hoping Alice doesn't notice. His skin is hot. Everything seems brighter.

The pair are silent as they leave the mini supermarket. A van crawls across the car park, then speeds up and hoots as it passes them, making Alice jump. Nik turns just in time to see the driver drinking from a can of Monster, a St George's flag taut across one of the windows.

12

May 1979

'Not that one,' Chand said, pulling Avani back by the strap of her dungarees. She followed her brother's eyes to the bright curtains hanging inside the pub window.

'Why?'

'Because I said so. Just hold it until we get there.' She frowned at the door. She really needed a wee and the activity centre was a whole ten minutes away. Before she could protest, Chand flicked the kickstand with his foot and pedalled on. Avani rushed to keep up with him on her roller skates. He was still in his school uniform, though his tie had been removed and the sleeves of his shirt pushed all the way up. Summer was coming; it was the first time she'd been allowed out without a cardigan in the evening.

'Because of the curtains?'

'That's not a curtain,' he said gently. 'It's a flag. If you see it, don't go in, all right?'

Embarrassment rose to her cheeks. It was the Union Jack, she should have recognised it. 'But isn't it our flag?'

He didn't respond. She thought of the photos she'd seen a few weeks earlier in the papers, when the man had died in the riots. It had been in Southall, where her mum sometimes went shopping for shak. The flag had been in those photos too. The army of men with their rolled-up jeans and big black boots had been waving it.

She looked at Chand, wondering why he wouldn't answer her question. He was moving his way down the gears. She pushed her skates harder against the road, giving herself a head start, knowing what was about to come.

'Race you,' he yelled. She tried her best but gave in after just a few strides, grabbing on to his seat instead, cruising along, letting him tow her down the street.

'You're cheating,' he shouted, swerving the handlebars as he sped up. The sound of his complaints was drowned out by the tune of an ice-cream van overtaking them. 'All right, all right,' he said. 'Get back on the pavement and slow down. Mum'll kill me if you fall over.'

She did as she was told and tried to concentrate on where the pavement looked uneven so she could skip those bits and go round them, like her father had shown her. She knew she'd get told off if she tripped again. Her mother had confiscated her skates for a whole week last time she came home with bleeding knees.

'Av.'

'What?'

'Remember those boys who scratched my bicycle?'

Avani glanced up at him. They hadn't talked about that day since it happened. He'd been only a few weeks into his new secondary school. He'd come home with one of the lenses in his glasses cracked and bruises along his arms. Their father had buffed out the scratches in the frame of his bicycle and painted over the word that had made her brother cry, the one that she often saw graffitied onto bus stops and people's houses.

'That's their flag. Just stay out of the way when you see it.'

She nodded, concentrating on the sound of the ticking bicycle beside her.

'Is that Elliot?' Chand said, squinting at the activity centre. She spotted a figure in a bright red T-shirt going round and round in the revolving door.

'How d'you know him?' Avani asked, as they stopped. She pulled her trainers out of Chand's backpack.

'He's neighbours with Gopal so we let him play football with us sometimes when he's locked out of his house. It happens a lot. I don't think his mum and dad are very nice. Do you know he used to live in Manchester? Right next to the football stadium? How cool is that?'

'All right, Elliot?' Chand said as Elliot emerged.

'All right, Chand? Hi, Avani.'

'I want to do that.' Avani skated straight into the revolving door, becoming part of his little world, going round and round. Elliot laughed and sped up while Avani grabbed on to the rail, feeling like she was on a fairground ride. When she got dizzy and told him to stop, they slowed down and escaped out the front to speak to Chand.

'Oi, Av! I'll be back at six, all right? Wait here for me,' Chand called to her. She nodded, rushed inside for the toilet and then hurried to look for Maya in the main hall. When she reached the old wooden door, she pressed her face against the glass panel and peered inside. It was dirty, with grey fluff all around the corners and her eyes fought against the lines in the glass, reaching for the figures in the distance. Maya was at the front of the hall, as always, her long curly hair down, twirling. Avani changed into her trainers, keeping her eyes on the dancers the whole time.

'Why're you so early if your painting class isn't until five?'

Avani jumped. Elliot was coming back into the hallway. She wondered how he knew what class she was in.

'I like watching the dancing,' she told him. She looked back at Maya and the rest of the girls in their pink leotards and tutus. They looked like fairies. 'You can't tell from here,' she murmured, 'but they have sparkling gems stuck on their skirts. It's called tulle.'

'I like your tie better,' he said.

Avani looked down to Chand's school tie tucked into the front of her dungarees. She murmured a *thank you* and swelled with pride. She'd forgotten it was there – she'd got into the habit of pestering Chand for it when he picked her up from school each day, then wearing it until bedtime. She and Maya were currently obsessed with 'Sunday Girl' and were spending most evenings taking it in turns to dress up in a black T-shirt and Maya's father's check blazer. When they could get their hands on it, Chand's school tie would be tucked between the collar. They'd try to copy Debbie Harry's sugary vocals, getting half of the lyrics wrong, not knowing what the rest meant. One hand would be pushed into a blazer pocket, the other curled around a hairbrush, bopping along to the words, mimicking Blondie's recent performance on *Top of the Pops*. Even at seven, Avani had been dazzled by how beautiful and cool Debbie Harry looked in the contrast of an oversized suit with glittery eyelids and glossy lipstick and fluffy hair like candyfloss.

'Why don't you do it too?' Elliot's eyes were on the ballerinas. 'Instead of just watching?'

'My mum won't let me.' She said it before she could stop herself. Her father had tried his best with her mother, saying Avani could still take part, that she could do it in her T-shirt and leggings. But it was still a no. It was always a no. 'She says the clothes are too naked.'

He looked back to the girls then made a face. She giggled. 'What are you here for?'

'Nothing,' he said, shy now.

'What d'you mean? Everyone does after-school club on Wednesdays.'

'Not me,' he said. His eyes were a blur of green and brown, forming a colour she didn't yet have a name for. He had more freckles on his face now than last time she saw him up close.

'You should come to painting club with me,' she told him. 'It's so much fun.'

'My dad won't let me go to the ones you have to pay for,' he said. This confused her because she was sure you had to pay for all of them. 'But I don't mind, because if one of the boys doesn't show up Mr Asare sometimes lets me join music class. I get to write poems that he turns into songs.'

'Oh,' said Avani. She didn't know what else to suggest so turned back to the glass. The girls had moved out of sight.

Elliot tapped her on the shoulder. 'I've got an idea.'

'What is it?'

'Come with me.'

'Where are we going?' She threw her skates over her

shoulder and tried to keep up. They smacked against her tummy as she ran.

'Hold on,' he said, taking the stairs two at a time.

The top floor was dark and smelt of wet socks. They hurried along the corridor. When they reached the other side of the building, Elliot nudged a door open to reveal a pocket of light. He put a finger against his lips and beckoned her through. A yellow glow filled the centre of the room, keeping them in darkness. Below, in the middle of the hall, classical music played and twelve tiny ballerinas moved in circles.

'Whoa,' Avani whispered. 'Are we allowed here?'

'No. If we're quiet they won't see us and you can learn by following along. I come up here when Judo class is on so I can secretly copy the moves,' he whispered, punching the air.

Avani told him to shush. Her eyes were on the girls. She couldn't believe how clearly she could see them from here. She put her skates down beside her and, when she was ready, twirled and pliéd along, stopping to check what they were doing every time she got stuck. It was the first time she felt like she was a secret member of the group she'd watched for weeks. She learned to do a wobbly arabesque that day, and when she turned to show Elliot, she was surprised to see that he'd been dancing beside her all along.

13

October 2017

Nik stands on a low concrete wall, looking out to the sea, the sound of his friends' chatter drowning against rolling waves. The beach below stretches for two miles. Running parallel to it, behind the wall, sits a neatly lined collection of boutique shops and independent delis that supposedly hum with tourists in the summer. The short street bleeds into a cluster of cottages, mostly holiday homes, before meeting the edge of a nature reserve thick with pine trees. Dog walkers dot the bays along the main road with their cars.

One by one, Nik's friends hop down onto the beach, burying their chins into thick scarves, hands tucked into their underarms for warmth. They crunch their way along the shingle, enjoying the momentary softness under their feet when they come across a pocket of sand. Nik lags towards the back of the group with Dan and Alice, zoning in and out of their chatter, drinking in the saltiness of the air and taking strange comfort in the icy breeze that runs through his hair and finds its way across his back. Dan and Alice have removed their shoes and socks so that the foamy water washes over their feet as they walk, making their toes grow red with cold. They're moaning about an essay that's due soon for the only module that overlaps across all three of their degrees. Nik nods when one of them turns to him for input and he throws in the odd 'yeah, man' but he is not fully paying attention. Instead, he searches the beach for a figure whose cheeks are blistering pink against the sea air, with hands stuffed into coat pockets to protect them from the cold. It is the image of a man plucked from the winters of Nik's childhood, a man who once meant everything to him.

'Kid!'

He looks up to see Paul approaching. Despite the lack of phone signal, he has managed to find Nik's group with minimal directions, and has somehow arrived earlier than planned. Nik watches him for a moment then calls to Dan and Alice, who are strolling along the water's edge, 'Right, I better cut.'

'Oh, is that him?' Alice asks, her eyes on the figure behind Nik.

'Yeah,' Nik says, watching Paul navigate the shingle in a pair of suede Chelsea boots. 'Ah, man,' he mutters, zipping his puffer coat all the way up to his chin. 'This was a bad idea.'

He'd finally replied to Paul's Diwali text this morning, on a total whim, saying that he'd be out by the coast today instead of on campus, fully expecting Paul to withdraw his offer of meeting up. Instead, Paul drove for an extra hour to catch Nik at the beach. A sticky guilt crawls over Nik as he thinks back to their conversion at that cafe. He knows that if he were in London, around Teo and Will and the comfort of home, he would not have agreed to meet Paul again today.

'We'll be in there,' Dan tells Nik, nodding to an old pub

with a thatched roof in the distance, the lights of the next town twinkling behind it, 'when you decide to bail.'

'It'll be fine. Text us if you need an excuse to get away,' Alice says.

Nik looks over his shoulder to see that Paul is just a few metres away now. He greets Paul with a nod and introduces his friends.

'In a bit, yeah?' Nik tells them.

'Later, buddy,' Dan calls. He points to the pub again when Paul's back is turned, grinning.

Once they run out of small talk, Nik and Paul walk side by side in silence for a while, falling into step. Nik looks out to the sea, which is murky grey, and the sky above it, colourless. He hears laughter and looks back to see his friends walking in the opposite direction, to the warmth of the pub. One of Alice's flatmates, a tall ginger rower, has thrown Melanie over his shoulder and is running back towards the front of the group barefoot. He is the one who organised this spontaneous day by the sea, promising the girls a glimpse of baby seals along the beach. His eyes had widened hopefully when Alice showed up with Melanie in tow, but he'd seemed less than thrilled when he spotted Nik and Dan a few steps behind. The rower had sized the boys up through a tight stare when they'd joined the rest of the group. It wasn't until they stepped off the bus an hour and a half later that they realised they were, by some epic misfortune, both a month early for the seals and also at the wrong beach altogether. Instead, they traipsed up the high street, staring through shop windows at camel-hair coats and Hunter boots, before stopping for fish and chips and coffee. They'd filled their coat pockets with cans of beer and packets of crisps from a posh offie before wandering up the beach towards the pub for a proper pint.

It is nestled quietly among this that Nik begins to feel his old self reappear. He realises that this is the first time since moving away that he hasn't had the urgent need to get back home tingling through his limbs. Escaping the bubble of campus has helped, and there's something about this chocolate-box town that reminds him of the lanes around the boys' school in Harrow, the ones he would walk through with Will and Teo on his way to college each morning, feeling, for a moment, like they'd stepped into another time.

'No university on Fridays, then?' Paul asks eventually, clearing his throat.

'Nah, we bunked off today,' Nik says, with zero shame.

'I see. How're you finding it?'

'S'all right. Not exactly what I imagined. It's proper quiet up here, man. Not like London.'

In the silence that follows, he can sense Paul searching for the right question to follow up with, but he doesn't want to talk about university, so before Paul can find it, Nik asks: 'What d'you do now? Mum says you have your own business or something.' It's a lie. Nik googled Paul on the bus ride out to the coast. He found an interview Paul had given for some actuary magazine, where he also learned that Paul now lives in south London, not far from Layla's university.

Paul nods and says, 'Pretty much. I'm doing the same thing, just working for myself. I was actually meeting a client just around the corner from your university this morning.' He slips slightly on the shingle as he speaks, but Nik pretends not to notice. They're approaching the edge of the coastal village now. Soon, the colourful cottages will give way to the nature reserve.

'Looks like it's going well, yeah?' Nik says, nodding to Paul's expensive-looking wool coat. 'And you've still got all your hair as well, or is that a toupée?'

Paul's face creases into a smile. He stares down at the shingle and says: 'We'll wait for the wind to pick up to find out, shall we?'

'How was the Maldives by the way?'

'Gorgeous. Was good to fully switch off, you know?'

'Lads' trip, was it?'

Nik thinks he sees colour rising to Paul's cheeks as he says, 'Not quite. Forest or beach?'

'Huh?'

Paul points to a gate in the distance leading into the nature reserve. 'There's a little pub about a mile down, hidden at the edge of the forest. We can either stick to the beach or walk through the reserve. What do you think?'

Nik shrugs. 'Whatever, man.'

Paul dawdles, then carries on down the beach. Nik glances back once more, but he can no longer see his friends. He realises that the further he walks with Paul, the longer they have to spend together, as if each step they walk actually equals two. He pulls a rollie from his jacket pocket and searches for his lighter.

'D'you mind?' he asks. The sea ebbs towards Nik, licking the heels of his trainers as he lights the cigarette.

'I don't think I have a say any more, kid,' Paul tells him.

'Don't tell Mum, yeah?'

'How is she?' Paul is suddenly engrossed by a piece of fluff on his sleeve.

Nik walks as close to the water as possible without getting his shoes wet. 'She's good,' he says. 'Just getting on with it. Have you lots spoken since the funeral?'

Paul shakes his head.

'You should call her, man,' Nik says, but the words surprise even him. They weren't planned. He wants to take them back.

'Really?'

'I mean, whatever. You know what she's like. She'd never reach out to you first, even if she wanted someone to chat to, as a mate, or whatever.'

'True. Whole thing still twinges at the old pride though.'

'What does that mean?'

A pause, then: 'I shouldn't bring it up.'

'Bring what up?'

They've stopped walking now. Paul looks over to him and says, 'Me and Av.'

Nik has thought about this moment over the years, more so since Paul reappeared at the funeral, but he never imagined it arriving so neatly this soon into their encounter. He puts his cigarette out on a pebble and tries to sound casual, as if he's just making polite conversation, when he says, 'Go on, then. What happened?'

Paul's watching him closely. Nik stares right back. 'Tell me,' Nik says, standing a little taller. 'I still don't know why you left.'

Paul looks out at the sea, pushing his hands deeper into his coat pockets. 'I didn't leave, exactly.'

'She kicked you out?'

'I ah . . . I wanted to marry her.'

'Mum?'

'Yes.'

'What, like, properly marry her?'

'How do you not properly marry – Christ, never mind. Yeah, I proposed to her.'

'What, like, with a ring?'

'Yes, Nik. With a ring,' Paul says tightly. He rubs the bridge of his nose and looks away. Nik watches him. Surely not. Surely his mother would have said yes. He wonders if his mother had shared this with anyone at all, if his grandfather had known.

'When?' Nik asks.

'Just before she ended it.'

'That makes no sense. You lots were basically married anyway.'

'Yes, exactly. You were like a son. I was on the mortgage. It was just signing another bit of paper, really.'

'Well . . . go on, then. What happened?'

Paul shakes his head. 'It isn't that simple, kid.'

'Why the hell not, man?' This comes out much louder than Nik intended. An old couple walking slightly ahead turn to stare at him.

Before Nik can apologise, Paul says: 'There was a lot going on, Nik. It was complicated.' The words rush out of him in a flurry.

Nik searches Paul's face, but his jaw is tensed and his eyes narrowed, fighting against the wind. Then, he says, in a low voice, 'She wouldn't let herself move on properly after your father. She wouldn't let go of the blame.'

Nik stands very still. Everything feels much colder than

it did a few seconds ago. Paul's words wring his core, but his mind is still on the proposal. He's trying to catch up with himself, trying to untangle all of this information, when Paul says, 'She's still got his name.'

'Huh?'

'Av. She's still a Harrison.'

The thought has never crossed Nik's mind before. They're a family, the two of them, so of course they'd both have his father's name.

'So hold on, like, she broke up with you after you proposed?' Nik asks, but his voice is strained. Something Paul said earlier is nipping at him, and he circles around it, not able to fully see it.

'Pretty much. I wanted to stay, even though she said no. But I think it made her realise that she wasn't totally over what happened with Elliot.'

Nik's chest pulses uncomfortably at the mention of his father's name. It feels strange to consider Elliot and Paul in the same conversation. The space feels too small for the two of them to occupy. He wants to ask what Paul means by this but there is a discomfort growing in Nik's stomach. It doesn't feel right to ask Paul about his father; he never knew him.

The old couple have doubled back. They nod at Paul as they pass, the man grumbling 'afternoon', while totally ignoring Nik. An overweight French bulldog heaves himself up the shingle beside them, snuffling loudly. Paul and Nik continue along the bay, the beach growing thinner as they walk. Nik wonders if they've gone too far, but then Paul points to a raised walkway that cuts through the pine trees and says, 'Quick pint by the fire?'

Nik nods. 'Yeah. Go on, then.'

They walk with their backs to the sea in silence, Nik wading through everything Paul has told him, trying to make sense of it. A pocket of space seems to have opened in him, and, in it, he feels a quiet sense of shame for pathologising Paul into something worse than the plain truth of it all. There is also a pool of irritation that simmers on a low heat for his mother. She pushed away their chance of being a proper family. This was all Nik had wanted as a child.

Their footsteps are loud against the walkway as they move deeper into the pine forest. It is much darker here but Nik can make out a faint light in the distance, spilling through gaps in the foliage. A building comes into view, red paint peeling away from the window shutters and ivy crawling around the walls. As they reach the entrance, Nik looks at Paul once more and murmurs: 'Listen, man. She never really spoke to me about why you left. Just said it didn't work out.'

'She's not a woman of many words, is she?' Paul says, holding the door open.

'On a level though, like, I just assumed you didn't want to be around any more.'

Their eyes meet for a moment and Paul says, 'Wasn't the case.'

Nik nods, and walks in. He knows, now that this conversation is out of the way, they'll soon fall into bantering over Arsenal's transfer policy and *Vikings* and that Paul's chat will be peppered with careful, guarded stories that give Nik insight into what he's been up to for the last five years. But there is still something pinching at Nik; words

Paul dropped in the thick of their conversation which have laced themselves around Nik's core.

The warmth of the makeshift pub draws them in. It's made up of just one room; the bar is pressed into the back wall where upturned bottles of liquor glint in the light. Thick, grand curtains line the windows and dim lamps throw an orange glow across the wooden floor. The walls are covered in framed maps, so close to one another that Nik can't make out the colour of the wallpaper behind them. The old chap behind the counter eyes Nik, then spots Paul and tells the pair he'll bring over a couple of whiskies.

It is only when they take a seat at a weathered table, Paul making a joke about how it feels like they're in a speakeasy, that the words Nik's been searching for come back into focus, the ones that stuck out to him when Paul spoke about his father's death, the ones which didn't sit right: Nik's mother blamed herself.

14

October 2017

13:07 Avani H: Good afternoon, Peter. I'd like to enquire about the litter of poodle puppies you're advertising. Your advert asks for some basic information about myself, I hope this is sufficient: I've never been a dog owner per se but do have lots of exp with dogs – spent many years looking after my neighbour's husky. I'm a CFO and can bring the dog to the office with me once they're trained. I'd like to know more about the process/next steps and potentially come up to Norfolk to meet the puppies before committing. Kind regards, Avani

13:08: Pete C: Funky name. Wear u from Darlin?

Avani rolls her eyes and clicks away from the message, muttering darkly into her pumpkin soup. Not one of the people advertising puppies online seems reputable. Perhaps she will adopt instead, she thinks, perhaps an older, already-trained companion might be a better fit for her lifestyle. She watches her colleagues through the glass wall of her office as she tries to imagine caring for a dog, waking up to walk it, finding someone to look after it when she goes on holiday. This idea is one that she has toyed with before – her husband had always wanted a greyhound called King, but it was something they were forever pushing further into their future, telling themselves they'd do it once they had children, a bigger home, more time. She came close to getting a dog the summer after her break-up with Paul. But meeting Maya the other week has made her sure she should finally take the plunge. She needs something new to focus on now that her son has left home and her father is no longer just up the road. She clicks onto a pet adoption website, scrolls past photos of smiling dogs, and stops on a three-year-old lurcher. Her mind begins to wander elsewhere. There is something budding underneath these thoughts, brought about by the idea of adoption, of scrolling through photos, searching.

It starts as a familiar itch, growing in her chest. She tries her best to ignore it, to push it down, but soon it stretches along the surface of her lungs like fog. She closes her eyes and tries to breathe it away. This untouched piece of her past is best left alone; there was a time when this itch turned into an obsession that very nearly broke her. Here it is again, the shadow of a conversation that unfolded in the early hours of a Saturday morning in whispers, over two decades ago.

Before she can stop herself, she opens up a browser with the Facebook sign-in page. She can hear a voice shouting to stop, not to yield to this, but she ignores it and works quickly, before the voice has a chance to catch up with her moving fingers. She can feel the adrenaline fizzing through her arms and towards her hands as she clicks onto the search bar and types: N I C K

She chews her bottom lip as she flicks past profile after profile, her heart beating loud in her chest. She used to spend hours doing this after her husband died, searching the faces of strangers for a glimpse of his strong jaw, for tight chocolate curls dappled with strands of gold in the sun, the ones that once felt like silk in her hands. The chances of finding the man she is searching for are slimmer than ever now that her husband is gone, but she cannot stop. She is sitting in the juicy centre of madness, revelling in it. The voice in her head grows louder, shouting that this is a dangerous game, something worse than just a waste of time, and besides, he is not called Nick. He never was, to anyone other than her husband. If he survived, his name would have certainly changed. She knows the only way of possibly ever finding him would be through a DNA search; an avenue that hadn't been available when she and her husband had tried. But for that she would need a blood relative. She would need her son. The idea is a pipe dream; letting Nik in, sharing this all, would be far too much.

A pair of knuckles drum against her door.

'Avani?' Francesca, one of Avani's analysts, leans against the frame. 'Do I need to be in this two o'clock meeting? I still have the reports to –'

'You're fine to skip it,' Avani tells her. 'I'll give you the headlines.'

Avani sighs and throws her head back to stare at the ceiling, shame filling her. She makes a promise to herself that she absolutely will not do this again. It's a slippery slope, one that took her years to climb up from, and she can already feel herself stumbling. She stares at the small squares of various Nicks, then watches them disappear as she deletes the letters from her search bar one by one. But then her fingers begin typing another name, a ball of nerves pulsing in her throat: P A U – she deletes the letters as quickly as they've appeared. She just needs to get a dog, she tells herself sternly. A new focus, to fill the void since her son left, to signify the end of this nonsense.

Her main feed refreshes and she whiles away time ambling through photos of her old school friends boasting new homes and videos of their little Amelias playing the clarinet and their happy Oscars doing the backpack kid dance with granny and grandpa. Avani looks through the posts of people she'd half forgotten about and their picture-perfect performative lives, lives which always make her feel more and more like an outsider.

She glides past targeted ads for puppy beds and running trainers, before refreshing the feed. The last spoonful of cold soup disappears into her mouth. But the liquid sits on her tongue – she finds herself unable to swallow it down. A blurry photo that's been uploaded less than a minute ago sits proud, watching her from the top of the feed. It winds her, this old photo from the late eighties, showing a woman dressed in a silk sari, chopping potatoes by the kitchen sink and looking round to whoever stands behind the camera. Avani's eyes shoot across the caption under the image, the soup turning sour like bile in her mouth, blood rushing to her cheeks, as she is confronted with words that scratch at her skin like long, sharp, nails.

Chand Rigvedi says: Today would have been the 70th birthday of my beloved mother, Agniben Rigvedi. My mother was a gentle, beautiful and kind soul, taken by the grace of God well before her time. She was always smiling, forever keen to feed anyone who passed the threshold of her door. My mother's divine duty shone out of her, and even as a young man who was yet to find my faith, I could always see how much pride she took in being an integral part of the growing Hindu community when she and my father moved to Harrow from Mombasa in 1968. She set up one of the first bhajan groups in our area, where she'd invite fellow devotees to her home for a day of worship, something she continued for the rest of her life. I found my own faith only after she passed, and it is one of my biggest regrets that –

Avani slams the lid of her laptop shut.

*

October 1989

Avani padded carefully around the first floor of her home on the balls of her feet, still in last night's clothes, pausing every now and again to track her mother's heavy footsteps one flight below. She knew to stay out of her mother's way when it was just the two of them. Her mother had never enjoyed an audience.

She pushed the bathroom door open and swallowed mouthfuls of cold water straight from the tap. Her mouth had a dryness to it that wouldn't budge and her face was puffy from just a few hours of sleep. She sat on the edge of the bath, yawning widely into her towel as she turned the tap. Steaming water splattered down into the large bucket resting in the tub. Fragments of the previous night slipped back into focus, the flashing lights, the dancing, the elation that had bubbled in her chest and shot through her limbs, but there was something else too, something that brought with it an acute nausea, making her double over and dry-heave into the sink. A cry from downstairs sliced through her. 'Avani!'

She caught her reflection in the mirror; her hair was still big and crimped and backcombed from yesterday. Eyeliner and dark eyeshadow had smudged all the way down to her cheeks and large hoop earrings glinted from her ears.

'Chalo! Jaldi.'

'One second!'

She grabbed the bar of soap on the side of the bath-tub and rubbed it between her palms until they were thick with a soft lather. Then, she dipped her face into the hot water and scoured the foam over her face until it stung in her eyes. She gargled a palmful of the soapy water and rushed back to her room to swap her pink miniskirt for a pair of high-waisted stonewashed jeans. A couple of rollies wrapped in toilet tissue fell out of her bra as she peeled off her mesh tank top, trying to ignore how it was patched together with safety pins from the bottom of Maya's handbag. The nausea rose in her again. She kicked last night's clothes under her bed, grabbed an old T-shirt and forced her arms through it as she headed downstairs.

Her mother was waiting for her at the foot of the steps, impatience etched across her face. Her hair was tucked into a tight bun at the base of her neck, and her polyester salwaar kameez made a staticky sound as she shuffled across the hall in a pair of wedge flip-flops.

'Heh! Why aren't you washed? You look so dark,' her

mother said, watching Avani through tight eyes as she followed her into the kitchen.

Avani checked her reflection in the hallway mirror as she passed, looking for any signs of last night's kohl smeared across her face in the rush to get it off. There was none there. Her mother was merely reminding her she wasn't as fair as she'd like.

'I was about to shower but you –'

'You're disgusting. They're going to be here in an hour.'

'Who?'

Her mother started reeling off a list of names.

'For what?' Avani interrupted.

'Ganapati puja. I've been cooking all morning.'

Avani sighed. Her breath still tasted sour, the hot-water gargle hadn't managed to dilute the yeasty scent of beer pressed into her tongue. She eyed several large steel bowls glinting from the worktops, a piece of perforated kitchen roll placed over each to cover the contents. She checked that her mother was distracted before she took a peek under the tissue. The bowls were brimming with bhajia and farfar and jalebi and penda. Saliva gathered in her mouth.

'Leh.' Her mother slid a bowl of flour and a mug of water towards Avani. 'Make the loht for the puris.'

'There's so much here,' Avani said, looking down into the bowl of flour, which was bright with turmeric. She could smell marchu and jeeru. 'How many are we making?'

'Ek so.'

'Jeez. I better get cracking then.' She pinched a handful of sticky jalebi from the nearest steel bowl, chowing through it like popcorn. 'Oh, Mum, these are so good,' she said, her mouth full.

'Eh! They're not for you,' her mother shouted from across the kitchen. 'You're getting fat, look at your hips.'

'Lay off, Mum,' Avani huffed, her brow furrowing. 'I haven't eaten yet today.'

'And get that hair out of your face. Put it up.'

'But I like it down.'

'Avani.'

Avani slumped to the sink to wash the jalebi syrup from her hands. She caught a whiff of stale alcohol as she moved and wondered how long it would be before she could retreat back upstairs. She reached up to work her hair into a bun, pausing to glance across at her mother, who was running a knife through a skinned potato, using her thumb as a chopping board. Condensation dripped from the glass beside her, bhajans leaking out from the cassette player that was perched on the windowsill. Avani lowered her hands and simply tucked her hair neatly behind her ears, willing it to stay there.

She made a small hole in the middle of the flour, filling it with tel and water. When the dough was sticky and damp in her hands, she dipped the tips of her fingers in tel and rolled even portions of it between her palms to form little balls. She placed the first couple down on the worktop, pressing them into the white flour dusted across the surface, so similar to the powder she and her friends had rubbed onto their gums as they walked from the bus stop to the nightclub. She closed her eyes and fought against the memories of last night, the rush that had followed, the chill of sweat that had coated her skin, the man on the dance floor who had forced her away from her friends and into a circle of his own mates, pushing her between each of them to the beat of Royal House. Her heart leapt. She could still feel the way he had held her tight, one arm wrapped around both of hers, his face burrowed into her neck as she tried her best to break away. All she could think of during those few minutes was that she should have stuck to the daytimers, the comfort of her own. Maya had found her eventually, grabbing her by the waist and almost carrying her out of the crowd.

You should report that, a surly blonde told them in the toilets as Maya attempted to calm Avani down. Maya had placed a sobbing Avani on the seat of a toilet and was kneeling in front of her, trying to pin Avani's top back together again. They both ignored the blonde. Avani wondered if Maya was thinking exactly what she was; of how unhelpful the police had been when Maya's older brother had been attacked the previous summer.

Oi, did you hear me? the girl asked, louder, offering no help. *You should report that,* she ordered.

To whom, exactly? Maya spat impatiently, standing up to face the girl.

Avani blinked away the images in her mind, trying to focus on the feeling of the dough, soft and warm and smooth in her hands, when the sound of a knife clattering around in the sink yanked her back to the kitchen. Avani flinched, her arms stiffening as her mother approached her from behind. She froze, not daring to move, as her hair was tugged roughly into a braid, sharp nails scraping against the nape of her neck as they worked.

'Mum,' she pleaded, already knowing it was too late, 'that hurts.'

Her mother ignored her, holding the end of Avani's plait tight while rummaging through a drawer beside her for an elastic band.

It was almost over, she just had to stand still for another moment.

The sound of her mother's hungry fingers scrambling around in the drawer stopped. Something was wrong. Avani could feel her mother's hot breath rolling off her neck and along her exposed shoulder. She moved her head slightly to see that the loose neck of her T-shirt had slipped down her arm. It was a Led Zeppelin T-shirt, inherited from her brother. She'd cut the neckline so it hung loose around her. But today, gravity pulled it a little too low, exposing the purple marks on her neck from last night. Thumb prints. A bite. She braced herself, her stomach full of fear.

'Aa su che?' A voice shouted from behind her. Avani flinched.

'It's nothing.' She moved away from her mother and took the bowl of dough to another worktop, the plait unravelling.

'Leh! Dhoiri bunigay?'

Avani tucked her hair behind her ears again and yanked the T-shirt back up towards her neck. She pressed the balls of dough into the worktop, ready to be rolled, trying to steady her hands. She did her best to focus on the fading tiles lining the wall in front of her, distracting herself by thinking of how she would render the vases of sunflowers etched into the tiles onto canvas. But she couldn't focus; the silence between them was charged, like the heat before a storm. She knew what was coming; she could hear her mother's breath growing louder, she could feel the frustration and anger radiating out of her. A dark flash shot across her fingers, slamming them into the worktop. She heard it before she felt it, the sound of wood hitting bone. The pain of the velan whipped through her, forcing the air out of her lungs. She had trained herself, over the years, to step out of her skin, to watch from above. Not to feel. But this pain was higher in pitch, the scream of it echoed through her bones, making her double over.

Her mother stood over her, shouting: 'I can smell daru. You're drenched in it. You think you're a white girl now? Wearing stupid sexy bras. Letting men put their hands all over you.'

Avani smelt starch as her mother's fingers passed her face, reaching for the red lace strap resting on her shoulder. Avani ducked away from the hand and made for the stairs, her mother right behind her. As she reached the first step, her mother's nails cut into her skin, tugging at the strap of the bra so hard that the underwire dug into Avani's armpit. Avani flailed, trying to get up the stairs, but she was being forced backwards, her mother tugging on the bra, through her T-shirt. The sound of fabric slicing in two cut through the air. Avani felt a cold blade against her skin. She froze, her bra sunk away from her breasts, limp. Her mother stood behind her, a pair of kitchen scissors in her hand. She had cut through the band of Avani's bra. The T-shirt was collateral damage.

She thought it was over, that she'd be able to grab her keys and escape to Maya's. But then she followed her mother's gaze down to the carpet. Three inches of hair still stiff with hairspray rested over her mother's toes, which were covered in socks then shoved into flip-flops.

'Oh my God. What've you done?' Avani reached round to run her fingers through her hair. Tears swelled in her eyes as she found a thick strand on her nape that was several inches shorter than the rest.

Her mother watched from the foot of the staircase, the scissors still in her hand, a triumphant glint in her eye.

'WHAT THE FUCK HAVE YOU DONE?' Avani shouted, spit flying onto her mother's face as she yelled. Her heart felt as though it had crawled all the way up to her throat, where it sat now, beating wildly. She grabbed the scissors from her mother's hand and threw them aside, then pushed her mother with as much force as she could muster.

Avani's mother barely moved against her hands. Fresh rage rose to her face. 'Sali vandri!' she yelled. Avani sobbed and ran up the stairs, hearing her mother's feet just behind her. When they reached the landing, her mother pulled Avani towards her by the waistband of her jeans, making Avani crash down onto the floor, jaw first. Her teeth clacked together painfully. Something warm and metallic filled her mouth.

Her mother's nails left red crescents and long scratches, like shooting stars, across the sides of Avani's neck as she tore the T-shirt off her, snatching Avani's favourite red lace bra from her chest. Avani was forced through the threshold of her bedroom.

It was over.

She lay still, her eyes closed, every inch of her rigid.

The sound of a key turning made her look up. Blood pounded in her ears. Her mother had locked her in, and was now thumping back down the stairs. A flight below, the kitchen door slammed shut, the melody of bhajans growing louder.

Visitors arrived one by one, calling 'Jai Shree Krishna' as they walked in. Avani listened from her bed, ignoring the growing pressure in her bladder as the hours ticked by. Outside, the world darkened and fell into the grip of night. She watched the jay bird that lived in the eucalyptus tree outside her window flutter from one branch to the next, until she could no longer make out its blue wings against the night. Drizzle fell onto her window in neat lines. Hunger and thirst grew in her and when the pain in her abdomen grew into a prickle, piercing her, she knocked on the door, hoping someone moving from the lounge to the hallway for more food would hear her. She swallowed her pride, tucked her hair behind her ears once more, and prepared a smile, along with it a story of how it was all just a silly game, how her mother locked her in by accident and then forgot about her in the excitement of the day. But nobody heard her knuckles against the wood, nobody followed the sound up the stairs. Her knocks were drowned out by a never-ending stream of prayer.

When the pain in her abdomen became unbearable, she squatted into a bin liner and peed until it was gone. She tied the bag in a knot, then searched her coat pockets with trembling fingers for some old chewing gum or a half-eaten packet of crisps. The dull ache across her temple matured into a throbbing. She kneaded her temple with her knuckles and when her arms grew tired she rested her forehead against the coolness of the wall. Eventually, she drifted into an uncomfortable sleep, one where her mother's face blended with the circle of greedy men from last night. She was pulled from it by the sound of her mother's voice rising through the chatter downstairs: 'Maro daayo dikro.'

Avani's heart leapt. Her brother was home. She heard him speaking to their mother, greeting people in the hallway, his voice growing louder as he got closer, followed by the sound of him taking the stairs two at a time. The handle on her door moved up and down.

'Av! Mum says you have a headache. Get your arse out of bed, you hung-over fuck!' Chand called.

Avani swallowed, searching for her voice.

'What're you up to in there? Why's your room locked?'

She couldn't speak. The door rattled and she pressed herself flush against it, finding strange solace in the way it shook her.

'Avani? C'mon. I made that mixtape you asked for. D'you want it or not?' She could hear worry in her brother's voice now. The rattling stopped. She listened as he descended the stairs – slow and uncertain. He paused. Groaned. Then, the sound of metal on metal. He'd found the key. The door pushed open, into her. He took one look at her and the lie she had prepared choked in her throat.

'Av?' he said, his eyes growing round as they ran over her face. She burst into tears.

*

Before he left that evening, Chand showed Avani how to navigate the edge of the flat roof under her window, climb down onto the bins and hop into the safety of the garden. Her father came up to her room in the early hours of the next morning after his double shift, clutching a battered toolbox, to remove the lock from her door. She woke to him sitting beside her with the toolbox on his lap, his cheeks wet. When he saw she was awake he pulled her close to him. He held her, like he always did, whispers of how sorry he was, promises of how he wouldn't leave her alone at home with her mother again sweeping between them. Her mother didn't meet her eye for a week. Each time Avani passed a mirror, she tried not to look at the shape of her mother's nails pressed into her neck; those little crescents that punctuated the damage from the ring of men, the two blending together seamlessly and developing into dark scabs, before peeling to reveal new skin, shining underneath.

15

November 2017

'Rah, bruv, these beats are dead,' Ade says, walking into the smoking area.

'Don't even get me started,' Nik mutters, following him.

'Who plays Taylor Swift in a club, man? How're you meant to move to that?' Rajvi asks, grimacing. Rajvi, Nik's favourite cousin, is visiting with her long-term boyfriend Ade. They're both in their sixth and final year at UCL's medical school, due to graduate next summer, and are several years older than Nik but seem even keener to let off some steam tonight. They've just paid to get into the third club of the night, each playing a more painful mixture of music than the last. *No chance of Candy playing here, fam*, Ade had said when they walked in.

Nik spots Alice and Dan tucked into a corner of the smoking area and heads over to them. Alice is perched on a low wall. Her lips are red to match her dress. Nik had tried not to linger on that dress when she met them outside the first club, an oversized denim jacket draped over her shoulders. Rajvi had spotted him staring, though. She'd whacked him on the arm after he'd introduced them and raised her eyebrows in that way she does, throwing him a look which said everything she wouldn't. It wasn't until later, when Alice had disappeared into a group of her rowing society friends, that Rajvi had asked Nik: 'Is that the one you had a little crush on back in day, yeah?'

'Oi!' Ade's looking at Nik. 'D'you hear what I said?'

'Huh?'

'It's bare old school up here, innit? Where all the brown people at?'

'I wish I could tell you, man,' Nik laughs.

'Nik, did you tell your cousin what happened at Sainsbury's?' Alice asks, assembling a fresh rollie. A full glass of Archers and lemonade balances on her knee.

Nik shakes his head and sips his drink. The spicy and sweet scent of the rum, and perhaps the warmth it brings, reminds him of Layla, and he ignores the urge to check his phone. He stares at the inch of caramel liquid at the bottom of his glass, wondering what she's up to. He was back in London last weekend, but hadn't heard from her. It's her birthday soon. If he was at a London university, they'd have probably run into each other on a night out by now.

Dan's low, calm voice pulls him back to the smoking area. 'You didn't say. What happened, buddy?'

'Yeah, what happened?' Rajvi asks, in her older-cousin-sister voice, as if she's getting ready to whack someone.

Nik looks up to see the four of them staring back at him and he thinks of the least dramatic way to summarise what happened. 'There was just this man . . . staring at me. Like I shouldn't be here.' He thinks of that flag, of the look on the man's face, of how – as he and Alice ambled home – they'd googled the difference between patriotism and nationalism.

'Ah, the white gaze,' Ade says, nodding.

'He was off his bloody rocker,' Alice says, lighting her cigarette. 'Came and asked me if I was all right, as if Nik was holding me hostage or something.'

Nik adds: 'I mean, he didn't actually say anything explicitly racist, but he –'

'He didn't have to,' Alice says, her eyes fixed on him. For a second, everyone else falls away. 'I wish I'd said something.'

'My dad can be a bit like that,' Dan says, in a small voice.

'Really?' Alice asks.

Dan nods and puts out his cigarette. 'Yeah. We're working on him.'

'Mine's also a bit of a dick with that stuff, to be fair,' Rajvi says.

'Just a bit, yeah?' Ade repeats, smiling widely.

'A proper dick, then,' Rajvi says, downing the last of her drink.

Alice looks between them. 'What d'you mean?'

There's a moment of silence during which Nik, Rajvi and Ade all look at each other. Nik sifts through the many conversations he's had with Rajvi over the last few years, searching for a way to vocalise the prejudice, the double standards, the anguish he knows it has caused her.

'Just say it, it's calm,' Ade tells her, bumping her arm with his elbow.

Rajvi closes her eyes and sighs.

'Her dad doesn't like me cos I'm Black,' Ade says quickly, nodding gently as he addresses Alice and Dan.

'What?' Alice says.

Nik shakes his head, thinking of how much he loathes

his uncle. 'Rajvi's dad is proper . . . difficult.' He had wanted to say 'traditional' but didn't want to tarnish the word. 'Wants the girls with good Gujarati boys.'

'Slim pickings, man. All the ones I know just act cute in front of their mas, then they're out smoking weed and dicking down on the weekends.'

The others laugh. 'Fair, man,' Nik says, after a moment.

'We met in first year,' Rajvi tells Alice. 'Dad was just about all right with Ade when we were just mates. But as soon as he found out we were going out he flipped. Like, our grandfather died this summer, yeah –' Nik feels the air leave him, his grandfather's face flooding his mind – 'and Ade tubed it all the way to Harrow from Walthamstow to help Nik's mum clear out our grandad's home, bless him. But all Dad cared about was what "people would think" seeing a Black man going in and out of the house.' She sighs, then nudges Nik with her elbow and says: 'You got so lucky, Nikhu, with Avani Foi.'

When he doesn't respond, Rajvi tells the rest of the group: 'Our grandad was cool too, way ahead of his time. He loved Ade.'

'Ah yeah, man, Rohan was the best. Proper made me feel at home,' Ade says.

'I wonder what went wrong with Dad,' Rajvi murmurs. 'Proper messed up that Bapu was so chill and then his son turned out to be a nutter. It's like we're going backwards.'

'What about your nan – what's she like?' Dan asks.

Rajvi shakes her head. 'She died when I was little. Nik never met her. She was pretty stern, you know. Maybe that's where Dad gets it from.'

Nik zones out and focuses on the sliver of golden

liquid sitting in his glass. He tips it over the cubes of ice, watching it dance around them. Talking about his grandfather doesn't mix well with rum. He feels a sadness so deep that it ripples through him, making his hands grow numb, his breath jagged. No one is speaking, but the air feels suddenly heavy.

'Listen, the music in here is some next shit,' Ade says after a long moment. 'My mate who went to uni here said there used to be this one random bar on the other side of town. It was old-school R&B vibes. Should we cut?'

'Yes, let's,' Alice says, getting to her feet. She pops herself in the space between Nik's arm and his torso, as if it's the most natural thing in the world. It makes the pain in him fall away almost instantly.

Later, as they walk back to campus in the early hours, Nik notices Rajvi stopping behind the others to remove her heels. He's busy finishing the leftover crusts from Alice's pizza, and interrupts her impassioned soliloquy on the gentrification of Brick Lane to say, 'I'm just going to hang back for Rajvi.' Alice smiles and skips ahead without a second glance to join Dan and Ade, who are talking loudly as they lead the way back.

'Here, hold this,' Rajvi says, handing Nik a single stiletto. She pulls out two black leather pumps from her bag that have been folded into each other like socks. 'That's so much better,' she says, taking the shoe back from Nik. 'You all right, broski? Had a good night, yeah?'

'Yeah, man, I'm so glad you guys came up.' Nik watches the others as he speaks. Alice has also removed her shoes and is trying to convince Dan to give her a piggyback.

'Are you enjoying it, or still not quite settled?'

He can hear the alcohol making her vowels curl into themselves, bringing out her mild Leicester accent. Having Rajvi and Ade come up for the night has made him acutely aware of how much he hates this place, and how far away home feels. He doesn't tell her this, though. Instead, he says: 'I mean, it's boring as hell but I'm just getting on with it.'

She tuts and says, 'Ah, broski. I can tell, man. You don't seem like yourself.'

He thinks back to the last time he went home – before setting off, he'd brewed a cup of chai in the communal kitchen, which resulted in another unpleasant run-in with Simon.

That's Nik, by the way, who wants it to be clear he's from Harrow, not Pakistan, Simon had said, sniggering, when his girlfriend asked for an introduction over the kitchen sink.

Irritation had whipped through him each time he replayed those words, the white heat of it maturing to shame when he recalls how he'd failed to summon a retort, failed to correct Simon, failed to stand up for himself even a little. It had stayed with him, this othering, lingering around him like a persistent headache all the way down to London, until he got on the Metropolitan line at King's Cross and sat across a young family conversing in Punjabi as they passed round a tiffin of aloo paratha. Just behind them stood a greying uncle dressed in an impeccable suit, speaking into his phone in Twi, one hand clutching a yellow pole for support. Further along the carriage was a woman cradling her sleeping son, a quiet, melodic stream of Arabic leaving her lips, looping around him like a lullaby. Nik couldn't help but watch, his body sinking deeper into the seat with a sigh of relief, comfort rippling through him. He felt something then, something he later recognised as the feeling of being home. These are details he never paid attention to before – these small pieces of London that call to him, beckoning him.

'It'll be fine,' he tells Rajvi, as they stroll back to campus. 'It's annoying, though. In London, I just am. Up here, it's like I'm "Nik the Brown One".'

Rajvi lets out a loud, dirty chuckle, and then says, 'I'm dead, bro. Sounds like a character from *Lord of the Rings.* You should talk to Priya, y'know. She proper struggled at uni too. Hated it. It's hard, when a big multicultural city is all you've ever known and then suddenly you stick out for no reason.'

'I feel like I don't have a right to moan, though.'

'What d'you mean?'

'It's nothing compared to what it must have been like for our parents when they were kids. Or the bullshit Teo and Ade have to deal with. Did you notice how we got searched at every single bar? That never happens normally.' He thinks of how many times he's heard the crackle of 'IC3' over a radio, the sound of heavy boots approaching, the dreaded '*Can I just stop you there for a moment, chap?*' when he's been out shopping or partying or just existing alongside Teo.

Her eyes run over Ade and she kisses her teeth. 'Your experience is still legit, though. Doesn't mean you have to stiff-upper-lip it.' Nik doesn't respond, so she adds:

'Speaking of wastemen, I can't believe that dick Paul had the balls to show up at Bapu's cremation.'

This turn in the conversation surprises Nik but when he thinks about it he realises Rajvi will have been itching to bring it up. He chooses his words carefully. 'I think Mum invited him. He . . . I met up with him a couple of weeks ago.'

Rajvi's eyes widen. 'Fuck off.'

'It was all right, you know, catching up.'

Rajvi stops in her tracks and watches him. 'Are you taking the piss? I thought we hated him.'

Nik keeps walking. 'I dunno, I feel like I've been a bit hard on him. He actually told me his side of the sto—'

'Wow. Just be careful with that one, yeah? He's sav nakamo, man. Proper sleaze vibes.'

'Have you spoken to my mum recently, by the way?' Nik says, trying to move on. He can feel the fresh air sobering him up.

'Nah. I should call her, really. Why?'

'So she hasn't told you about finding my dad's car, then?'

'What? No.'

'It's this peng Beemer, man. So cool. Bapu kept it for me. It's at Will's now. I've been fixing it up with him and Teo.'

'Ugh.' She rolls her eyes at the mention of Teo's name again.

Her reaction makes Nik laugh. 'It's calm, man, he's got a girlfriend now.'

'Still likes every single one of my Insta photos though, as soon as I put them up, as well.'

'No way. Does he?'

'Yeah, so keen. I think Alice might like the look of him, you know. She was asking me if he's single earlier. Anyway, tell me about Fua's car again.'

The word is like a sip of warm chai. He has never thought of his father being called 'fua' before. He thinks back to the photo he found of the girls with his father, his arms wrapped around all three of their tiny frames. Nerves bud inside him as he asks: 'I always forget you knew him. D'you remember him?' He's never felt able to ask her this so directly back home, within earshot of their parents.

'Yeah, I do. He was awesome.' She walks beside him in silence for a moment, then says, 'Dad was never very cuddly with us, but Fua was. We've got this cute home video of him lifting us one by one to his chest and spinning us around in the air.'

'Really?' Nik smiles. 'What else d'you remember?'

'He proper loved your mum. I remember that clearly, even as a kid. Like, he'd always be rubbing her back or reaching for her hand. They were goals, man.'

Nik nods, clinging to her words, thinking of the couple in the photos his grandfather secretly handed him each year. He can only just make out the sound of others' chatter in the distance. He deliberately walks slower than usual to prolong this moment with Rajvi. 'What else?'

Rajvi looks across to him. 'I can't remember much, Nikhu – I was only five when we lost him. I think everything I remember is jumbled up with Sarita's and Priya's memories of him too. But he was also close to Dad when they were younger, you know. You should ask him.'

Nik thinks about what his grandfather had told him that evening in hospital: *Chand will be able to tell you more than I can.* He doesn't want to go to his uncle. He doesn't want to involve him, to taint what might be. Instead, he asks: 'What happened, Rajvi? Why can't Mum talk about it?'

'I think it was the shock, broski,' she tells him gently.

'D'you remember what happened?'

Rajvi takes a deep breath before she says: 'Dad said it was late, and he was walking home from work and someone, like, ran over him and drove away.'

The words pile up inside of Nik as he hears them, as though they are slowly suffocating him. He has never been told this before. A numbness pulses through his limbs, fizzing at his bones like acid. He thinks of his father lying in the middle of a road, alone, the life seeping from him. Nik is filled with the sudden, desperate, impossible urge to find him, to protect him.

'They caught the guy though,' Rajvi says. 'He was way over the limit.'

'I didn't know,' Nik murmurs through tears.

'Oh, broski,' Rajvi says, wrapping an arm around his waist.

'No one's ever told me that.'

'What? Really?'

'Yeah, not even Bapu.' He rests his hand over her shoulder. 'They just said it was an accident, and I always assumed he was driving.'

'Nah, I'm sure Dad told me he was walking,' she says. 'It was that massive roundabout near your ends, in Harrow.' Nik immediately knows the one she means. The one near Northwick Park Hospital, the one which, for years, his mother has avoided, even if it meant adding an extra twenty minutes to their journey. The one that, when Nik passed his test and would drive her down, would result in her turning pale and growing silent, her nostrils flaring slightly. Why had she never just told him? Why couldn't she just let him in? A sob escapes from his chest.

'It's okay, broski,' Rajvi says, her arm tightening around him.

Nik wipes his face with the sleeve of his shirt, hoping the others don't turn to see. Rajvi fetches a tissue from her handbag then says, 'I hate that they don't ever talk about him.'

'You've noticed it too?'

'Yeah . . . I mean, I feel like it's okay to chat about him now cos we're away from home, but I'd never have been able to tell you this with Avani Foi around.'

'There's something else there, man. If they were so happy, why doesn't Mum want to remember him? If anyone brings him up it's like she takes it so personally, as if they're insulting her.'

'Yeah, I know what you mean – it's all been left unsaid but it's there.'

'I'm going to figure it out,' Nik says, pushing back fresh tears. 'I want to know what happened.'

16

November 1989

Avani stepped off the bus, pulling her oversized blazer tight around her. She checked her watch as she walked. It was well past midnight. She would have to sneak back in the way Chand had showed her – her emergency escape doubled as a discreet entry route.

The pavement glowed orange under the street lights. Her heeled boots echoed into the night as she walked. Her favourite shoes – a pair of blue second-hand Kickers – were tucked in her bag but she hadn't bothered to change into them as she left the party. She could feel the silk band tied around her hair threatening to unravel as she rushed against the cold. Harrow at midnight sounded quieter than she expected, though the music from the party had been so loud that it had left her ears ringing.

She slowed as she approached the road running parallel to the park. Two options presented themselves before her: either she could walk straight through the park, taking her home in just five minutes, or she could carry on down the well-lit road which kissed the estate where Maya's brother had been mugged and battered the previous summer. She stopped to look between the two, weighing up which was the lesser of two evils. The park was enveloped in darkness and Avani found herself strangely drawn to it; something about the enclosed pocket of grass made her feel safer than walking down the exposed street. Without thinking about it, she found herself climbing over the locked gate and stepping into the shadow of an old oak tree. She walked as quickly as she could, very aware that her steps sounded like those of a scared woman coming home late. She focused on the end of the path, moving as fast as she could without breaking into a nervous run. Then something shifted in the periphery of her vision, making her flinch. She slowed, squinting against the darkness to spot a large horizontal mass on one of the benches lining the path. There was someone asleep on the bench. Shit. She could hear her mother now: *Fari rkhadva gayti? This is why our girls need to stay at home.*

Fear wrapped itself around her, clawing its way up to her throat. Half of her was screaming to turn round but the other half of her reasoned that she'd have to climb over the gate again. If he wanted her, he'd catch her, even if she ran. She could feel an anxious heat growing under her arms and around her chest. She should have changed her bloody shoes. Then the rhythm of Royal House beat inside her, growing, stirring memories of just weeks before, memories she still couldn't find the words for. She stifled this away, breathing deep and steady, trying not to shake, trying not to look scared, trying to walk fast but make as little noise as possible. She was almost at the bench now, and she was terrified. Her mother's voice grew quieter in her mind, fighting another which was kinder, which she recognised as her own: *Just keep walking. Keep your head down. You're almost there.*

Her attention was fixed on the ground as she passed, her pace quickening to match the pounding in her ears.

'Av-Avani?'

She flinched. It was her name. He knew her name. He even pronounced it correctly: Uv-nee. Despite herself, she glanced at him. A pair of hazel eyes found hers. She looked quickly away, tucking her face down into her scarf, fear exploding in her chest. It took the length of four clean steps for her to place those eyes, for the urgency to fall away, for her feet to slow and then stop altogether. She turned to the figure on the bench, despite the voice in her head still telling her to run. Grey with cold, he stared back at her. A flutter of recognition passed between them. Avani's mouth parted and she took a step towards him, two almost-strangers studying each other's faces in the thick of night, trying to match what they saw with memories dipped in sunshine and innocence.

She tried to arrange his features in the order that they belonged but he was a Picasso painting. Parts of him were misplaced, swollen, and she could see, now that she was closer to him, that the section of his face she'd assumed was in shadow was actually another colour altogether; purple with bruises. Dried blood like kumkum powder was pressed into his forehead. The only reason Avani was sure this was the Elliot of her childhood was because of the stranger's kind eyes; warm like honey and full of comfort.

'Oh my God,' Avani took another step towards him and he recoiled, as if out of habit. 'What are you doing out here?' Puffs of grey left her mouth as she spoke.

'I . . . it's been a while, eh?' His voice was hoarse. The

northern twang of his childhood was much less pronounced than Avani remembered, diluted by a decade in London. 'Sorry, I didn't mean to scare you.'

Her eyes reached for his. 'Ell. What happened to you?'

He didn't respond.

Her gaze moved back to the darkness, empty-handed. She hadn't seen him since the summer before they were to start secondary school. Avani and Maya had been watching him from their hiding spot outside his home, crouched behind a butterfly bush, giggling as Elliot called their names in a game of hide-and-seek. A bee had been bothering Maya, buzzing around her ponytail, the sound of her frustration punctuated by the engine of a black cab ticking across the street.

Despite how close Elliot was to the girls – just metres away, searching for them behind a lavender bush that stood like a guard outside his front door – the game of hide-and-seek never concluded. He never found them. Instead, the door beside him opened and his heavily pregnant mother appeared in a cotton dress printed with lilies, taking him by the elbow and forcing him into the house. Avani can still remember the words that rang through the quiet Harrow cul-de-sac before the door slammed shut, the pure spite that had dripped from them: *Where the fuck have you been, you dirty little cunt?*

Avani and Maya had exchanged a nervous glance through confused eyes, before mother and son reappeared. Elliot was crying as his mother launched him out of the door, a backpack as big as his torso hanging from his arm. A fresh cigarette drooped from his mother's mouth. Before getting in herself, she loaded four bags of belongings, then her son, into the waiting cab. It left Harrow and never returned.

Avani remembers skating immediately to Chand, as she always did at that age when something went terribly wrong. She found him on the football pitch with his friends, and still remembers the boyish scent of sweat that they left in the air as they circled the streets on their bikes, searching for Elliot until the sky grew grey, then black. But the cab was long gone. He was gone.

Before he disappeared, Avani recalled how her childhood friend, bright like the sun and brimming with energy, grew more and more withdrawn as his age slid into double figures, how he developed a stammer, how he would constantly hunch his shoulders, stoop his head, as though trying to make himself smaller so that he'd become less of a burden. So that he'd become easier to love. His parents had pulled him out of school for a short stint and then dumped him in another. Eventually, he fell through the cracks. There had been plenty of rumours about the Harrison household; both parents finding themselves on the wrong side of the law, their son unsuccessfully trying to run away from home on multiple occasions. Avani's own mother had warned her about spending too much time with him as a child, which she wholeheartedly ignored.

Avani thought about this, watching him, wondering how she could condense this all into one question without seeming too nosy. 'I thought you'd moved away,' she said eventually.

'We did, yeah. St Raph's.'

'What're you doing back here?'

He gnawed on his bottom lip. 'Had a bit of a barny,'

he said in the manner of someone simply describing the weather.

'With whom?'

He didn't answer. The red-faced man Avani had seen as a child stumbling back from the same park they were in came to mind, a carrier bag clinking in his hand. She remembered a young Elliot staying out later than the rest of their group on the days his father had been particularly thirsty. Sometimes he could still be found lingering around Harrow well past dinner time.

'Where – you can't stay here tonight,' Avani said.

'No.' Then: 'D'you remember Phil?'

'Yes. I've just come from a party he's still at, actually,' she said, her voice clipped. She felt her jaw tense.

'Ah, makes sense. I crash at his sometimes, but he wasn't in.'

Avani looked at the plastic bag by his feet, with a change of clothes and toothbrush poking out of it.

'How's Chand?' he asked.

Summers of their childhood exploring the abandoned industrial estate and playing stuck in the mud diffused through her mind, like a flavour she'd forgotten the taste of, she and Maya forever in roller skates, the boys behind them on bicycles.

'He's at university now,' Avani said, taking a seat on the bench beside Elliot. 'Lives in a cloud of music and grass.'

'How poetic.' The end of his words were met with a chuckle that rolled into a wet chesty cough.

'Christ, that sounds awful.' Elliot rubbed a rib as if it was the source of his cough. 'Look, I don't think Phil's going to make it back tonight,' she said, checking her watch again. 'He was totally off his face.' The image of Phil trying and failing to do the Running Man earlier that evening came back to her, ending with him falling face first into a window.

'Damn,' he sighed. 'What about Ian and Pete?'

'Yeah, they're both still at the party. It was only just really getting started when I left.'

He swallowed and the sound was dry, almost like a croak. He picked up the plastic bag, his eyes searching the darkness for an answer.

'Why d'you even hang out with them?' Avani asked, before she could stop herself. 'That Phil's a right piece of –'

'I know. I know. I just . . . there's nowhere else.' His eyes flashed away from hers.

'What about your auntie? The one you used to stay with sometimes when we were kids?' She thought of the kind woman who always opened the door in an apron when Avani used to knock for him.

'She moved to Spain a couple of years ago.'

Avani could feel the true weight of this statement in the white space between his words, in the monotone of his voice as he spoke; she knew what it would have meant to him, losing her. She had been, in every sense, his safe space growing up.

'You could crash at ours or something,' Avani said eventually.

His eyes flicked up to meet hers. 'What about your mum?'

Avani opened her mouth to respond, then looked away when words failed her. It wasn't just the Harrison household people talked about, apparently. She noted he didn't ask about her father though, and it warmed her that Elliot remembered his kindness.

'Fuck her,' she said finally, thinking of the chain she'd managed to screw to the inside of her door just last week. 'You can kip on my floor.'

'I couldn't,' he said, shaking his head.

Avani found herself slightly taken aback by this and wondered how sleeping on her floor could be worse than on a cold park bench. Her mind raced and landed on Phil and his cronies, who, for years, had switched between treating her like she was one of them and acting like she was an outsider as quick as the wind changed. Phil had come up to her as she was leaving the party, his pupils alive with speed, squeezing himself in the space between her and the wall, his breath hot against her ear: *Wouldn't mind adding a bit of Indian to the list,* he winked, swaying slightly, *if you're up for it.*

Goose bumps ran across her arms. She assumed the worst, that Elliot would rather sleep on a cold park bench than admit to his friends that he'd stayed with the Rig-vedis. She knew she was jumping to conclusions, being paranoid, but she found that, often, it hurt less in the long run to assume the worst. It numbed the sting, somewhat.

'Right,' she said, standing up. 'Well, suit yourself.'

She strutted back along the path, her head held high.

Before she climbed over the gate, she paused for a moment, pretending to adjust her blazer. The swish of a plastic bag grew in the darkness behind her. Footsteps, too.

17

November 2017

Nik puts out a rollie and slides two pieces of chewing gum into his mouth. He flaps the body of his unzipped puffer coat, trying to get rid of the acrid scent lingering around him, pressing itself into his hair and hoodie. There was a time when covering his tracks was a careful three-step process, which included standing downwind, only blowing smoke away from himself, and carrying a bottle of Lynx in his college backpack at all times. Now, a makeshift breeze and a couple of pieces of spearmint Extra will do. His phone buzzes in his pocket as he walks into the station.

12:28 Mum: Train pulling in now. Love, Mum xxx

12:28 Nik: Yeah, I can see it. I'm just by the ticket barriers

He catches his reflection in a shop window and tries his best to sort his hair out. He has spent the last forty-eight hours in his room, rising only from bed to use the bathroom and to smoke out of the window. The world outside seems brighter, busier, more overwhelming than he remembers. He doesn't feel as though he is part of it. He has nothing to contribute. He is tired, despite having done nothing the last couple of days, and is already itching to get back to the safety of bed. Since the start of term, he's been to only a handful of lectures and seminars and has read none of the books or essays prescribed as weekly reading. Alice slipped their latest assignment through the gap under his door last night and he'd scanned it, thinking it may as well be in another language, before scrunching it up in a ball and lobbing it out of the window. He thinks of how, just six months ago, he was getting rinsed by the boys for always handing in his coursework early, for always getting straight As. His phone buzzes again.

12:30 Mum: Great. I have a surprise for you, by the way . . . xxx

He knew there was another reason for her sudden trip. She'd messaged him last night asking if he could spare a couple of hours to meet her for lunch. She had the day off and wondered if she could take the train up to visit him for the afternoon. He told her he could meet whenever, curious as to why she was taking the train; she hated them and drove absolutely everywhere. It must be something to do with this surprise. For a fleeting moment, his imagination takes him back to his childhood when the very same words had preceded his mother arriving home with Paul smiling at him from the passenger seat of her car. He'd flown back earlier than planned from Christmas in the States with his parents to spend New Year's Eve with Nik and his mother. In his mind's eye, Nik sees Paul helping his mother off the train, the two of them walking down the platform towards him. The thought is so inviting that it makes him feel something he hasn't in weeks. It's warm, this feeling. It's hope, he realises. Happiness. He blinks away the mirage and yanks the zip of his puffer coat up to his chin. She's probably just brought Maya up with her, he reasons, or got a new haircut.

He spots his mother walking along the platform among a flurry of other passengers. She moves in and out of view as she bobs towards him. She's dressed in her long burgundy coat and has a black beanie hat on that blends into her shoulder-length hair – it's the one that she borrowed from Nik last winter and still hasn't returned. As she comes into view, Nik notices there's something different in the way she's walking; her steps are shorter and quicker, as if she's being tugged along by a taut string. It's only when the ticket barriers open, and she picks up a scruffy yet elegant-looking grey-haired dog and carries it through with her, that Nik realises her steps were those of a dog walker being pulled along by an eager companion.

'Surprise!' she says, putting the dog down and opening her arms to hug him. Nik stares at the dog and it looks back at him inquisitively, its tail beginning to twitch.

'Whose is it?' he asks, bending down to stroke it.

'Mine. I just rescued her last week.'

'Rescued? From where?' The dog sniffs Nik's palm and licks the centre of it when he tries to stroke her ears.

'Adopted, I mean. From Battersea. They made me fill in loads of forms and had someone come round to look at the house and everything. Very thorough,' she says, fussing over the dog as if it's personally responsible for such a meticulous adoption process.

Nik shakes his head, trying not to overreact.

'What?' she asks, her smile faltering slightly.

'I can't believe you got a dog as soon as I left, man. You told me I couldn't have one like a hundred times when I was a kid,' he mutters. He is aware of how spoilt he sounds, but his mother has fully hit a nerve. He'd pleaded with her for years for a dog, increasing his efforts significantly after their neighbour's husky, who Nik used to walk daily, was run over. He knows he is being ridiculous, but her timing feels deliberate. His mother doesn't seem bothered by his response though, and simply picks up the medium-sized dog and places her in Nik's arms as if she's a toy that he's not showing enough gratitude for. She wriggles until Nik drops her back to the floor. She sneezes then shakes off the encounter, her ears flapping noisily, before rising to put her front paws on Nik's abdomen.

'Ah look, she loves you. Her name's Rani,' Avani says, stroking the dog's head. 'It means –'

'Yes, I know what it means. C'mon, then. I'll show you around town,' he says, striding out of the station.

The ten-minute walk takes closer to twenty due to his mother stopping every time Rani wants to sniff a wall or lick a piece of pavement. Nik slows down, biting back telling his mother that she should probably get the dog used to walking at pace if she ever wants to get anywhere on time. He notices his mother seems chirpier than usual and totally oblivious to his bad mood; she's delivering a steady stream of chatter, as if to fill the silence on Nik's part. 'Goodness, there are so many churches around here, aren't there? Oh look, another little cafe. Don't know if this number of independent eateries would survive in Harrow, what with Costa and Caffè Nero basically already opposite each other. Oh, that's a pretty building. Lovely bricks. When's Alice joining us, Nikhu? And where would you like to eat, beta?'

'Dunno,' he says, looking back down at Rani. She wags her tail every time their eyes meet and he stops to stroke behind her ears. 'Nando's?'

'Oh, let's go somewhere proper,' his mother says.

'We'll have to find somewhere with outside space though,' Nik grumbles. 'Unless you want to tie her to a lamp post while we eat.'

'She is *such* a sweetheart,' Avani says, watching Alice walk back towards town. Avani hasn't seen Alice since Nik's final year at primary school. It surprised her to greet a charming nineteen-year-old with a nose ring instead of the giggly eleven-year-old with blonde ringlets that she remembers.

'Yeah, she's all right.' Nik yawns. He strokes the top of Rani's head absent-mindedly.

Avani had hoped coming up to visit Nik and surprise him with Rani – the docile three-year-old lurcher-poodle cross she's adopted – would make him snap out of whatever it is that seems to be going on with him. Instead, he'd eyed the dog with suspicion when Avani stepped off the train, and said something along the lines of 'Are you serious? I begged you for a dog for years and then you get one as soon as I leave?'

This drew the air from her, the smile slipping slowly off her face. It hadn't crossed her mind; she thought he'd love to have a new friend to come home to. She spent lunch ignoring the bowl of steaming broth in front of her, instead trying her best to prise full sentences out of him while he mumbled bland responses in between mouthfuls of pho, Rani resting her head on his feet. Their afternoon brightened significantly when Alice joined them for cake in a cafe, merrily telling Nik to *stop being such a miserable bastard*, while fussing over Rani, which made Avani smile.

'I'm so glad you two ended up at the same uni.' The words are her father's. They're the ones he spoke to her once, years ago, when she finally found the courage to tell him that she and Elliot were in a relationship.

Nik doesn't respond, so Avani glances at him as they walk towards the station. There is something about these last few moments with someone before boarding a train, she believes, that has a 'now or never' feeling to it. She can feel the question on the tip of her tongue and considers biting it back but it tumbles right out. 'How's Layla doing?'

'I knew that was coming,' Nik says, laughing without any warmth. 'Me and Alice are just mates, Mum, yeah?'

'Does she know that?'

'Mum.' Nik tuts.

'She looks at you like . . . oh, I don't know.'

'She looks at everyone that way. It's just Alice. She has a way of making every person she speaks to think they're the centre of her world.'

'Oh,' is all Avani can think to say. There is a certain coolness in her son's voice that tells her more than the words themselves. 'What about Layla, then?'

They're standing in front of the station now and Nik walks ahead and turns so they're facing each other. He leans against one of the brick arches that line the entrance.

'What about her?'

'Well, the pair of you hang out a fair bit when you come home,' Avani says, fiddling with Rani's lead.

'I see Teo and Will every time I'm home,' he says slowly, his voice flat. 'Shall we put a label on that too?'

Avani holds her hands up. 'Fine, Nikhil. I was just wondering.'

Nik kisses his teeth. She's always told him off for this habit, but now they're away from London and in this strange little town, she feels comforted by him making this noise that is so synonymous with home. It makes Nik Nik.

'I actually haven't seen Layla since I left.' He doesn't meet her eye as he speaks. She wonders, then, where he's been going when he's back; he's rarely ever in the house. 'Stop being nosy, man,' he warns, before she can ask any more.

She tried, years ago, to get him to stop calling her 'man' but she eventually gave up and began to see it as a term of endearment. This is the first time the word has been used to create distance between them. She tries to gather herself, then says: 'I'm just worried about you, Nikhil. I barely see you when you come home and you . . . you look low, beta.'

'I'm fine,' he snaps, running a hand through his hair.

Avani watches him. She wants to tell him how she has noticed an edge, a darkness to him since his grandfather's death that doesn't seem to be lifting. She wants to tell him it's okay to take a term off if he needs to, or to transfer to London if he's unhappy. She wants to tell him he can talk to her, about anything.

'Go on, then. You'll miss it if you don't hurry up.' He nods towards the train.

She swallows down the words she'd gathered and instead says, 'Well, I had fun, Nikhu. Thanks for showing me around,' and reaches up to hug him.

He rests his head against hers for a brief moment, holding her tighter than he usually does. When he speaks, his voice is softer again. 'Yeah, thanks for coming, Mum. And for lunch.'

'When are you next home?' Avani asks, rummaging through her handbag for a tissue. There is something about leaving her son behind after spending the afternoon with him that she is struggling with. It's the same feeling she felt trapped inside her chest when she helped him move into his halls in late September. She wants to take him back to London with her.

'This weekend. Will's helping me source a new exhaust for the Beemer so I'll be home la—'

She looks back up at him, the words not quite sinking in. Surely she's misheard.

'Fuck.' Nik squirms slightly and his cheeks grow pink – a trait he has inherited from his father.

'What did you say?'

Silence. There is panic – a raw fear – rising from the pit of Avani's stomach. It lodges itself in her lungs and she tries to breathe it back down. 'Did you keep that bloody thing?'

'Mum, let's not. Your train's about to leave.'

'I . . . we discussed this. You said you'd sell it. We agreed you'd purchase a second-hand Polo instead.' He doesn't respond, and something slots uncomfortably into place, making the hairs on her arms rise as if ready for battle. 'Is that where you've been sneaking off to every weekend when you come back home? To fix that bloody thing up?'

'Mum, you're shouting, man.'

'I don't want you to have it. What don't you understand?' she says, placing a hand firmly on his shoulder. Rani nudges at her legs. Avani can hear a bark growing behind her whimpering.

Nik shrugs her hand away and looks around before murmuring: 'Mum, listen –'

'No, Nikhil. Why would you do this?'

'Do what? It's just a car.'

'Exactly. Look, we have Bapu's inheritance. You can buy any car you wa—'

'Why're you so against me having it? It's all I've ever had of his.'

Avani is no longer listening. She speaks over him. 'I don't want you to keep that car. I don't know how many times I have to –'

'I don't care. I'm keeping it.'

'No, you're not.'

'All right, fine,' he says. 'Explain why I can't have it and I'll get rid.' Their eyes meet. 'Tell me why and I'll obey you.'

Avani stares at him with eighteen years of emotion jammed in her throat. She tries to speak, but the words she seeks can't be summoned. They fester in the space below her throat and above her chest, forming a painful lump. She stares up at her son and, for a second, sees somebody else. He has never been stubborn. She cannot find a way to respond to him, to this, without unravelling a piece of her that she keeps packed away safely at her very core. Instead, she shakes her head, brushes past him, and walks towards her train, Rani padding obediently beside her.

18

September 1990

Avani woke up to the image of the number eight, looping deliciously around itself against the black of sleep. Eight. It was the number of nights left, the number of days she had to get through. She was just over a week away from the wide expanse of freedom. She stretched, feeling the tiredness squeezing its way out of her muscles, then threw her curtains open. Neatly stacked boxes lined her walls. She was fully packed for university, ready to go, making do with the pile of fading clothes she was leaving behind. She refused to reopen any of the boxes, sure that something would go wrong if she did, that the spell would be broken. This was a liminal state of waiting, where her mind was full of all manner of disasters that might occur, part of some collusion her mother had cooked up to keep her tied to her little life in Harrow.

It had been a journey, to say the least, getting her mother to come round to the idea that she was going to live away from home. She'd agreed to study the course her parents chose only if her mother accepted that she was not going to live at home while completing it. She'd spent the last twelve months' worth of Saturdays stocking shelves and balancing the books of a family friend who owned the newsagent's down the road, saving up every penny she earned for her new life. The promise of adulthood, of freedom, was just eight short days away. She brushed her hair while peering down onto the flat roof outside her window, her tired eyes searching for any sign of movement, then changed into jeans and the Deep Purple T-shirt she'd inherited from Chand.

When she removed the door chain from its clasp and stepped into the hallway, her foot met something cold and smooth. She looked down to see a masalyu, like the one her mother kept in the kitchen. A note sat on top of it with her mother's strong hand pressing hard into the paper: FOR UNIVERSITY. She crouched down and opened the lid to find a cluster of six small bowls circling the perimeter of the container, curled around the seventh, which sat snug in the middle. They were filled with ajmo, marchu, garam masala, hardar, methi, rai and jeeru, each covered carefully with cling film. She was filled with a wash of warmth, which stayed with her only until she noticed another package next to the steel dabbo. A cardboard box. Inside: a face cloth and a tube of skin-lightening cream. Avani shook her head. She stuffed both the dabbo of spices and tube of cream into her bin. She wanted no piece of her mother following her into her new life. Her mother's words just the week before came back to her, crawling over her like a chill; she'd stepped away from her family at Tesco to say hello to a school friend, only to walk back into the cool mist of her mother's mutterings: *I've given up trying to stop you hanging around with these white boys. You'll regret this. You'll fall pregnant. The only small benefit will be that at least the baby will be a reasonable colour, white mixing with your dark, dark skin.*

Avani shook the memory from her and made her way downstairs. She was pleased to see that her mother's shoes were missing from their place by the front door. Her father was sitting at the kitchen table, sipping a cup of chai and reading the paper.

'Morning, Puppa.'

'Morning, beta.' Her father folded the newspaper carefully in half. Avani watched Thatcher's face disappear behind a sheet. Her father was dressed in a crisp white shirt tucked into suit trousers. A sharp crease ran down his sleeves. Dark socks twitched under the table.

'Want some more chai?' Avani asked.

'You sit, beta,' her father said, getting up. 'I'll do it.'

Avani plucked a grape from the bowl in front of her and bit into the sweetness of it. 'Dad,' she said, inspecting the green jelly-like flesh, 'Chand's invited me to go to a gig with his colleagues tomorrow night. I won't get back 'til late. Will Mum be around?'

Her father checked his watch as he leaned against the worktop. 'Tomorrow night.' He ran the words around his tongue slowly. 'Yes, beta, she'll be home all day.'

Avani swore under her breath, then popped another grape into her mouth.

'Could you stay at Maya's?' he asked.

'She's away this weekend, but I could crash at Chand's.'

'Okay, beta,' he said. 'Just be safe.'

Avani nodded, preparing the half-truth she would deliver to her mother, when asked. It would be worth it. Music and art were her two escapes. Chand had very much tucked her under his wing over the last few years; sneaking her to gigs with his friends despite the four-year age difference, bringing home copies of all his favourite albums, introducing her to artists that bridged her two worlds. As a child, her father hummed to Asha Bhosle and Lata Mangeshkar, while her friends seemed to constantly be surrounded by the beat of Blondie and the Boomtown Rats. She flitted between the two, between the sitar and bansuri of her home and the electric guitar and synthesiser that sat waiting outside. And then, her mind had been quietly blown open as a ten-year-old when she watched Sheila Chandra performing 'Ever So Lonely' in that iconic purple sari on *Top of the Pops*. Over the next few years, while her school friends progressed to Wham! and Madonna, she began to search deeper. She looked further back to discover more. Eventually, she met herself in the mix of East and West that Chand presented to her; in the fusion of George Harrison and Ravi Shankar, in John McLaughlin and the Mahavishnu Orchestra, pressed between the melodies of Shakti. Maya, meanwhile, introduced her to daytimers, to the bhangra mixes and underground music that was just beginning to take off. It was as though these amalgamations gave her identity permission to ebb and flow in the way her mother would never allow. It was here, this possibility, in music.

Avani watched her father stoop over the pan as he added in chai no masalo and cardamom pods. The beginnings of a hole were forming at the back of his sock, by the heel. Flesh pushed against the worn thread. She felt a sudden wash of guilt for leaving him, a need to stay, to protect him.

'Beta,' he said, turning to her, 'I've bought you

something for university. I was going to wait until next week but since it's just the two of us, now seems like a good time.'

Avani searched his face as he spoke, thinking of the unwanted gift from her mother that had been waiting outside her bedroom door.

He tapped the side of his nose and disappeared into the garden. The pan hissed from the stove and a wave of creamy lather rose to the top, bringing specks of loose tea with it. She lowered the flame, took a bottle of milk from the fridge door, and poured some into the pan. Her father reappeared a moment later, carrying a package that was almost as tall as him.

'Whoa,' Avani said. 'Where've you been hiding that?'

'In my shed. Open it, beta.' He leaned the package against the worktop.

Avani unwrapped the brown paper to reveal the neck of an easel. 'No way!' she breathed. She tore the rest of the brown paper away, her eyes bright with delight. She had walked countless times past this very easel in the shop at the end of Harrow High Street, watching it move an inch to the left or the right every few days as other items nudged their way to the shopfront. She propped it up and ran her fingers along the beechwood. It was smooth and strong and smelt like happiness.

'Puppa,' she said, tucking herself into his chest, 'I don't know what to say.'

He wrapped his arms around her and she filled her lungs with the warm, earthy scent of him.

'I'm sorry you couldn't study Fine Art, beta. Mumma is right, you'll have better prospects with Mathematics.'

He pulled away from her to take her face in his hands. 'But that doesn't mean you should stop painting, chakli. When your studies are finished each day, you paint to your heart's content.'

'I will, Puppa. Thank you so much. I love it.'

'I've already checked with Kalpalbhai,' he said, 'and it'll all fit nicely in his van when he drives you to your new digs.' He raised his eyebrows playfully on the final word, as if to check he'd got it right.

Avani laughed, her hands exploring the easel. She adjusted it so that it was sitting at the perfect height. The canvases that filled the walls of her room had all been painted with her hunched over them at her desk, the muscles in her neck cramping as her hand danced across the cotton, a trail of colour behind it. The perspective was often slightly skewed when she worked like this, with pieces of dust pressing into the paint. She looked back up to her father, who was opening a packet of biscuits. 'You'll be okay when I leave, won't you, Dad?'

Her father waved her question away with a flapping hand. 'Areh! Now don't you waste any time worrying about me. I'm always just fine,' he said, 'so long as I have a crisp paper and garam chai. And maybe a nice bhajiu or two.'

'Saachi vaath, Puppa.' Avani went back to the stove to see how the chai was getting on. Her father had brewed enough for the whole street, it seemed. She carefully strained out three mugs' worth, stirring a spoon of white sugar into two, moving between them, hoping her father hadn't spotted the spare.

'Maya's university is near yours, heh ne?' he said.

'Yeah, just down the road. We'll be in the same digs.'

'And how about your friend Elliot, beta?'

Avani's eyes automatically flicked up to the ceiling, then to the clock on the table. 'He's doing really well, Dad.' She handed him a mug, trying to keep her voice light. 'He got a full grant to study Literature, did I tell you?'

'You did. Smart young man.' He watched her as he took a careful sip. 'It's interesting,' he said, casually, unfolding his newspaper and leafing through it, 'I'm sure I saw someone who looked remarkably like young Elliot climbing over our bins and onto the roof outside your window just now.'

Avani froze, her breath trapped in her throat. Her gaze met his. Something unspoken passed between them.

'Take some biscuits with you, chakli,' her father said, nodding at the ginger nuts he'd just opened. 'Looked like he hadn't eaten in a while, bicharo.'

Avani stared at the orange packet, wondering if this was a trick.

'Go on, beta.'

Avani tucked the packet under her arm, picked up the mugs and headed for the door before he could change his mind. 'Thank you, Puppa.'

He looked up at her from the paper. 'You're very welcome, beta.'

In the hallway, Avani stopped to gather herself. She took a deep breath, wondering how she had got away with it. Her father probably knew she was feeding Elliot and helping him study, as opposed to the things her mother would have accused her of. The thought of her mother spotting Elliot instead of her father made her stomach coil into a tight fist, pushing a wave of nausea to her mouth. Eight days, she reminded herself. Just eight more days. She navigated the mugs of chai up the stairs, nudging her bedroom door open with her foot. Waiting for her by the open window, his arms folded over the frame, was Elliot.

'Fancy seeing you here.' He smiled and she felt the worry fall from her face. He moved his hair sleepily away from his eyes. She'd spent countless hours sprinkled across almost half a year hunched over her oil paints, trying to recreate their colour by mixing various ratios of paint together. Yellow ochre. Burnt umber. Emerald green. She could never quite replicate their hue, but the act of failing itself felt right to her. His spirit was one that could never be captured, pinned to canvas.

'What're you doing?' he asked, cocking his head, his grin growing. 'Come over here.' He was shivering slightly, his eyes puffy, his cheeks red with cold. She handed him a mug and sat on the edge of the bed to face him.

He took a deep breath. 'Smells delicious. Thank you.'

'Did you . . . where was Phil last night?'

His mouth opened. Nothing came.

'Wasn't it his turn to have you over?'

Silence.

'I can tell you slept in the park again. You're almost blue.'

Elliot sighed and rubbed his eyes. 'I've had enough of his . . . I don't like the way he talks about you.'

Something caught in her chest. They watched each other for a long moment.

'It's not on,' Elliot said, an apology in his voice.

Avani perched her chai on the windowsill. 'Come and get warm,' she told him, lifting the duvet.

He placed the mug beside hers, removed his shoes and coat, then slipped between the sheets. Goose bumps rose along her skin as he wrapped himself around her. The cold seemed to have stitched itself into his core.

'Is this okay?' he whispered.

'Very much so.'

He laughed silently then asked: 'Are your parents home?'

'Only Dad. He was asking about you. He knows you've been popping in.'

'What?' She felt him freeze behind her.

She shook her head and said, 'He was cool. I think he knows you're just stopping by for chai and biscuits.'

Elliot's arms relaxed slightly and he sighed into her hair. She slid her hands into the arms of his jumper, warming up his forearms, telling him in whispers about the easel, about how sad she was to be leaving her father, how she hoped he'd be okay. They counted down the days until they would be at university together, comparing notes on the induction timetables they'd just been sent in the post, cross-referencing the afternoons they'd have free together.

'I caught up with Chand yesterday,' Avani told him, trying to sound as casual as possible. 'He said that you should go and stay with him next week, before uni starts. He's just bought a sofa bed.'

'Really? He said that?'

'Yes.'

'Ahhh. We'd have such a laugh.' He pulled Avani

closer and she entwined her fingers with his, rubbing her thumb around one of his nails. She thought of the English teacher at his school who had read his poetry and encouraged him to apply to university; of the circle of friends who had taken him in since he left home; of Chand's offer to have him stay. Despite the hand he'd been dealt at birth, the pain of his parents, life had begun to nudge small morsels of kindness towards him. He was so incredibly loved.

Elliot was murmuring about university again, but Avani was only half listening; her mind was on his parents. She recalled the last time she'd seen his mother, when he'd left Harrow in that black cab, the words that had rung in the air around them, the fullness of his mother's stomach under that floral dress. 'Ell,' she interrupted. 'Can I ask you something?' She searched for a way in, a way to lead up to the question that had been bobbing to the surface of her mind again and again.

A pocket of silence expanded between them. Then he said, in a voice slightly too chipper, 'What's that?'

'I think I might have imagined this,' Avani started, cautious, 'maybe I'm confusing your mother –' he took a short sharp breath in – 'with someone else, but I remember watching her pack that cab up when you moved away from Harrow. Wasn't she . . . pregnant?'

The word sat round and full in the air. Elliot sighed and his breath tickled her neck. 'Yeah,' he said. 'She was.'

Avani lay very still, listening to him breathing behind her. She'd been thinking about this for months, waiting for him to mention a younger brother or sister. 'What happened?'

Elliot untangled himself from her and lay on his back. 'I was a brother, for two short weeks.'

'What?' Avani said, turning to face him. 'Why only two weeks?'

His eyes were glassy but she could see a deep, devastating pain in them. 'They took him away.'

She thought she'd misheard. 'Away?'

'Mum gave birth a couple of months after we moved away from Harrow.' His eyes were on the ceiling as he spoke, as if watching his past unfold above. 'I think that's the reason we left in such a rush. She wanted to try and leave him . . . my dad, before she had the baby. But he found us. I was so bloody naive. I thought that everything was fixed when she took him back; that we'd be a proper family, that her and Dad would sort their shit out, that having another son would bring them together. We'd moved to a new flat, and I had a brother.'

Avani listened to his voice ringing through the stillness of her bedroom, her eyes wide open. It was so rare for Elliot to speak about his childhood, let alone his parents.

'I should have known something was wrong when they wouldn't name him. They just called him "it" or "the baby".' She could hear the emotion gathering in his voice now, making it break. 'I came home from school one afternoon and he was gone.'

'What do you mean?' Avani whispered.

'I mean he wasn't there any more. He wasn't anywhere.

I'd made a bed for him in one of the cabinet drawers in our lounge. When I got home, his blankets were gone, and the drawer was full of coppers and receipts and old pens. His formula wasn't in the kitchen. His clothes were missing. It was like he had never existed. They wouldn't tell me what happened to him, where he went. Dad got riled up when I kept asking but . . . he was my little pal. When he used to wake up in the night, he'd stop when I held his hand, or when I picked him up. I was his person. I was the one who fed him and changed him and loved him. I was only a kid myself, but I was all he had.'

'But where did they take him? Where did he go?'

Elliot shook his head. 'The day he disappeared, Dad didn't get home until early the next morning. He'd borrowed someone's van. I reckon he drove as far as he could and dumped him somewhere.'

'Oh my God.'

'I fluctuate between wondering if they gave him away or if they just left him. Or . . . if something much worse happened. Whenever I tried to ask them, they just told me never to mention it. That it had never happened. That he'd never existed. It was almost like they started to believe it themselves. Then, last Christmas, when I went back home to get the rest of my stuff and properly move out, I found one of his socks. It had been trapped in an old pillowcase, probably from the washing machine. A little white sock. That was when Dad and I . . .'

Avani pressed her eyes shut, remembering the phone call just a few weeks after she'd run into him on that bench, an unfamiliar, staticky voice telling her Elliot was in the ICU. She'd gone to visit him in the hospital and had barely been able to speak for days afterwards, the shock of seeing him so weak, so nearly gone, almost stifling her. Her hand searched for his under the sheets.

'Have you ever tried to find him? There must be . . . like . . . hospital records at least.'

'Of course I did. But it was like fresh heartbreak all over again when I came to a dead end. I searched newspaper archives, tried to speak to social workers, but I didn't know who I was looking for. They never registered his birth. They refused to talk about him, to admit he even existed. All I had was the sock. And what was the point? He's hopefully somewhere safe and happy, loved, looked after. It would be so selfish to tear him away from that just because I miss him. He has no memory of me, anyway, no idea that I exist.'

Avani took a deep breath, her mind alive with his words. Hearing these rare snippets from the years they'd spent apart always whipped the air from her lungs. When they were children, she'd seen the verbal abuse from his mother, the bruises on his arms, the round shining scars she spotted on his shoulders one summer when they all went swimming. Elliot would never say a word about any of it. He never complained. She'd never heard him speak about what happened when the front door of his home swung shut.

'I feel so alone without him.' His voice was straining under the weight of tears. 'I think about him every day.'

'Ell –' she tucked into him – 'don't be alone with this. We're all with you. You know we all love you.' It was true, she loved him, so deeply. In a way that seemed to eclipse everything else in her life. He nodded, but there was still a resignation – a hopelessness – in his face that filled her with fear.

'Maybe Maya could help,' she said. 'She's going to be studying law, so she'll have access to all sorts of –'

He shook his head. 'I don't want anyone else to know. I want to try to find him once more, on my own.'

The silence between them grew heavy, holding the weight of unspoken words. The image of him as an eleven-year-old, left to look after a baby, filled Avani with a sudden rage that sat hot on her skin. She was livid with his parents, that they'd produced such a wonderful son and neglected him, then gone on to produce another they didn't even try to care for. She bit back her pride and told him: 'I'm here too, you know. I can help.'

Elliot nodded. 'I'm living in the hope that one day, I'll find him.'

The words 'you will' grew against her lips, but she caught herself just in time; it wasn't a promise she could give. Instead she wiped his cheeks and asked, 'How old would he be now?'

'Seven,' whispered Elliot, burying his face in her hair. His voice was hoarse, the wet from his eyes pressing into Avani's neck. 'It'll be his eighth birthday soon.'

Later, when the untouched chai on the windowsill had cooled and rain landed neatly on the glass beside it, Elliot murmured to Avani: 'I always thought, when I have a son one day –' he paused and something fluttered in Avani's stomach, finding its way up to her chest – 'I'd name him after little Nick. That's what I called him for those two weeks, my nameless brother.'

Avani lay still, wondering if he would go on. When he didn't, she skimmed her lips lightly against his jaw and murmured: 'What do you think of Nikhil?'

'Nikhil.' Elliot moved the word around in his mouth slowly, as if trying it out for size. 'I love it. It makes me think of a circle.' He drew one on Avani's abdomen with the tip of a warm finger.

'Yes,' she said, taking his hand in hers. As her fingers laced through his, intertwining, she whispered: 'It means complete.'

19

November 2017

Nik's on a cold, creaking train chugging its way towards the capital. He rose before the sun to catch the first service to London. This journey has come to provide a sense of solace to him. He finds that in the time between departure and arrival, the whirring of his thoughts stops for a while, the burden of them seemingly left behind, only to overtake him and greet him at his destination once more.

The air around him hangs heavy and damp. The floor is muddy with wet leaves and empty beer cans which have gravitated towards each other, forming small piles in the corners of the carriage. A tired-looking teenager with a ponytail meanders along the aisle, carefully collecting rubbish with a litter-stick and placing it into a clear bin liner. Nik watches from a window seat in the first carriage, his head pressed against the glass, slipping in and out of sleep. Beside him, expanses of frost-bitten fields and forests still thick with foliage shoot past, eventually giving way to the concrete towers and shiny windows that make up the skyline of central London. Dawn breaks slowly, beautifully, behind it. Nik's not paying attention though, because he's just received a text from Layla – the first in weeks.

7:56 Layla: Hear you're home this weekend, stranger x

Nik blinks sleepily at her words for a while. He types several replies out, but eventually settles on:

7:58 Nik: Morning! Yeah I am, stalker. How you been? x

8:03 Layla: I'm doing a birthday ting tonight. Have invited Will and Teo so you're welcome too, obvs. Most of the college lot are gna be there x

8:03 Nik: Nice! Central? x

8:05 Layla: It's in south. Pres at my halls then going to a club round the corner. Come x

Nik is typing out a reply when another message comes through from Will. It's a photo of the new exhaust for the Beemer followed by: Broski! Look what the postie just delivered.

8:06: Nik: BRUV. My train's just pulling into London, can I come straight to yours yeah?

8:07: Will: Yeh come over, we'll get it sorted this morning. Dad can sort the MOT for you this pm

8:08: Teo: I'm coming too. Hanging so will bring McD. Do you lots want?

Nik's phone signal cuts out as the train approaches King's Cross. He looks back at the picture of the exhaust. It's taken weeks to arrive and is the final piece of the car that needs replacing. The process has been much more difficult than he'd expected; the car was particularly difficult to transfer to his name. He'd found a mouldy logbook in the glove compartment but had to make several lengthy phone calls to the DVLA and send them his grandfather's death certificate, which he pinched from a stack of papers on his mother's dressing table. He'd managed to tax it, eventually, but knows the car is going to be extortionate to insure under his name. He doesn't care, his student loan should cover most of it, and he has some inheritance tucked into his savings. Everything going well, it could be up and running by the end of the day, and it'll be all his.

Later, when Nik receives an email from his university adviser telling him they need to arrange a meeting to discuss his attendance, he turns to Will and Teo. 'D'you guys actually go to all of your lectures then?'

The boys are leaning against the bonnet of Will's Fiesta, watching Papa Burns use an angle grinder to remove the Beemer's old exhaust. It has seized up and a thorough dose of elbow grease hasn't made the slightest difference.

'Yeah. Don't you?' Teo says, navigating the words around a mouthful of egg and sausage.

'First year doesn't count towards my grade,' Nik says, deleting the email and stuffing his phone back into his jacket.

'Neither does mine, but I still go,' Will says. 'Get my money's worth, innit.'

Nik thinks about this and senses the boys exchanging a glance.

'What's up with you, broski?' Will asks. 'Used to be some next mission trying to get you to bunk at college.'

Nik rolls an alloy plug under his foot as he speaks. 'Just got a lot of stuff going on that feels bigger than uni.'

'With your mum?'

'Yeah. And this,' he says, nodding to the car. They are so close to finishing it and Nik can feel himself tensing up, worried something is going to come up last minute which means he can't drive it after all. He swallows a final bite of breakfast and asks, 'You guys up for Layla's tonight, yeah? Or should we skip it and go shisha instead?'

'Nah, man. Let's go to Layla's. It's gonna be lit,' Teo says.

'You legit only wanna go because Rach is gonna be there,' Will says, smirking. Both Will's and Teo's relationships have recently ended and tonight is the first time their old group of college mates are hanging out, exes included.

'Should probs get a fresh cut, y'know. Just in case,' Teo says, running a hand over his stubble. Nik and Will both crease up. Then Will nudges Nik with his elbow and says: 'What's up with you and Layla, then?'

Nik shrugs, his ears growing hot. 'Haven't seen her since I left.'

'Is it? Rah, I bet something happens later,' Teo says. 'You two are taking bare time with this, you know.'

'Is she with anyone?'

'Dunno, man,' Will says, scrunching up the paper his breakfast was wrapped in and wiping his hands on his joggers.

Nik runs a hand through his hair and stands a little straighter.

'Bare guys are trying it though,' Teo says. 'Apparently,' he adds, when Nik throws him a look.

'Ready, lads!' Papa Burns calls, moving out of the way.

The boys get off the bonnet and circle the Beemer. Nik dribbles the alloy plug between his feet as he walks, as though it's a tiny metal football. 'You know what,' he says, his eyes on the car, 'if I hurry up and insure this thing, we could probs drive there tonight . . .'

Nik cruises through Wembley with the windows down, despite the bite of November wind weaving its way around the car. 'Did You See' blasts out of the stereo. Teo jams to it from the passenger seat and Nik joins in, all arms, whenever they stop in traffic. Will eggs them on from the back, and when the song bleeds into 'Bestie' all three of them rap the lyrics. Teo turns the radio up even louder, just in time for Yungen to spit about getting blocked on Instagram. Nik laughs at the timing, remembering how Rajvi recently blocked Teo on Instagram, too. He punches Teo's arm and Will shouts over the music: 'Peak, Teo got blocked.'

'Oi, piss off, man,' Teo says, punching Nik back. He swerves slightly into the right-hand lane, narrowly missing a bus.

'Did she actually block you then?' Nik asks, waving an apology to the bus driver.

'Yes, bruv. Since when is it a crime to like someone's Insta?'

'Every time she uploads a photo you're literally the first one on there. Fire emojis all over the shop.'

'It's jokes watching you tryna chirps her,' Will says.

'I'm single now, though, remember? And she's fire.'

'Ugh, she's my cousin, you sicko,' Nik says, overtaking a cyclist.

Teo ignores him, turns to Will and says, 'Oi, I beg you text Layla to ask if Rach is coming tonight.'

Nik zones out of their chatter and merges onto the A40, still surprised by how smooth the Beemer is to drive. It's both heavier yet quicker than his mother's Volvo. As he weaves his way across London, the knowledge that his father once existed in the same seat that he occupies now keeps rising in his mind, bringing with it a wash of pride. A little piece of his father's life has found breath once again. His feet once worked the same pedals, his hands once warmed the same steering wheel. It was important to Nik to get this car running again. It has made him feel closer to the man he never knew, the same way Layla told him she felt when she pulled her father's old sweatshirt over her, curling into it as she searched for sleep in the nights after he left. This is Nik's equivalent of a watch or coat or jumper that's been passed down to be worn and cherished. Why else would Bapu have kept it after all these years?

He turns off the A40 and heads into central London, taking the road that cups Hyde Park and Buckingham Palace. Will and Teo jam to 'Unforgettable', passing a bottle of rum between them. When Nik speeds onto Vauxhall Bridge, he feels a shift in the air around him. The sun is settling down into water either side of them, its reflection dancing in the ripples. He drinks in this moment, feeling comfort in the London that stands tall and resolute around him. He feels so enveloped by it, so at one with the city, as if this is where he belongs. Something loosens in his chest, like a chuckle that rises then falls, not quite finding its way up to his mouth. This is the first time in months that the fizziness under his skin has fully dissolved away, the sensation that he is tense and waiting to walk into battle is gone. The distraction of finally fixing the car, the excitement of firing the ignition and driving out of the garage, seems to have cast a fresh light across his thoughts. It's like he stepped into the car to greet his old self, the self he left behind that summer day in hospital, when he had to summon a courage that never came.

'Broski, no permit parking up there,' Will says from the back, pointing towards a road Nik has just driven past.

Nik checks his rear-view mirror, reverses a few metres, and swings into the road. He's cautious as he parallel parks into the only empty space, the boys clapping him on the back as he slips neatly in on the first go.

'Saved you a bit,' Teo says, handing him the bottle of rum as they pile out of the car. They head towards Layla's halls, Nik feeling the excitement bubbling gently through his veins. He skies the last of the rum, then pulls his phone from his pocket. His mother rang him twice as he drove, but he rejected her calls to keep the maps app running. Now, she has messaged him:

16:45 Mum: Are you coming home this weekend or not? Please let me know

16:52 Mum: Love, Mum xxx

Nik is about to reply when a call comes through. It's Alice. He stares at her name for several seconds before answering: 'Yo, Alice! S'up?'

She laughs, her voice smooth against his ear: 'Wow, is this Harrow Nik, yeah?'

'Eeyes, speaking,' he says, loud and posh.

'Thanks for ditching me this morning, you knob.'

'What d'you mean?' he asks, following the boys down the main road. Teo raises his eyebrows and shoots Nik an upwards nod, silently asking who Nik's talking to. When Nik mouths Alice's name, Teo grins and reaches for the phone. Nik bats him away, not sure what's going on, until Will says, 'Teo, stop begging it, man.'

Nik turns away from them, remembering when Teo first spotted Alice on one of Nik's Snaps and replied to it with Ayyyyy who dis? He pushes this out of his mind and tries to focus on her words.

'I thought we were meeting at the station for the 9am to London,' she says.

'Nah, I wanted to get down first thing.'

'Well, cheers for letting me know. I saw the car on Insta, by the way. How does it drive?'

'Ah, it's incredible, man. We just drove across London in it.'

'Oh, really? Whereabouts are you?'

'Somewhere in south.' As he says this, Paul rises in his mind. He lives nearby, Nik recalls, in Dulwich.

'Well, I'm heading to Ministry with my sixth-form mates this evening. Thought we could join forces later, maybe.'

'Did you now, Yoda?'

He can almost hear her rolling her eyes. 'You should come. I want to meet your mates,' she says.

'I think Ministry is ages away from us though. That's gonna be some next mission.'

'Ugh, well, let me know where you end up, yeah?'

'Will do, man. Have a good one.'

He looks up to see the boys heading into a tall building block and decides to leg it the last few metres. Layla meets them by the door. Something swoops through Nik's stomach. She wears an off-shoulder dress the colour of summer. It takes Nik a moment to notice she holds herself differently. She seems taller.

He has no idea what is about to happen or which way this will go; whether she's going to be cold and haughty or if they'll immediately fall back into the rhythm of what they had earlier that year, as though no time has passed at all. He's just a few steps away from her now and is suddenly overcome by the fear that she may have invited him tonight to flaunt a new boyfriend, to show Nik what he lost out on. Surely not, though. She's never been one for games. Their eyes meet and Nik can't help but smile. 'All right, stalker?' he says, nodding as he passes her.

She nods back. Her eyes are still on him when she says: 'Oi, Teo, your ex is in there. Behave yeah, or I'll kick you out.'

'Yes, ma'am,' Teo calls, as he and Will take the stairs two at a time.

'So here you are,' she says, closing the door and turning to Nik. 'Alive and well.' He seems to have lost the ability to form words. He smiles like an idiot and reaches down to hug her. As she moves, the sweet, warm scent of her jolts something in him, reminding him of the start of the summer, of who he used to be, of how he spent most afternoons with her in a carefree haze of cinnamon and honey, Burna Boy and Wizkid and Drake and Trey Songz on repeat in the background.

'Your hair's grown,' she tells him, her hand running through it and resting on a strand behind his ear.

Nik notices the space between them appears to have shrunk somehow. He's moved closer to her without realising. 'Happy birthday for next week,' he begins to say, but his words don't quite make it out, because Layla has risen to her toes to press her lips against his.

20

September 1993

Avani pushed the front door shut with a click and turned to drink in the comforting mess of her home. Remnants of the house-warming party greeted her: crispy leaves and soft mud dotting the wooden floor of the hallway, surfaces brimming with empty glasses tinted red from wine, large bowls sitting among them with straggling ganthiya or crisps lining the bottom. Mary J.'s 'Real Love' played from the lounge. Avani walked into the kitchen, where Elliot was at the sink, running a scourer over a stack of plates. She watched him – he was so gentle, so precise. There had been a stolen moment earlier that night when they had held each other's gaze, surrounded by their friends, laughing and dancing through the flat. No words were said. That quiet moment – at the very beginning of their lives, with their friends speckled through their new home – felt, to her, more intimate than if they were wrapped around each other in bed.

'Let's go upstairs,' she said, resting her head against the space between his shoulder blades. 'We can sort all of this in the morning.'

He turned to hug her, his hands wet, the tap still running.

'I can't believe we did it, Av,' he murmured into her hair.

'I know,' she whispered. 'It's mad.'

They had, just a few days earlier, moved into their first home together, a humble one-bed in Neasden, which they could barely afford between both of their graduate salaries and second evening jobs. The bathroom walls were peppered with mould and they still hadn't figured out how to switch on the central heating, but they did not care; they had graduated and escaped the baggage of their childhood homes to build a new one, together. The impossible had been achieved. Over the last three years, the edges and borders of their minds, their bodies, their very beings, had blurred and bled into one another, forming a new entity in itself. Away from the glare of her mother's judgement, Avani had let herself grow towards the shape of a new sun.

They debriefed each other on all the best gossip from the night while they brushed their teeth side by side at the bathroom sink, then stepped out of their clothes and into bed. Avani talked Elliot through which of their university friends were in new relationships and which had secured jobs with fancy titles at companies their godparents owned. When they moved on to the other guests and landed on Chand, Elliot said, 'I still can't get my head around how much getting married has changed him.'

Avani could hear the crackle of Elliot's hand running across his stubble. 'I know,' she murmured into his chest. 'He's become such a bloody bore, hasn't he?' Her Doc Martens-wearing, Nirvana-obsessed brother had, since marrying earlier that year, morphed into someone who wore chinos at the weekend and spent three hours a day commuting to a corporate job in central London.

Something had shifted in him; within the space of six months, he'd gone from being madly in love with a waitress called Poppy to being engaged to a dentist that their mother had introduced to him. They'd married and were already expecting.

'I think it's the first time I've ever seen him turn down dope,' Elliot pondered through a yawn.

'Rukmani keeps him on the straight and narrow, bless her,' Avani said, yawning too. Someone in the flat above turned up their music, and Avani could make out the baseline to Madonna's 'Fever'.

'How exciting that they're already having a little one.'

'Yeah, Chand said they've finally decided on a name,' Avani told him.

He tilted his head when listening to her, which Avani had only recently discovered was because he was partly deaf in one ear, a childhood injury he could not recall the details of. 'Can you tell me?'

'Of course. It's Rajvi.'

'Rajvi,' he repeated. 'Beautiful. I can't wait to meet her.'

Avani held her breath, already knowing what was about to come. Sure enough, a moment later, Elliot shifted to face her and asked: 'When are we going to start trying?'

Avani ignored the swooping in her stomach. 'When we move to a proper house. And get married,' she said through a smile.

'So next summer, then?'

She laughed and heard him doing the same beside her. 'We have so much time. We have forever.'

'Chand having one on the way is making me so broody.'

'I know, Ell.' Her eyes following the sliver of light

moving across their ceiling. 'You're going to be such a great dad.'

'I don't know.' The music faded, giving way to the hum of Neasden in the early hours. A scooter shot past their open window. She knew he was thinking about his lost brother. Little Nick, who he wasn't able to save, who they hadn't yet been able to find.

'You,' Avani told him, 'will be the most *amazing* father.'

'I hope so,' he whispered into her hair. The rhythm of their words grew slower. Sleep was so deliciously close. She sunk herself snug into the darkness that was waiting for her. Images from her day flickered across her mind; the bouquet of hydrangeas their new neighbours had brought round, Chand and Rukmani in the corner of the lounge clutching a couple of glasses of squash, stealing glances at the clock on the wall, Elliot and Maya dancing in the kitchen to 'Ain't 2 Proud 2 Beg'.

She could hear Elliot's breath slowing, stretching deeper into his lungs. Then it stopped altogether. She heard him sit up suddenly.

'Are you asleep?' he said.

'Hmm.'

'I want to ask you something.'

'Go on.'

'D'you fancy . . . would you like, one day, to get married?'

Avani's eyes snapped open. 'What?'

A soft glow ebbed towards them from under the curtains. She could see that his face was bright, there was a confidence to it that reminded her so much of the boy from her childhood, her first ever crush, before the burden of adulthood had found him and prematurely rested its weight upon his shoulders.

'I'm going to propose to you properly, I promise,' he said, taking her hand, 'but I don't want us to move in together and for you to sit wondering if there will ever be more. I know how hard you fought with your mother just to get us here. So, I want you to know, now, that I'd really love to marry you one day soon, if you'll have me.'

'Oh my God.' Avani was overcome with tears, her heart sparkling with joy. 'Absolutely,' she said. 'I absolutely want to marry you.'

'Excellent,' he said, smiling between kisses. 'Can we have a Hindu wedding?'

'Whatever you want,' she said, laughing and crying at the same time.

'I'm going to propose to you properly. With a ring and everything,' he said, again.

'You don't have to bother with any of that nonsense.'

'I'd like to. I just wanted you to know now, that it's coming,' he whispered, pulling her close. 'It's waiting for us.'

Later, half dreaming, half awake, her mind whirred with images of what their wedding might look like. She saw her whole family there, all of them, her mamas giving her away, the heat of the fire they'd sit in front of, Elliot walking into the mandap with his friends and family dancing around him . . . the mirage wrapped itself into a dark knot, slipping away from her. He had no family to dance with him, to bring him into the hall to the sound of the dhol, as she had done for Chand.

She had never been to a mixed ethnicity Hindu

wedding, let alone with one side of the wedding party totally missing. She thought of how much fun Elliot had had at Chand's wedding, how gorgeous he'd looked in a sherwani, how he'd embraced every single tradition, how he'd helped stop Chand's new brothers-in-law stealing his shoes as they walked in, how he'd danced to bhangra at the reception, how he'd followed the rules and abstained from running his hand across Avani's back or giving her a quick peck like he always did. He was trying so hard and it devastated her that she had no reference point for how she could bring him in any further, or what a Hindu wedding might look like without his family there.

They would figure it out, she told herself. They would find a way.

21

November 2017

Nik wakes up to a shooting pain slicing from his temple to his left ear. Layla's head rests on his chest, her body tucked neatly against his. He rubs her forearm absent-mindedly as he looks around for some water. A glass has been left by the windowsill next to him, his phone face down beside it. His mother has called three more times in the night and a list of messages fills his lock screen.

23:49 Mum: I assume you've stayed at uni, then. Call me because I think we should talk. Mum

01:16 Alice: COME TO MINISTRYYYYYYYYYY

01:42 Alice: OI

03:49 Alice: Where are you? A bunch of us are heading back to a house party in the flats next to Elephant & Castle station. Bring your mates if you want, specifically Teo

04:02 Alice: helloooooooooo???????

04:18: Will: Broski! Me and Teo are heading back yeah? Gonna Uber it. Nandos tomorrow?

Nik stares at his phone, not knowing who to reply to first. It's just gone 10am; he and Layla have been asleep for less than four hours. Moments from last night flash across his mind, fragmented, like shards of glass. The memory of leaning against a bar presents itself vividly, Nik telling anyone who passed by: *I drove my dad's car today*, his speech slurred, until someone clapped him on the back and said, *Cool story, bro. D'you want a medal or something?* He laughs at this, realising how ridiculous he must have sounded. It was probably the best night out he's ever had. Twenty of his college friends plus a dozen of Layla's university friends had crammed themselves into an eight-person student hall kitchen, before piling out onto the street and heading round the corner to a club that played J Hus and Mr Eazi and Charly Black and Serani. He hasn't had fun like this since before his grandfather passed away, and definitely not back at his own university. Yet here, life as he imagined it would be is unfolding, for everyone apart from him. It's everything he expected university to be, back when he was hopeful and excited for it, before he'd moved away from London. He recalls speaking to two of his mates from college who he hasn't caught up with since he moved away. They told him they'd deliberately checked which universities had South Asian societies before applying: *You should see if they have a soc for us, man. They must have something.*

Nik thinks about this, wondering if he's Indian enough to join an Indian society, even if his university has one. He picks his phone up with the aim of checking, but instead finds himself on Instagram. He turns the volume as low as possible and watches his stories from last night. There are only three. One is of the Beemer before they drove across London, Teo and Will standing in front of it. The next is a blurry video of his college friends dancing in Layla's kitchen. The final story is one that he's reshared from Will's Instagram of Nik with Layla, the words 'THESE TWO' across the photo. Alice appears in the watch list. Fuck. He clicks on her profile to see that she's had a very similar night out, until he comes to a story that she's reshared. Someone is videoing people at the house party, dancing and downing Jägers, before the camera moves to Alice, her arms wrapped around someone's neck, her lips on his. *Ayyyy! Alice being Alice!* someone yells.

Nik's mouth feels drier than it did a moment ago. He knows he has absolutely no right to feel weird about seeing Alice with another guy, especially after last night, and especially since they've been on nights out which have ended with her going home with people, but seeing her actually kissing someone has made his stomach writhe. He watches the story once more, just to punish himself a little longer.

'Who's that?' Layla asks, after he replays it for a third time, her voice thick with sleep.

'Nothing,' Nik says, locking his screen.

'Put it away and come here.'

Later, when Nik's navigated Layla's tiny bathroom for a shower and helped her clear several bin bags of bottles from her kitchen, he leans against her door, sipping a cup of tea and eating Ritz biscuits. She hums as she does her make up, stopping occasionally to skip a song on the playlist that's cascading out of her phone.

'Doesn't that tickle?' Nik asks, watching her.

'What, mascara?'

'Yeah, whatever that is,' he says, waving a biscuit towards the little black instrument that reminds him of a honey dipper.

She laughs, tells him it doesn't, and then says, casually, 'You should transfer to London.'

'Huh?'

She swivels slightly on her chair to face him. 'You said last night how much you hate it up there. If you're not happy, just transfer.' When he doesn't respond, she adds, 'It's really not a big deal. Loads of people do it. My sister did, remember? It's not like you're dropping out completely. You got five acceptances, right?'

Nik has a sudden flashback to the early hours of the morning. They'd been sitting on a set of concrete steps in front of a glass building. The sky was dark, Layla was burrowed under his arm, picking at a cardboard box of chips, listening to Nik tell her about how much he hates being away from London, how he's only been to a handful of seminars so far, how much he misses his friends. He thinks, his breath catching, that he may have cried.

His cheeks grow warm. He feels suddenly exposed, annoyed with himself for telling her these things, impatient with her for bringing them up again now. He takes a seat on her bed, exhaling.

'I know how you feel,' she says, turning back to her mirror.

'As if.'

Layla stops rifling through her make-up bag to glare at him. 'I'm studying English with Creative Writing, remember? I'm literally the only person who isn't white in my poetry class. I have zero friends on my course.'

'I have mates,' Nik says, a little louder than he intended to.

'Are they nice?' Layla barely moves her lips as she speaks, focusing intently on applying a layer of lipgloss.

'Yeah, man. They're both from London. Dan's in my halls, and I've known Alice from day. They're not on my course but our lectures overlap.' He's absent-mindedly flicking through an open notebook on her bedside table.

Her voice is sharp: 'That's private, by the way.'

'Rah,' Nik says, looking from her to the curly black words dancing across the page in neat stanzas. 'Is this your prize-winning poetry, yeah?'

'Is Alice that blonde girl with the nose ring?'

There is a vulnerability in her gaze that he does not expect. All of the photos featuring Alice on his social media flash through his mind like a deck of cards. There isn't anything super intimate on there, maybe a drunken piggyback at worst.

'Yeah, that's her.' When she doesn't respond, he adds: 'C'mon then, let's get some breakfast, yeah?'

Her eyes are still fixed on him, unblinking. Beyoncé's 'Sorry' dances out of her phone. 'I would –' she pauses, meeting her own eyes in the mirror, searching her face for something she can't seem to find – 'but I'm meeting the girls for a birthday brunch in a bit.'

Nik is filled with an urge – one that grows in the depth of his stomach and pushes itself through his limbs, all the way to his fingers – to go over to her, to wrap his arms around her. Instead, he watches her stand up and pull a pair of jeans on. She stuffs her phone – which is still playing music – into her back pocket, then reaches for her bag.

Something in the rhythm of her movements has changed. He doesn't like it. He doesn't want to leave just yet.

'All right, babe.' She shrugs on a coat and pushes the door open. 'Avocado on toast beckons.'

Nik sits in the Beemer, the engine ticking over quietly, staring out of the windscreen. It's midday, and he still has four hours to kill until he meets the boys. He doesn't want to go home and face his mother yet. The tightness in his chest is creeping back, the numbness in his limbs not far behind, made worse by a night of too much alcohol and not enough sleep. He doesn't know what to do with himself or where to go. But the longer he leaves facing her, the harder it will be. Not only does he have the car to explain when he pulls up on her driveway, but now also the lack of replies and unanswered calls. He opens his chat with her to read through her messages and assess the damage. She's sent him three in a row, the last asking him to just let her know he's okay. She's online too, and he can imagine her now the other side of London, sitting on the edge of their sofa, a cup of cold chai by her feet, staring at the same screen he's looking at, wondering if he'll start typing. He closes the chat and opens up the one he has with Paul. On a whim, without really thinking about it, he presses the call button.

Paul answers almost immediately. 'Nik.'

'That was quick.'

Paul chuckles, then says, 'I had my phone in my hand, kiddo.'

'Just waiting for me to call, yeah?'

'Of course. Nice to hear from you. How's tricks?'

'Yeah, good, man. I'm actually in your ends.' Nik runs a hand through his hair as he speaks.

'In my what?'

'I'm in south,' Nik says. 'Lucas Street,' he adds, squinting at a road sign.

'Ah, yeah?' He hears footsteps. A door being pulled shut. 'What brings you this way, kid?'

'Night out. I'm heading back to Harrow in a bit. Was wondering if you're about.'

There's a brief moment of silence, during which Nik's heart crawls up to his mouth, before Paul says, 'Well, why don't you come over for coffee, if you've got time?'

'Yeah, that would be cool,' Nik says. 'If you're free.'

'I am. Just give me fifteen to sort the house out.'

Ten minutes later, Nik parks up outside a tall town house with a dark green door. 'Whoa,' he whispers, staring three storeys up. Paul appears, dressed in a black T-shirt and grey jeans. His hair's wet and slicked back.

'Congrats on the new ride,' Paul says, wrapping him in a hug. Nik expects it to be loose, quick, for there to be a clap on his back. Instead, Paul holds him tight, like he's genuinely glad to see him.

'Uh, yeah, long story,' Nik says, lingering on the front steps.

'Can't wait to hear it, kid. Come in.'

Nik wipes his shoes carefully before taking them off altogether and follows Paul through the hall. The ceilings are high, everything below them white or grey and expensive-looking.

'I thought I might as well check in, since I was in the area,' Nik says, trying to fill the silence. *Check in?* Since when does he speak like that? It sounds like something Paul would say. He realises that he's using his white voice, the one that he put on for the police last year when Teo got stopped and searched after that night out in Watford, the one that seemed to come out during his university interviews or when he speaks to particularly boujee-looking lecturers. It's not the voice he uses when he's at home – the one that comes naturally, where *t*s melt into the vowels either side of them, where *v*s occasionally take the place of *th*s. It's just Paul, man, he tells himself, it's calm. He clears his throat.

Paul leads him past an open door and Nik glances into his lounge. A well-stocked wood burner sits under a navy wall. Photo frames dress the mantel. Paul carries on through to the kitchen, where the herringbone floor stretches all the way to the back of the property to meet a neat garden, sliding doors separating the two.

'Are you hungry?' Paul asks.

'Yeah, starving.' Nik perches himself on a stool by a marble kitchen island. Wine glasses hang precariously from a rack above him, their curves sparkling where they catch the light. The worktops are speckled with bottles of herbs and various liquids. He reads the labels on a couple that stand taller than the rest. *Apple cider vinegar. Gluten-free tamari.* He wouldn't know what to do with these strange fluids. The radio plays quietly in the background, and he spots a splayed newspaper and half-eaten piece of toast on the dining table. There is so much comfort in this small arrangement.

'Big night, then?' Paul leans against the island, a dish-cloth thrown over his shoulder. The stance reminds Nik of his grandfather, who would rest his hands on the kitchen table in the same way when he abandoned making dinner to help Nik with his homework.

'Yeah. Nice place, man,' Nik says, distracted. He rubs the beard growing around his chin absent-mindedly as he speaks.

'Ah thanks, kid. We – I renovated it last summer. Coffee?'

Nik notices the stumble, so is barely paying attention when he accepts the cup of steaming, black liquid. He's only tried coffee once, years ago, and remembers how much he hated it. He stirs in three spoons of sugar when Paul's back is turned.

'Have you eaten?' Paul says, bringing him a glass of orange juice. 'I'll make us some pancakes.'

'I didn't know you cooked.'

'I don't think pancakes count as cooking, kiddo.' Paul cracks a couple of eggs into a clear bowl and adds flour. 'So where did you end up last night?' he asks, carefully measuring a spoon of baking powder and adding it to the bowl.

'Just up the road near Goldsmiths. Was lit,' Nik says, taking a careful sip of coffee. He screws up his face and tries not to gag. It literally tastes like melted shoe polish. He swallows it reluctantly, feeling it mingling with the remnants of last night's rum, and this morning's Ritz biscuits. He takes a quick sip of orange juice straight after, which seems to make things significantly worse.

'Nice. Uni friends?'

'Nah, with the college lot.' He watches Paul pour a scoop of batter onto a frying pan with the same spoon his mother would use to serve daal.

'Are you still a Gunners fan, by the way?' Paul says, picking out a jar of Nutella from his cupboard, then a bottle of maple syrup.

Nik throws him an incredulous look. 'What sort of question is that?'

Paul laughs, raises his eyebrows. 'I've got a spare ticket to the home game against Tottenham next Saturday, if you fancy it?'

'Ah sick, yeah definitely.' He hasn't been to a game since Paul took him to a Fulham match in 2010. They'd won 4–0. Baird had scored an own goal. The crowd had been electric. Nik can't wait to tell Teo and Will. He takes another sip of the coffee, wanting to like it.

'Tell me about this car, then,' Paul says. 'Interesting choice for a student. I'd have thought you're more of an A1 kinda guy.'

'Nah, I'd have a Golf if I could choose.'

'How did you source it?'

'Ah, yeah . . . it was actually my dad's.' Nik mumbles the words, giving Paul the opportunity to pretend he hasn't heard.

Paul is still facing away from him, but Nik sees the back of his neck grow pink. 'Your father's?' he asks carefully.

'Yeah. Bapu kept it all this time.'

Something is buzzing behind him. Nik looks around to see Paul's phone lighting up from the dining table.

'Interesting,' Paul says, his back still to Nik, but the word is flat, and spoken so fast that it folds into just two syllables. 'How's your mum about it?'

Paul places a plate on the island in front of Nik as he

speaks. Nik looks down at a stack of three fluffy American pancakes, dripping with maple syrup. Sliced bananas and dollops of Nutella dot the top of them.

'This is next level,' Nik says, picking up his fork and knife. He always holds them in the wrong hands, and goes to swap them, but then reminds himself that he doesn't have to pretend with Paul. 'Where's yours?'

'I'm stuffed,' Paul says, leaning against the fridge, his head tilted slightly as he sizes up his work.

Nik looks back down at the plate. This is the Paul of his childhood; the super-laid-back easy-going guy who could fix everything. Who never seemed to rush. Who was so damn effortlessly cool that Nik, at an age when being cool was all he cared about, hoped more than anything that Paul's personality would rub off on him. The buzzing behind him starts again and Nik is slightly warmed by the fact that Paul isn't answering his phone, that he doesn't want to be disturbed from this, whatever this is.

'Fuck. These are good, man,' Nik tells him, slicing through all three pancakes at once and taking a bite almost too large to manage.

Paul laughs and downs his coffee. Neither of them speaks for a while, the sound of the radio and Nik's cutlery on the plate filling the space between them. He meets Paul's gaze and is reminded of the unanswered question that's still hanging between them.

'She doesn't know,' he says, his mouth full.

'About the car?' Paul raises his eyebrows slightly.

Nik nods, taking another large bite of pancake. They're so moist and soft that he only chews twice before swallowing. 'She knows I kept it but I reckon she didn't think I'd be able to get it up and running again.'

Paul lets out a low whistle. 'When will you tell her?'

'Ugh.' Nik puts his cutlery down to rub his face. 'Today at some point, when I stop putting off going back home.' He sighs and looks at Paul. 'She's gonna proper flip, man.'

'It makes you happy, though, right?'

'What d'you mean?'

'The car.'

'Yeah, it does. It's sick.'

'There you go then. It'll be worth the drama. It might even give her a bit of a push, help her finally process everything properly.'

The end of Paul's words are met with a loud bell echoing through the hall, towards them. They both turn to look through the sitting room and out of the front window. Nik is filled with a sudden rush of hostility for this person who has burst their bubble. Worry pulses in his stomach. He hopes it's just a delivery.

'Gimme a sec,' Paul says. He closes the kitchen door leading into the hallway, but the lounge door is ajar, so Nik hears perfectly clearly when Paul reaches the front door and swears quietly. The sound of the street floods in as the door swings open.

'Hello again, sweetheart.' The woman's voice is so high-pitched and posh that it makes Nik think of icing sugar.

'Oh hey, babe, listen, I'm just in the middle of a conference call –' Paul says, his voice low.

'Gosh, I'm *sorry*, darling. I was in such a terrible rush earlier that I forgot my boots.'

'Which ones?'

'The Louboutins. They're by the wall next to the en suite. I need them for the opening tonight. It's at seven, sweetie, don't forget.'

Nik has padded through Paul's open-plan lounge to look out of the window. A tall woman stands on the front steps, her thick blonde hair almost reaching her waist. She's wearing a red fedora hat and an expensive-looking coat that sweeps down to her ankles, which are hidden by black leather stiletto boots. Her face barely moves as she talks and Nik notices an artificial plumpness to her lips. A brand new BMW Z4 sits in the middle of the road, right next to Nik's father's car, the roof down and the hazard lights on. He can hear Paul taking the stairs two by two and moving around on the first floor, but he's not paying attention. He's thinking about the words ringing clearly in his mind from an afternoon late in the summer, the score of his favourite Marvel film playing in the background:

Are you?

What?

Single?

Yes.

Nik shakes his head and makes his way back to the kitchen via the lounge, stopping by the mantel, where a collection of photo frames rest, one careful inch between each of them. The first shows an old couple who Nik recalls are Paul's parents, against a blue sky, the Golden Gate Bridge behind them. He never met them in the flesh; they only existed to him as pixellated faces that appeared once every few months on Paul's laptop screen. Nik scans the rest of the photos for any signs of a girlfriend, but they're all of Paul living the bachelor life, in fancy restaurants, golf courses, at what looks like Machu Picchu, the same group of white friends peppered around him. But there's a space between the fifth and the sixth photo. A gap.

Nik looks around for a while before his gaze rests on the loveseat next to the fireplace. He can just make out the corner of a photo frame that has been stuffed hastily behind a cushion. He stares down at the face of a woman who could by no means be confused for the person currently standing on Paul's porch. The woman in the photo has stern, chin-length, black hair. She's dressed in a tiny pink bikini, Paul's arms around her waist, a white-sand beach behind them. Something in Nik's memory whispers to him that this photo was taken in the Maldives. It punches him in the gut, this photo. Little pockets of heat burst in unison across his skin, crawling over him. Two bottles of nail-varnish, one red and another clear, have also been stuffed behind the cushion. There is something so pathetically juvenile about this that it makes Nik feel sick. The overly sweet pancakes feel like they're suddenly making their way back up to his mouth. He places the frame carefully back on the mantel, where it belongs, perching the nail-varnish bottles either side of it, like two beacons. A memory seems to be pushing its way through Nik's subconscious, one from his childhood, infused with the scent of Tipp-Ex and old books. He can feel it breaking the surface, but it's hazy, all he can grasp is the shallowness he'd felt in his chest, the unease in his mouth.

The sound of Paul rushing down the stairs and pulling

the door back open shoots through him. 'Here you go,' Paul says.

'Thanks, honey. When's Mags back?'

'Couple of weeks.'

'I'll pop back tomorrow night then, sweetie?'

Nik doesn't want to hear any more. In the kitchen, he rinses out the glass of orange juice Paul handed him, then fills it with cold water from the tap and downs it. His phone is buzzing in his pocket. Paul is walking back through the hallway. Nik listens to his steps. Paul pauses, probably by the open lounge door, the one Nik assumes he thought was shut, the one which tells Paul that Nik has heard everything. Nik wonders if he's staring at the photo frame that's suddenly grown feet and climbed back onto the mantel.

Nik's phone stops buzzing for a second then immediately starts up again. He answers the call and turns towards the garden. Silence presses against his ear. He can hear Paul moving around the kitchen behind him. Nik's plate and cutlery clink as they're placed in the dishwasher.

He looks at his phone screen to check he's still connected. 'You there?' he asks.

'Are you okay, beta?' His mother's voice comes out in a rasp.

'Yeah, yeah I'm all right,' he says, rubbing his forehead.

'You didn't come home this weekend?' It's pitched as a question. She sounds like she's been crying. A sticky guilt oozes through him.

'I did, yeah. I came down yesterday morning.' He switches the phone to his other ear.

'Kiddo. More coffee?' Paul asks, loud, from behind him. Nik waves his hand, shaking his head.

'Oh God.' His mother's voice, laced with betrayal, pushes its way through the phone. 'Are you – are you with Paul?'

22

November 2017

Avani puts the phone down and tilts the back of her head against the wall. Her eyes sting behind closed lids. She spent most of the night lying in bed, switching between checking her phone and watching shadows dance across the ceiling, waiting for the sound of her son's keys in the front door, her heart hammering in her chest every time a pipe gurgled or one of her neighbours slammed a door shut, terrified that this night would form the mirror image of another, one that belonged nineteen years ago, when she spent hours staring at the space next to her, picking paint from her fingernails, wondering why her husband hadn't come home.

She got into her car twice, Rani in the passenger seat, ready to drive to the university to check he was okay, then forced herself back into the house, telling herself she'd drive up if she hadn't heard from him by midday the next day.

The worry that coursed through her, keeping her awake all night, has now bled into a muddle of humiliation and resignation. She cannot understand how her son, who she has always been so close to, has changed so much in the last couple of months. They've always been a team. But moving away has brought a stubbornness to him that feels like it belongs to someone else altogether. First the car, and now Paul. Paul, of all people. She shakes her head. Rani's tail thumps against the floor.

'Fine. Come on,' Avani says. She throws on a coat and steps outside.

Avani focuses carefully on her surroundings as she walks down Northolt Road, Rani's nails scraping across the pavement as she trots along, stopping occasionally to sniff front gates and brick walls. A breeze wraps itself around Avani like a hug she hasn't asked for, but she breathes it in, feeling it wash through her lungs. Her mind slips towards her son, gliding backwards, landing on when he was a newborn, during that blur of pain and grief and loss that she sleepwalked through which ended with a child being suddenly thrust upon her one cold morning at a hospital she couldn't even remember arriving at. A dull pain builds in her when she thinks of him. She fought for him from that very first day, the day she named him Nikhil, despite her brother telling her 'N' wasn't one of the two assigned letters for his name, as per his raashi chart.

These thoughts threaten to overwhelm her, so she forces herself to clear her mind as she walks, counting each step, and it is only when she reaches Alexandra Park that she frees Rani from her lead and ambles around the perimeter of the grass, her pace slowing, allowing her thoughts to catch up with her.

She's comforted by the glistening green before her, wet leaves the colour of sand sticking to her shoes as she walks, the wind playing around the naked trees. A young father is teaching his daughter to ride a bicycle further along the path, his hand hovering between her shoulder blades, his feet quickening to keep up with her. Rani runs ahead, past the father and daughter, but turns every few moments to check Avani is still there. Avani has never known a dog to do this before, one that is so full of curiosity yet requires so much reassurance. She's grateful for Rani, knowing that if it weren't for her new companion, she'd be spending the rest of the day in bed, wishing for the nothingness of night to hurry towards her, the promise of a fresh day in its wake. She leaves the path to follow Rani's quick steps across the grass. It begins to drizzle slightly, though not enough for Avani to put her hood up. There is a strange sense of comfort in the mist that fizzes in the air as she walks and the cold that presses into her cheeks.

It is among this that she acknowledges how hearing Paul's voice just behind her son's has reopened an old wound, one with an uncomfortable heat bubbling at the edges of it. Now that she is outside, she allows herself to confront it. It's the wound of not being enough. She wasn't enough to satisfy Paul, her love was not enough to heal her husband, and now she is not enough for her son, either. She cannot give him what he needs. She walks around the park with the weight of this realisation crushing down on her, the toes of her Converse growing green from the damp grass. She feels so far away from Nik, in every sense. She cannot understand how their relationship has disintegrated to this, to him choosing to stay with Paul when he comes back to London instead of her. It is blindingly clear that her son has desperately been searching for a replacement since his grandfather's death. It's why he agreed to meet Paul for that coffee in September. It's why he went behind her back to keep that bloody car, the one she is still sure he will not be able to fix up. These thoughts nudge another inside her, clicking it into place. She has known this for a while, but had pushed it away, simply because she didn't want it to be the truth: her son will always be searching. Nobody will be able to fill that empty space as well as his grandfather had. There is no one left to buy her time. He will always want to know more about his father, and she must find a way to let him. But she does not know how she can do this without holding some of the truth back; she could not bear to burden him with all she knows. It would be too much. It would shatter something in him, like it did her. It would only destroy him.

Even just the thought of this, of opening Nik, and therefore herself, up to the life she once lived, is too much for her. It scares her, to let the tide of memories come, not knowing what the ebbing waves will bring with them. She needs time. She is not ready just yet.

Avani whistles loudly when she realises she has lost sight of Rani. She scans the park, searching for moving grey between the still green. She spots Rani trotting up the path towards her, her tail pointing to the sky, her tongue lolling. When they reach the main road once again, Rani stops to sniff a lamp post with flowers tied around it. Avani does not wait for her, does not look at the face of the deceased smiling at her from behind a plastic sleeve, wrapped taut around the lamp post. It reminds her of a day she has turned over in her mind so much that, over the years, the shape of it has changed under her hands, as though it were a painting that she's revisited more often than needed, layer after layer of paint being added, until eventually, the canvas grows so thick that she can no longer tell if what she's left with is the same subject she started with. There is no way to scrape the layers down again, to unearth the messy truth. Now, she isn't able to distinguish the reality of what happened that night from the horrors thrown around in her dreams.

She calls for Rani over her shoulder, refusing to glance back. She doesn't want to look at the shrine, because her mind is already full of the wave of cards, flowers and letters that had spread across the roundabout by Northwick Park Hospital. Her husband's pupils had come one evening, in their masses, to light candles for their teacher. As she walks home, she thinks of the package she received through the letter box a few weeks after his death. She had been lying in bed, watching the sky move above her, when she heard the doorbell ring. She rose in his T-shirt to the window, watching from behind a net curtain, as the French teacher from Elliot's school stood in their driveway. She had been his favourite colleague, the one who got him into André Breton and Patricia Kaas and chouquettes. Small and pretty, she was dressed in a long summer dress, her strawberry-blonde hair up, the sun falling happily over her. Avani went back to the darkness of bed, hearing the letter box flap shut and something fall with a thud on their welcome mat. It was a book, created by Elliot's pupils, with anecdotes, poetry and letters detailing how he had inspired them. Together, these stories sang a song of pity Avani felt she did not deserve.

On the cover of the memorial book, someone had superglued a Polaroid photo of him laughing in front of a blackboard, white chalk dust pressed into his dark jumper. He looked so content, so full. The image of him did not match what was tucked between the folds of Avani's memory, the version of him she remembered from those final months. She realised, then, that she had never seen him at work; she never knew the Elliot that he presented to his pupils and colleagues. This variation of her husband was one she had never met.

Avani had spent a long time wondering who had taken that Polaroid, before sitting on the bottom step of her staircase and flicking through the book, growing hot as her eyes ran across the surface of the words on each page. The school had held a memorial for him the week before, which former pupils from across the country had attended, their letters filling the final pages of the book. One, from the first year of pupils he taught, was a published poet now, and was dedicating his latest collection to Elliot.

When Chand stopped by to check in on Avani later that day, she'd thrust the book into his hands, telling him to get rid of it. He stared at her like she'd gone mad. He hadn't understood her pain.

How can you be angry about this? he asked, looking between her and the book. *It's so incredibly thoughtful.*

I'm not angry. I just don't want to see it. They didn't know him like I did.

He stared at her for a long time after that, and she felt like a child in his gaze. She hadn't known another way to express what she had felt then; the need to protect her husband's memory, for people not to make performances of their grief. It was a reminder of her culpability.

When Nik parks up outside their home, his mother opens the front door to greet him, in the same way Paul had earlier. There are little black smudges under her eyes where her make-up has run. The tip of her nose is pink, her face paler than usual, like it always is when she's been out in the cold. Rani appears in the hallway, her mouth breaking into a happy pant when she spots him. Nik takes a deep breath, burrowing his fingers into his pockets. He notices that his mother's eyes are not focused on him. They run across the bonnet of the Beemer, drinking in the shape of it. Something shifts in her face, making Nik's stomach churn. In that moment, he knows that this is one surprise too many for her, that whatever conversation she had planned for his return home has disintegrated in her. He regrets not parking round the corner. Her lips press together in a hard line before she turns back to the house. Nik simply follows her indoors and removes his shoes.

He is desperate to change out of last night's clothes and for a long, hot shower. His mother continues into the kitchen, murmuring about preparing a fresh pan of chai, as if Nik is right behind her, but he has stopped in the hallway. He takes a moment to notice the scent of agarbatti that Layla once told him is synonymous with his home. He has never really paid attention to it before, but today stops to watch the orange tip of the dark stick spiral away into wisps of scented smoke which weave delicately into the air, moving towards the large copper

Ganapati that looks over their entrance. He stares at the conch in Ganapati's hands, then at the lotus and the ladoo. A photo of his grandfather, with a sandalwood garland strung around it, sits just beside. The sight of him, of his warm, comforting face, cuts straight through Nik. Tears rise and he blinks them away, but he cannot do the same with the feeling that overwhelms him; the desperate urge to drive down the road and spend an afternoon basking in the light of his grandfather.

Rani is by Nik's shins, sniffing at something on his jeans. She explores it with her tongue. He picks the dog up in one large sweep and carries her into the kitchen. Her coat is damp and she licks his chin as he walks.

Nik takes a seat and watches his mother pour water into a steel saucepan, then throw in some chai no masalo and loose black tea before placing it on the stove. 'I see you managed to fix that car up,' she says. Her voice is even on the surface, but Nik can hear the defensiveness bubbling underneath.

'Yeah.'

'If you're going to insist on driving that thing, then all I'll ask is that you do not park it near my house.' There's a sharpness in her voice that Nik's never heard before. Anger rolls off her like heat.

'Why? Because it reminds you of him?'

Silence. Nik watches her through narrowed eyes. He is filled with a sudden courage. 'What did he do to make you hate him this much? You can't even *talk* about him.'

His mother lights the smallest ring on the stove and turns, standing with her back against the hob.

'Not now, Nikhil,' she says. 'Just drop it.'

He shakes his head. Rani nudges at his hand when he stops stroking her.

'Why are you so desperate for this? I've already told you everything there is to know about him. Pushing for more isn't going to solve anything. It's not going to bring him back.' Her voice is strained and it breaks before she reaches the end of the sentence.

'I'm not trying to *solve* anything.'

'There's no point,' she says, almost to herself.

'And just because I didn't know him, it doesn't mean –'

'Yeah, that's right, you didn't know him. You didn't lose anyth—'

'He was mine, too,' Nik shouts at a volume that surprises even him, willing her to understand. 'He was my dad. This isn't just about you.'

She looks out of the window, her mouth set in a way which Nik knows precedes tears. He watches as she picks a couple of leaves of mint from the windowsill and drops them into the pan with a shaking hand. She stirs the chai, pours in some milk and turns up the heat. When she adds another pinch of loose black tea to the mix, the air in the kitchen grows heavier with its scent. She stands taller as she moves, the strain in her shoulders falling away. The tears Nik expected do not fall. A thought seems to be surfacing in her, fed by fresh confidence. Nik holds his breath, wondering what is coming.

'Well, you have Paul now, so . . .' she says.

Her words spin around him like bullets before settling in his chest. 'That's so unfair.'

Thoughts pile up against his tongue. Before he can stop himself, he finds himself saying: 'I know you fucked that up too, by the way, rejected him when he wanted to be a proper family, when he wanted to marry you. You pushed him away, like you do everyone.' He knows, before the final word has left his mouth, that he has dared to play a card he shouldn't have, one from an altogether different deck. He waits for his mother to round on him, to shout, to tell him to mind his own business and to piss off out of her house. Instead, she simply shakes her head and says, in a voice that almost glistens with spite, 'I see. Is that what he told you?'

Nik finds himself sitting very still. He doesn't speak. He knows he has taken a wrong turn; he wants to inhale the words, to pull them back. A glimmer of something dances across his mind, just out of reach. A memory, flickering, struggling with all its might to break the surface.

'I asked Paul to leave,' she says, her voice fuller now, her eyes bright, 'when I discovered he was having an affair with a colleague.'

The words don't register at first. He doesn't want them to be true. He can almost feel the contempt in the air around him, powdery and warm like the residue that escapes when a gun is fired. A sharp ache sears through him. He thinks of the slip when Paul mentioned the renovation, the woman on Paul's doorstep, the other woman in the photo he found, the fact Paul had told him he was single back in the summer.

'And that was just the tip of the iceberg, Nikhil. He's the definition of a womaniser. His proposal was just a panic move, a desperate attempt to win me back. You were so young when it happened. I didn't want you to know.'

Something primal and raw and full of fear stirs and rises slowly within Nik, telling him to turn away from this, to stifle it all into a small manageable box that he can keep buried in a dark corner.

'No he didn't,' he says, shaking his head. He tries to meet his mother's eye, but she won't face him. She lowers the flame, sighs and pours some chai into her favourite mug. 'No he didn't,' he says again, louder this time, willing her to look at him.

But then it comes to him, acutely, as if from nowhere. At first it is not recognisable as a memory; it is simply a sensation, carrying the weight of what it feels like to be winded by overheard words. It's appearing, this thing that he has blocked and buried, clawing its way back up. It was his first taste of devastation, his first glimpse into the messy business of adulthood.

He remembers sitting in a hidden corner of the school library with Will and Teo, carefully applying a layer of Tipp-Ex to the 'e' on a pair of Air Force Ones to change the 'Nike' to 'Nik'. They were bunking drama class. It was his third week at secondary school, the autumn after Paul left.

Does 'betrayal' always mean cheating? he asked. The boys were silent for a moment. *I overheard my mum on the phone . . .*

He looked up to see Will shaking his head: *That prick.*

Allow him, man, Teo said. *If he bells you just air him.*

As quick as it comes, the memory snaps back shut like a clam. He's shocked, frightened even, by how well he'd stifled it as a child. He knows why he would have done so; he didn't want it to be real. He recalls having plans to meet Paul the next weekend for a game of football in the park. He didn't want to cancel. He was split in two; filled with the need to protect his mother, filled with the desperate desire not to lose Paul. So he told himself to forget about it, convinced himself that he'd misheard.

'Did you hear what I said?' his mother's voice is louder than usual. She is at the sink now, rubbing a soapy scourer around the inside of a mug.

'What?'

'If you're going to come home on the weekends then don't mess me around like last night. If you're staying with *Paul* now, for God knows what reason, just text me to let me know. This isn't a hotel. And don't park that disgusting bloody thing on my driveway.'

'Yes, all right, I heard you the first time, man.' He buries his face in his hands as he talks. He's desperate for a cup of chai. His mother hasn't poured him one, and he feels like going to get a mug himself would be some sort of figurative white flag. His phone buzzes in his pocket. It must be the boys; they're meant to be meeting in an hour. He looks up to his mother and adds, 'And I didn't stay at Paul's last night. That would be so weird, man. Stop jumping to conclusions.'

'Where were you, then?'

Nik doesn't respond.

'I don't know what's going on with you at the moment, but you need to think carefully about what you're doing,' his mother says. The sound of utensils smacking against the sink cuts through him. 'Do you even have the money to insure it?'

'The car?' Nik asks, struggling to keep up. He needs some air. He nudges Rani off his lap and stands up.

'Yes, the car.'

'That's none of your . . . I can sort myself out.'

'Right. Well, you go and do that then,' she says, pouring the rest of the chai into a mug and pushing it into his hands.

23

December 2017

The photos hang at eye level, light glowing around their frames like halos. It is the final night of the exhibition, showcased in a south London gallery with the sort of exposed brick walls and colourless floors that could only belong to an old factory, the kind her father had worked in. Art students from the university round the corner traipse in with wet boots and pastel raincoats the colour of sweets. Raindrops sit like dew on their sleeves. Avani watches them from a corner of the gallery, white wine in hand, searching their faces; she remembers her son saying a few of his college friends had moved to this part of London for university. Maya's new boyfriend, Richard, stands next to her, humming along to what sounds like 'You Know I'm No Good'. He's shorter and slighter than Maya's usual type and has a habit of yawning without covering his mouth. One end of his scarf has fallen off his shoulder, its fringe kissing the floor, but Avani can't be bothered to draw his attention to it. The pair have exhausted their supply of small talk and are now standing awkwardly together, sipping on wine that is a little too sweet and much too warm, as they pretend to be utterly engrossed in the large photos lining the walls around them. Avani's hungry gaze lingers on a tall woman in knee-high leather stilettos who flicks her long blonde hair with an air of authority. She wears a red fedora hat. Avani watches, not quite able to place where she's seen her before.

'There you are,' Maya says, squeezing past the woman.

'We're exactly where you left us,' Avani says, trying not to sound irritated.

Maya takes her wine glass from Avani and says, 'I didn't think my call would go on for that long. What have you two been talking about?' She smiles, hopeful eyes moving between them.

'Well,' Richard says, 'Avani was just telling me all about her lurcher. My mother had greyhounds, isn't that funny?'

Avani purses her lips, knowing Maya will tell her off later for not trying harder, but for now her friend is busy pulling Richard's scarf back over his shoulder. Avani's lips meet the last sip of her wine and she excuses herself to fetch a fresh glass. She feels out of step as she passes through the crowd. Being in spaces like this always makes her think of that other path, the one lined with impasto strokes, the one which may have led her to exhibitions like this as another person.

She scans the crowd as she walks, as she always does when she is in a busy room, searching for a pair of hazel eyes, for curly brown hair, toying with herself. Even if she did find him one day, what would she have to offer? A story about how he had a brother once, a wonderful brother who loved him, who she wasn't able to save.

There is a crowd by the bar, but Avani abandons it just a few seconds into waiting, because a photo hanging nearby has caught her attention. It captures a mannequin through a shop window, a shadow splitting the body neatly in two. Half of it shining in white light. Half hiding in grey obscurity. The photographer's reflection is translucent in the window, like a ghost. The street reflected back in the glass is alive with colour.

Avani walks towards it, noticing how the sound of the room behind her seems to fade away. Something stirs in her; an itch behind her ribcage, one she cannot reach, one that grows, making its way down to her fingertips. The photo has pulled forward a memory, reminding her of another image she saw once, years ago.

Three summers had passed since her husband's death and she was on a date with a man so unremarkable that she cannot recall the slightest detail about him now, not his name, nor what he looked like, nor what he did for a living. He was vanilla in every way. She remembered thinking this on their very first date, as she watched him eat sushi at a restaurant which kissed the periphery of Primrose Hill. At the time, unremarkable was exactly what she needed. A palate cleanser.

The only thing that stayed with her from the two weeks they dated was the framed poster that hung in his lounge. This image has come to her, over the years, presenting itself in the most unexpected of moments. It was of a young Black girl, probably just a year or two older than Nik at the time. She wore a faded blue dress the colour of sky, the scalloped cotton collar of it white and curly like drifting clouds. The girl stood before a shop window, staring into the face of a mannequin behind the glass, sleek and white in its nakedness. The girl's mother was slightly stooped as she gazed down at her daughter, a hand resting softly on her shoulder. There was so much patience in that gaze. Avani remembered searching the space between the mother and daughter, hoping to find the secret to good parenting in it, a curious mix of both guilt and hope rushing through her. She thought of her toddler, asleep at her father's house. She thought of the way his tiny fingers would be wrapped around the corner of his blanket as he dreamed, his eyes moving behind closed lids, his mind full from a day of planting carrots and peppers at his grandfather's allotment. He was in the phase of finishing every sentence with 'plee', not yet having found the end of that word. It sufficed, getting him whatever he was asking for quicker, with a smile from the giver to boot. She still felt guilty leaving him, even just for the evening, and wondered if she would ever stand with him the way the mother in the photo did, exploring the world through his innocence.

The contrast between mother and daughter, of the child looking at the mannequin – so full of wonder and delight – against the mother's knowledgeable, patient gaze, also reminded her of the volume of poetry that had made a home on her husband's bedside table in the years before his death. He'd based his first lesson as an English teacher on those poems. He had practised the lesson plan on her the night before his first day, delivering a forty-five-minute class standing in his suit by the bathroom sink. Avani listened from the tub, bubbles that smelt of geranium leaf dissolving slowly around her. She couldn't recall the name of the poet, or any of the poems, but she could remember the cool controlled flavour of them, and the way they had made her feel as he read them aloud. *Innocence and Experience*. Those were the words etched across the cover of the illustrated collector's edition she had bought him as a wedding present. She thought of those poems as she stared at the young girl, who was looking up at a world that wasn't made for her, one that seemed so exciting and beautiful, brimming with hope and possibility, caught by this photographer before she grows to discover another layer underneath the glossiness of it all, a layer of injustice and prejudice and spaces that are not for her, that she has to fight to be in, just to breathe in. The gaze of the mother appeared to hold all of this in its quietude. There was so much richness to her silence. Innocence and experience. Avani couldn't yet recognise herself in the mother's contemplations. Instead, she saw her father – the way he looked at his grandson in the moments when little Nik's blindness to the cruelty of the world shone through.

She had risen to her toes for a better look, staring at this piece of art in her date's lounge, thinking of how the once rich, inky memory of her husband was diluting itself another drop with each night that passed, each new word their son learnt, each centimetre he grew. She thought of Nik, wondering what filled his dreams. She thought of her father, who would be watching the news in his slippers and dressing gown, the light of the television reflected back in his glasses. And when she looked away from the girl in the poster, what was left with her was this: she had not been taken by an image in this way since her husband's death. It called her name, making her fingers twitch, making her want to paint again.

She asked her date where he'd purchased the poster

when he returned from a notably long loo break, and he'd glanced at it, told her it came with the flat, sloppily topped up her wine, and said they should move to the bedroom, his eyes greedy. She ordered a taxi home after that, but the image of the daughter and mother had stayed with her, lodging itself permanently in a corner of her mind; a reminder of how a still image, a moment captured, could say so much without saying a word at all. This was the reason she had fallen in love with painting as a teenager; it was a way to express all the things she wanted to say but could never find the words for.

'Auntie?'

A hand presses into Avani's lower back and she turns from the photograph to see a young woman with friendly dark eyes standing beside her. It takes her a few seconds to recognise Layla.

'Oh, hello, darling,' Avani says, giving Layla a hug.

'You look so nice, Auntie. I love this skirt and boot combo.' They're both Maya's. 'You're so on trend.'

Avani thanks her, then asks Layla how she's been and how university is going. The gallery is much busier than it was a few minutes ago – a fresh wave of visitors have come in, bringing the cold December air with them. Somebody has turned the music up, and the hum of the gallery has risen to match it.

'Really good, thank you. My halls are just up the road so we thought we'd check this place out.' She nods to the group of students by the bar as she speaks.

'Oh, lovely. What do you think?'

'Yeah,' Layla says, her gaze skimming the photos. She shrugs and takes a careful sip of wine. 'It's nice. I'm not really into visual art, if I'm honest,' she murmurs. 'But I really like some of these. They make me think of Tyler Mitchell's work. Have you heard of him?'

'I have.' A smile passes between them. 'I hope Nikhil's kept in touch?'

Layla's cheeks seem to glow slightly pink as she says: 'Yeah, actually. We all went out together last time he came home, for my birthday. He was telling me all about his new car.' She removes her berry-coloured raincoat, folding it neatly over her arm.

Avani nods, trying not to look surprised. So he'd probably stayed with Layla that night, not Paul. Why hadn't he just told her that? 'Yes, it's all very exciting,' she says vaguely.

'Not long until you have him back for Christmas,' Layla says.

This draws fresh nerves up to Avani's throat. She hasn't spoken to her son since that weekend. 'Will you be back in Harrow for the break too?' she asks.

'I'm actually going to spend Christmas in Dublin . . . with my dad.' Layla says these words cautiously, as if she doesn't quite believe them herself. 'We haven't seen each other in almost a decade, so it could end up being a very short trip if it doesn't go well.' Her delicate gold earrings catch the light as she laughs.

Avani doesn't know how to respond to this, whether to simply wish Layla luck or to make some sort of dry comment about how Nik's return home is looking equally precarious. Before she says anything at all, Richard comes over to them and mutters, 'Ah, there you are. Thought I'd lost you again.' He pushes a glass of red wine into Avani's free hand. She doesn't want it; red always matures to sadness in her veins, presenting itself to her the next day with a foggy head and eyes continually on the brink of tears.

Avani introduces Layla to Richard, scanning the crowd for Maya.

'Well, I better find my mates,' Layla says, hugging Avani again. 'But it was so nice seeing you, Auntie.'

'You too, sweetheart,' Avani says. She watches Layla head towards a group of students by the bar.

'Auntie? I take it she's your niece,' Richard says, twirling his wine in a manner that suggests he's thoroughly impressed with himself.

'No. She's a friend of my son's.'

'Hmm.' His greying eyebrows draw together. 'Curious.'

Avani takes a deep breath. He's standing far too close to her, as he has been all evening. 'Where's Maya?'

'Work called again.'

'Right. Well, I've got an early start so I'm going to head back,' she says, handing him the untouched glass of red. 'Will you tell her I'll ring her tomorrow?'

The next morning, Avani abandons her weekly running club to lounge on the sofa with a bowl of fresh grapes and a pot of green tea. She has been overtraining. Her left knee throbs with tendonitis. She ices it, annoyed with herself for spending the day in heels yesterday. Rani nestles herself into the space behind Avani's legs, her head resting on Avani's thigh as she snores. Rani spent the previous day with a dog sitter so that Avani could head down to Deptford after work with Maya and Richard guilt-free.

She is extra needy today as a result, clinging to Avani like a wet leaf. Avani absent-mindedly strokes behind Rani's ears as the pair drift in and out of a nap. Avani is half watching a David Attenborough documentary, looking up at the screen every time he says 'years', her chest warming slightly. He pronounces it the same way her father did. She remembers her husband teasing him about his pronunciation – *yurs* – and watching her father try to explain that it was a hint of an Indian accent as opposed to being posh. She thinks of him, wishing he were still up the road so she could pop in. Today is exactly the sort of day when she'd wander down there for a cuppa and end up spending hours doing nothing with him. They'd potter around his allotment with a flask of chai, sit on the sofa and watch nature documentaries, cook khichdi and kadhi. She misses him, so deeply, yearning to hear his voice, wondering what words of comfort he'd share if he knew how unbearably lonely she feels.

The ring of Avani's phone interrupts her thoughts. She expects to see Maya's face lighting up the screen, ready for a guarded debrief of last night. But it's not her. Avani answers, hearing her estate agent's voice, the overfamiliarity of his greeting spreading across her skin like a rash. She tries to summon some patience, but then he says her name, drawing out the non-existent middle syllable like a piece of chewing gum in that way he does – *Ah-vaaan-knee* – even though she's already corrected him twice and made a dry joke about how the second 'a' is silent. It hasn't stuck. As he babbles on excitedly about the buyers, she holds back snapping at him; she wants to remind him that he's calling about the sale of her deceased father's house, that she's not some excited twenty-something selling a fixer-upper she purchased with her trust fund.

'Ah-vaaan-knee? Hello?'

'Yes, I'm here.'

'What would you like me to do with them?'

'With what?'

'The boxes in Rohan's loft.'

'What boxes?'

'I was just saying they wanted to have a poke about the loft and found a couple of boxes full of old artsy bits. There was an easel kicking about, too. You didn't tell me the old boy was partial to a bit of painting-by-numbers.'

Avani grits her teeth. In her mind, she sees her twenty-six-year-old self asking her father to pack up her husband's things for the charity shop. She remembers passing her old studio, which is now Nik's bedroom, and telling him to donate everything in there too. *Beta, you'll want to paint again one day,* her father had said, worry creasing his eyes.

Please, Dad. Just get rid of it all. I don't want to look at it.

'Now,' the estate agent says, 'I can arrange collection and disposal. Eighteen pounds per kilogram, plus VAT.'

'No,' she says. 'I'll pop over in a bit to pick them up.'

Avani knows she is in trouble when she sees Maya's make-up-free face compressed into the round peephole in the door. When she pulls it open, Maya immediately bends down to fuss Rani. This is still something Avani hasn't got used to – friends greeting Rani before rising up to hug her, passers-by on the street smiling at her dog instead of her.

'This is a nice surprise,' Avani says, worry gathering in her throat. 'How did you know where to find me?'

'I saw your car wasn't in the driveway so thought I'd try your parents' place. It looks so much smaller empty,' she says, scanning the bare walls.

Avani tucks her hair behind her ears and nods. Rani noisily laps at a bowl of water in the hall, drops darkening the carpet as she drinks.

'How's the sale progressing?'

'No hiccups so far. Probate went through super quick thanks to Dad being so organised.' The thought makes her breath catch and she steadies herself before she continues. 'The estate agent's a total pain, but he gets the job done. Reckons we'll complete by the end of the month.'

'I'll miss this place,' Maya says, still looking around.

Avani's eyebrows knot together. Maya would only ever come over in emergencies when they were kids; they always hung out at Maya's parents' home growing up, having dance parties, roller-skating in the garden, staying up late to talk boys and music and dreams.

'I'm glad we could do last night,' Maya says. Avani can see the shape of her hands in her coat pockets. They're bundled into nervous fists. 'I feel like you were upset, by the end of the evening. Did something happen?'

'Not at all. I was just tired. It was lovely to meet him, really.'

'We're going to live together,' Maya says, her eyes on Rani.

'Goodness. How exciting.'

'I'm worried about his cat getting on with the girls. It's got issues.'

'What kind of issues?' Avani remembers the adoption coordinator at Battersea telling her Rani's stomach could get runny from time to time.

'It's a feral little thing,' Maya says. 'Look at this –' she yanks up the hem of her jeans to reveal claw marks scabbing on her skin – 'it tried to climb me like a tree last week.'

'Three cats, wow. So you'll be moving to Crouch End?'

'No, no. My place is bigger, so he's coming to Highgate.'

This is the better alternative, but Avani can't summon a reaction.

'I know it's quick, but he makes me really happy.'

'How exciting,' she says again. Avani's busy thinking about just a few weeks ago – they'd glossed over their row and met for a bottle of rosé at their favourite wine bar in Kensal Rise. Avani had asked Maya outright what she saw in this Richard, and she'd responded with a humble: *he's just so incredibly kind*. They had ruptured something in her, those earnest five words, reminding her so much of why she'd fallen for Elliot – the kindest, most wonderful man she'd ever known. She's brimming with these thoughts, her heart heavy, tears threatening to rise, so isn't fully paying attention when Maya adds, quietly: 'We're thinking of starting a family.'

Avani's skin tingles with cold. She wonders if she has misheard. In spite of herself, she finds herself thinking about the fact that Maya is only six months younger than her. A baby at forty-five.

'This is a good thing,' Maya says, as if she is speaking

to a child, trying to convince it that a new sibling will be a treat. 'I won't be flitting all over the shop on cases any more. We'll set down some proper roots.'

'That's huge, Maya,' Avani says. She turns to the staircase and takes a seat on the bottom step. 'I'm just surprised; you've always said you never wanted children.'

Maya faces her, leaning against the front door, her hands still in her pockets. 'I just never met someone I wanted one with.'

Avani nods. This she can understand. 'It's just a bit of a U-turn,' she says. 'It's not like getting another cat. It's such a big decision.'

Annoyance flicks across Maya's face. 'Yes, I know that having a baby is different to getting a cat, Av,' she says, 'but we don't have the luxury of time. We're most probably already too late. I didn't ever think I'd have the chance.'

They watch each other, Avani struggling to size up the weight of this new development – yet another change.

'Look, I can't stay long,' Maya says. 'I was just passing through and thought I should drop in. Are you definitely up for the Cotswolds? I didn't know if you were just being polite last night, when we asked.'

Silence.

'Please come. It won't be the same without you.'

Avani fiddles with Rani's collar.

'At least join us for New Year's Eve, Av. You shouldn't be alone.'

Spending Christmas with three couples in the countryside is Avani's idea of hell, but she puts her pride aside; she knows it is important to Maya. 'I'll be there. I just need to check in on Nikhil's plans.'

'It'll be fun. We'll cook loads of lovely food and go for nice long walks with Rani.'

'Sounds great. And I'm really happy for you, honey,' Avani says, reaching up for a hug. Maya's face relaxes and a smile touches her lips. She rests her knees on the foot of the staircase as they embrace. As Avani holds her oldest friend, she realises this moment looks so much like another, from decades ago, when Maya had held her in this very spot after a phone call to the Rigvedis' landline, a voice telling Avani the doctors wouldn't know the extent of Elliot's brain injury until he woke up, telling her there had been an accident involving two flights of stairs. Avani imagines Elliot's father, red in the face, glaring down at his son from the stairwell railings, a little white sock clutched in his hand.

After Maya leaves, Avani sits on the bottom step of the staircase again, the quiet of the house reminding her of those first few moments when she returned from the hospital with Nik after her father's death. This time, there is no knock on the door, no family to come. She thinks of Nik again, of spending Christmas without him, her hand reaching for her phone. This is the longest they have ever gone without speaking. Realising that he'd probably stayed with Layla that night instead of Paul has made her feel both better and worse; why didn't he just tell her? She runs her hands through her hair, thinking of what her father would say, how he would help her to fix this, but she is met with silence.

Rani falls asleep in a ball by her feet, her nose tucked into the fur under her leg. Nerves have silenced the growl of hunger that was growing in Avani when she first arrived. When she notices the world darkening outside, she climbs the staircase, Rani by her side, her fingers tracing shapes on the wall. Rani sniffs under her father's bedroom door, and Avani wonders if the house still holds his scent. She pulls down the ladder to the loft. There is no light, and she is careful to walk along the beams, her eyes battling the darkness. She sees the boxes have been moved from the back of the loft towards the entry point, their journey marked in the dust. Rani whimpers from the bottom of the ladder and Avani calls to her as she brings one box down, then climbs back up to fetch the second, then the third.

She sits cross-legged on the floor as she peels away the soft, wrinkled cardboard and peers inside. Nostalgia washes through her as she picks through the box, her fingers meeting old tubes of paint and brushes and palettes. When these items had lived in her studio, they'd been spread across her table like a generous display of food at a dinner party. Her father had packed them so neatly, organising the tubes of acrylic paint into bundles, elastic bands holding them together in clusters. Her oil paints have been carefully stacked in a shoebox, her paintbrushes placed into old jars standing alert, like soldiers waiting to be called back to action. She rubs a finger over their bristles, frozen stiff with the paint she had been too exhausted to soak away the last night she had used them. Three palettes are stacked at the edge of the box, thick and alive with acrylic that glistens and rises from the wood as though it has only just been freshly released from the tubes which Avani knows will now hold nothing but dry, chalky powder. Feeling these items in her hands again is like listening to a well-loved song, but with the words taken away, just the beat is left, familiar but not quite what she remembers.

In the second box, Avani finds a number of canvases wrapped in old bed sheets. This small act to preserve her work sends a rush of emotion to her eyes. Shortly before Nik was born, she had removed the framed canvases that hung in her kitchen and bedroom, suffocating them in black plastic bags before dumping them in her grey refuse bin. She doesn't regret this destruction, even now. Those pieces of art had come from a different woman, one that was free and open and not afraid of herself. After she'd removed all the canvases, she'd paid a father and son duo to paint all of the walls white, including the mural of the ocean sweeping across a wall in her studio. Over the years, framed prints displaying line drawings of women looking over their shoulders and verdant monstera and magnolia took the place of the canvases and wedding photos. The only painting of hers brought forward into her new life sat proud in her father's kitchen. She asked him to take it down more times than she could remember. He always nodded, never saying yes. It was still there the day he died. Now, it sits in a charity shop in Harrow.

Her hands explore the series of oil paintings she had been working on in the weeks before her husband's death, the ones she'd asked her father to remove from her studio as she swapped them for pictures of smiling tigers and crocodiles to make way for baby Nik. They hadn't met the fate of the others, bagged and binned, as per the instructions she'd given her father. Instead, they'd been carefully stored away, silently waiting in the hope she would one day find them, these almost-forgotten pieces of her past. Most of the canvases before her now are just primed in green and blue, a couple have a first coat of foliage pressed into them, and one is almost finished. They're all derivatives of photos Avani and Elliot had taken in the Lake District, where they'd spent a week hiking, shortly before his death. He had wanted to walk in the footsteps of his favourite poets. She had wanted to drink in the countryside, to be charged with inspiration for a fresh batch of paintings.

Finally, she opens the third box. She turns away from it with a gasp when she catches a glimpse of deep, devastating crimson. She steadies her breath, then tries again. Her wedding sari sits at the top of the box. Beside it, her wedding album. But she does not want to revisit this. She does not want to think of that day, of her mother, unsmiling, in the plainest of saris, as if she were at a funeral. She does not want to think of how none of her mother's family were invited, how her mother would not allow witnesses to the crudest of betrayals; her own daughter, marrying a *troubled white boy with low earning potential*. It had been a quick registration with just fifty guests made up of Avani's father's family and the couple's friends. The Hindu wedding Elliot had asked for did not come. Avani did not want it, after the drama her mother had caused in the lead-up. Maya had hosted their reception in her garden. The only relative from Elliot's side was his favourite aunt, the one he'd go to when things got bad with his parents. She'd made the trip from Spain. They had tried so hard to find his brother in the months before the wedding, and it was exactly a week before the big day that the social worker had told them that he'd exhausted all options and found nothing. It had destroyed Elliot in a way Avani hadn't thought possible.

Once she has placed the boxes and easel into the boot of her car, she checks her phone again, staring down at the blank screen. Over the last few weeks, she has caught herself doing this more often than usual – waiting for her son's name to flash before her. She wants him to reach out, to make up a reason for them to speak, like when he called one morning during freshers' week, the hangover pulling the moisture from his voice, just to ask her if she uses semi or skimmed milk at home for chai. She had known then that he had simply wanted to be with her in some way, to talk about anything at all, and they had, until the worry had weaved out of him and he sounded like her son again.

Avani is full of these thoughts, certain this is the reason for her sudden obsession with checking her lock screen, so it is only when her fingers automatically reach for Paul's name in her contact list that she realises it is not just her son that she is waiting for. Finally, she confronts what she's been pushing away, what's bobbed to the surface after seeing her best friend in the thick of new love. She is frustrated at Paul for forcing his way back into her son's life. But at the same time, she was sure Paul would have called her by now or messaged her at least. He'd told her, when they broke up, that he'd always want to be with her. That he would wait. That he would never marry. She shakes her head at this as she pulls her father's front door shut, trying to gather herself as she leads Rani back into the car. She cannot revisit that mess. Nothing Paul ever does is straightforward, betrayal is always a few steps behind him, dogging him like a dirty shadow. She wonders, not turning to look back up at the house as she drives away from it for the last time, how many other women Paul may have repeated those beautiful, empty words to.

24

December 2017

Nik yawns widely as he trudges through the university car park, trying to recall where he left the car. He is running several hours behind but is too hung-over to rush. It is the first day of the Christmas break, and he was supposed to be meeting Layla in half an hour to say goodbye before she leaves for Dublin. This won't be possible, because Nik has only just woken up, and it would take close to three hours to get back to London, plus an extra twenty minutes if he stuck to the speed limit. He was out with Dan, Alice and Melanie last night, watching students clumsily two-stepping to Katy Perry while sipping on Smirnoff before flailing around to some next nonsense Nik has only recently learned is called 'Electro House'. Towards the end of the night, he watched through a daze of disgust and confusion as the club lit up with Panjabi MC, causing a sea of middle-class white students to attempt and fail to move to it, doing all sorts of interesting things with their shoulders and hands. He'd sent a Snap of the debacle to Rajvi, who'd replied immediately with: These lots, man. First they butcher our food now they butcher our moves.

He sends Layla a message as he walks through the car park, telling her he's sorry, he won't make it. She reads it immediately and tells him it's calm, babe, and that she'll message him when she's back. He stares at the screen, willing this not to be the end of her message, for the word *typing* to reappear, promising him more. It doesn't come. He wants her to tell him that she's disappointed, that this isn't good enough. He wants to tell her he's sorry he fucked up, that he'll FaceTime her later and that they'll chat loads over the break. But he knows this is her way; her succinctness has always spoken volumes. He sends her a message made up only of three *x*s, then stuffs his phone back into his joggers.

The Beemer sits right at the back of the car park; it takes Nik a long and stressful fifteen minutes to find it. When he does, he notices a brand-new Audi A1 has been parked almost flush against it. Nik grumbles, pulls the door open, then squeezes out of the space and back towards his halls. Alice is waiting for him by the entrance, her hair neatly piled into a complicated bun, her skin bright and pinched from the cold. She wears a shearling-lined denim jacket, ripped black skinny jeans, chunky army boots and a scowl. A flask of something hot is held by her chest, steam twisting away from it in grey wisps.

Nik parks up beside her on a double yellow and calls out of the window: 'Look at you, man. Dressed in your east London hipster best, yeah?' They had almost kissed last night. There had been a brief moment, at the end of the night, when Melanie and Dan had gone to bed and Nik had been helping Alice get out of her dress – which was backless and seemed to require a master's degree in fashion to get in and out of – when she'd drunkenly turned to rest her arms over his shoulders and stare up at him. There was a pause that felt like an aeon. Her eyes were warm on his. It would have been the easiest thing in the world to simply tilt his face down a couple of inches and brush his lips against hers. He'd been so close, but Layla's face had burst before his eyes, the honey and cinnamon haze of last summer pulling him away.

Alice opens his boot, grimaces and says, 'Christ, Nik. This is rats.'

He goes over to take a look. 'What's the problem?'

'You're so messy. And why do you have so many bags in here? You're only going back for a few weeks. There's no room for my stuff.'

'Just bung 'em on the back seat, man.'

'Ugh, give me a minute. I need to sort this out or it'll drive me mad. I honestly don't understand how you can live like this.' She picks up Nik's hoodies and jeans delicately with the tip of her fingers before flinging them into a pile. Then she removes old plastic bags brimming with empty sandwich boxes and old bottles of Coke, before placing her luggage carefully in the middle of the boot. While she works, Nik sips from the flask she handed him, thinking of home. He worries about what it will be like when he gets back. He's always moved around the weight of his mother's moods like a stream breaking into two when it meets an obstacle. This is the first time he's stood up to her. He doesn't know if time will have washed away their hasty words, or if he should expect the silent treatment.

The white Audi A1 from the car park pulls up next to him then and Nik sees Simon, the flatmate who he avoids as a rule, in the driver's seat.

'Fuck's sake, man,' Nik mutters. Last week, Nik had

opened his drawer in the communal kitchen to find a packet of sliced ham stuffed inside the masalyu his mother had sent him off to university with. *That little prick*, Dan had said, looking over Nik's shoulder. Nik had stifled the urge to barge into Simon's room and batter the actual shit out of him. Instead, he calmly placed the meat back onto Simon's shelf in the fridge. Dan had shaken his head, apparently lost for words, then taken it upon himself to stir a couple of spoons of Marmite into Simon's tub of Nutella.

Alice slams the boot shut and looks up. 'Just ignore him,' she tells Nik, tugging her jacket tighter around her. 'I'm going to the shop to get some lunch before we head down. Want a sarnie?'

'Yeah, go on, then,' Nik says, handing back her flask of tea. He can hear the sound of Simon's electric window rolling down and braces himself.

'What is that thing, like fifty years old?' Simon calls, his eyes on the Beemer.

'Look at the plate. It's only a little older than you, fucko,' Nik says, heading back inside.

'Oi, can't you read?' Simon says, pointing to the sign just above the Beemer's bonnet: No Parking.

'Nah, you're going to have to help me with that one, buddy,' Nik calls. He can hear students' footsteps thumping up and down the stairwell as they prepare to head home. He hammers on Dan's door. 'Broski, we're ready. You still want a ride, yeah?'

Melanie appears in one of Dan's hoodies. 'Sorry,' she says, her voice still thin with sleep, 'my alarm didn't go off. He's just in the shower. Won't be a minute.'

'No worries. We'll wait in the car. Have a good Christmas, yeah?' Nik says. She surprises him by pressing herself into his torso for a hug and telling him to look after himself. Nik nods, wondering what Dan might have told her, now they're together. He ambles back outside to see Simon grinning at him from the driver's seat of the Audi, his overlapping yellow teeth glinting slightly. Simon's mates pile into the car, merging into a dirty gaggle of shaved heads and navy Barbour jackets. One of them holds his backpack against his chest, his arms wrapped around it. Nik can just imagine the scent in the car; a nauseating mix of Red Bull and Versace Blue Jeans. They seem like they're in a rush, and Simon's A1 skids slightly on the ice as he speeds off. Nik walks across the pavement, wondering why they're so keen to get away. But the answer comes to him when his eyes run along a deep scratch carved into the body of the Beemer, the length of it stretching across two panels.

Nik stares at the long white line, noticing how the colour has been lifted from it.

He tries to rub it away with the sleeve of his hoodie, wetting it with saliva and buffing the scratch. It's deep, probably made with a key. His efforts don't make a difference. Then he spots something else, something finer, underneath it. Carved into the body, two small words. Initially, he thinks they read 'No Parking'. But they do not. The second word is missing a few letters, everything except the 'P', the 'A', the 'K' and the 'I' is gone. There's an 'S' at the end, too.

There is a moment when everything seems to suspend in the air, reality itself rising an inch or two, hitching up like a screen. Under it, the slow and measured crawl of those words, creeping closer, tapping at Nik's skin with spindly legs. A quiet, devastating rage soars through him, making him tingle with adrenaline.

'Is Dan still not ready?' Alice says, reappearing with three tote bags dangling from her shoulders like baubles. Nik stands in front of the scratch, hoping she won't notice. He knows she would fully kick off, and he doesn't have the energy for one of her rants. They are his alone to deal with, these scratches that do not belong to him, that have been forced upon him.

Alice tuts when Nik doesn't answer her and hands him one of the bags. His chest feels as though it has frozen over. His fingers are numb, his heartbeat loud against his ears. A chill washes over him, as if he is immersed in water, water he wants to step out of. He cannot seem to find his voice, so looks inside the bag to see a selection of treats: a sandwich, three packets of crisps, several chocolate bars and two cans of Coke. Her generosity cuts a slice of light through his rage. He asks her how much he owes. She waves his question away with an impatient, fluttering hand, then points to Dan's window and says, 'This is fully taking the piss. I don't have all day.'

They wait in the car, Alice fiddling with Nik's radio, Nik flicking through messages on his phone with trembling fingers, his mind still on the scratches. They are too deep for T-Cut. He wonders if Papa Burns might know someone who could buff them out. He scrolls down his contacts to message him but finds himself skipping ahead to Paul's name. He wants to call him. His finger hovers over the green button, but he does not press it. In this moment, he feels more alone than he has all year. The scratches have fractured a part of him that was already strained to its limits. He wants to melt safely into someone for comfort, for strength, but he doesn't know who. Layla is on her way to Dublin, his grandfather is gone, and he hasn't spoken to his mother for weeks. He shuts his eyes, breathing back tears, hoping that Alice isn't watching him. He turns once more to the chain of messages Paul has drip-fed over the last few weeks, the ones he still hasn't replied to.

14:59 Paul: Hey kid! Good seeing you yesterday. Still on for the game this weekend?

The next day:

12:34 Paul: So, I was thinking, there's a pub about a mile away I normally go to before matches. Should we meet there first for a bite and a pint?

Two days later:

18:52 Paul: It gets super busy on match days so I've booked us a table – it's the Hunter S near Dalston. About a 30 min stroll from the stadium so we can have a bite then amble over. Sound okay?

Another two days later:

08:12 Paul: Hope you're good, kid. Assuming you're not coming today. Won't bug you again, but you know where I am if you ever need me. Paul

He has stared at this same screen many times over the last few weeks, thinking about what his mother told him, fluctuating between wanting to call Paul to calmly have it out and messaging him to tell him he's a disgusting fucking weasel who Nik wants nothing to do with. He'd promised himself that he'd decide what he was going to do about the Paul situation before he drove back home for Christmas. He'd blocked Paul at some point last night for all of three minutes before unblocking him again. Now, a young and fragile part of Nik is screaming for Paul, telling him Paul will know exactly what to do about the scratches, that he'll make it all better. Despite this, Nik chooses not to listen. He'd rather figure it out himself. The boys will help. Papa Burns, in his humble quietude, will be there too.

Nik takes a deep breath, then deletes Paul from his contacts, so their chat goes back to the way it was before he started university. Paul's photo turns into a light circle. The place where his name once was is now just a random sequence of digits again. He is pushed back into the past, into a memory once more. Nik takes another slow breath and deletes their chat from his phone.

Beside him, Alice hums along to 'Wild Thoughts' in between mouthfuls of chocolate. When Nik puts his phone away and rubs his face, she says: 'You all right? You've gone a bit grey.'

'Nah, I'm good, man.'

'Looking forward to some time back home?' She fishes out another chocolate bar from her tote bag and offers Nik a piece. He takes it, then washes it down with a sip of her peppermint tea. They both watch as Dan comes in and out of view against his bedroom window on the ground floor, stuffing clothes into a backpack. It's almost as if they're in a drive-through cinema and Dan's window is the screen.

'Sort of,' Nik says. 'You?'

'Why only sort of?'

'It's a bit of a mess back home at the moment. My mum's proper vexed at me for keeping this car.'

'Why, because it was so expensive to insure?'

'Nah, because it was my dad's. I think it reminds her of him.'

'Oh,' Alice says. She tucks the half-eaten bar of Dairy Milk back into its wrapper and then places it on her knee. 'Didn't they get on?'

Nik shrugs.

'What happened to him?'

He looks across to her.

'Sorry,' she says.

'Nah, it's calm. Hit-and-run, man.'

'Fuck,' she says, just as Dan appears at the entrance to their halls now, Melanie wrapping her arms around his torso. It reminds Nik of how Layla had embraced him that day he stood in Teo's garden, before he found the car. He was just a boy back then. So much has changed since. He glances at Alice, who is staring straight ahead. His eyes follow the profile of her face. There's something strangely intimate about being alone with her in the bubble of the car, like they're set apart from the rest of the world. He winds his window all the way down to welcome in the outside, then props his elbow on the door.

'Christ,' Alice says, gagging as she watches Dan and Melanie say goodbye. 'Who knew these two would end up so grossly into each other?' She reaches over to the steering wheel and a horn fills the air, making Melanie jump. 'Chill out, Mel, he'll be back in a couple of weeks.'

Dan frees himself from her with one last kiss and runs towards the car, a backpack thrown over his shoulder.

'Sorry, guys,' he says, once he's in.

'About bloody time.' Alice throws a bag of treats back at Dan, then slaps Nik's thigh as if he's a horse. 'Let's go.'

When they've dropped Dan off outside a block of flats in Tottenham, Nik crawls down Kingsland Road, listening to Alice moan about east London traffic.

He swings into a little street and drives until Alice tells him to pull up outside a tall town house perched on the edge of a square. Nik does so and reads the sign on the black gate opposite: 'Welcome to De Beauvoir Square.' Behind the gate, he spots a rose garden filled with young families. A milk float-cum-bakery is parked up against it, a queue of customers waiting in a neat line.

After the bustle of Kingsland Road on a Saturday, which sits just two hundred metres away from them, Nik's surprised that he can now only hear the trickle of bicycles and the chirping of dunnocks dancing around a nearby hedge. Many of the front drives seem to sport the same naked trees with curved branches twisting around their trunks, which Nik knows will hold magnolia flowers in the spring. He knows this because he helped his grandfather plant one at the foot of his garden earlier that year. He wonders, with a sadness that dries up his throat, which stranger will be lucky enough to see that magnolia tree bloom one day.

'Home sweet home,' Alice says, stretching luxuriously.

'These are some boujee ends, man,' Nik says, unbuckling his seat belt.

Alice fetches her bags from the boot, then takes the steps up to the house two at a time. 'Come in for a cuppa,' she says.

Nik dawdles by the car. He is busy watching a young mother teach her son how to roller-skate in the rose garden, a sausage dog scurrying happily between his moving legs. Alice tuts. 'Hurry up. D'you want some tea or not?'

'Go on, then,' he says, following her in. Her front door is huge and heavy, with stained-glass panels. Her home smells like a hotel. Three pairs of wellington boots sit neatly by a brass umbrella stand. A selection of Jo Malone candles line a nearby console.

'Back in a sec,' Alice says, disappearing upstairs. 'Kitchen's through the hall.'

Nik feels strangely like an impostor as he pads through to the kitchen to put on the kettle. He can't find one, so instead looks at the collection of items pressed onto the fridge, held in place by magnets. A whiteboard takes up most of the door, telling the reader that they need to *please pick up some fresh eggs*. Beside it sits a photo of Alice and her parents. They are standing under the Eiffel Tower. Alice is the spitting image of her mother, the same height and build too, though her usually blonde hair is shorter and darker in this photo. Her father looks like he's come straight out of a menswear catalogue, with a thick head of silver hair, a sharp jaw, and the sort of eyes that make you feel like you could trust him in an emergency.

'Where are your parents?' Nik asks, when Alice comes

back into the kitchen. She has swapped her jeans for a pair of grey joggers that match Nik's, and is shrugging on a jumper that has a selection of smiling avocados dressed in Christmas hats. Nik can't decide if she's wearing it ironically or not.

'They're actually away for the weekend. In Cornwall visiting my gran.' She fiddles with the tap and boiling water spills straight out and into two mugs. 'I was going to say, you can chill here tonight, if you don't want to go back to your mum's right away.'

Nik feels his cheeks warming. He thinks again of last night, of almost kissing her, of the inevitability of what might happen if he stays. What he feels towards her is reduced to nothing when he thinks of Layla. But how can he have space for both of them? Is he no better than Paul for liking two people at once? Or is the fact that he isn't pursuing Alice enough to mark him apart? He can't help how he feels, surely. But should he? Alice is rummaging through the cupboards and Nik is grateful for the fact that she cannot see his face as he weighs up her offer. She turns to him when he doesn't respond, a dark tub of manuka honey in her hand. Nik watches as she stirs a heaped spoonful into each of their mugs. *Say something. Anything. Anything at all. Just answer her bloody question.*

'I'm having a couple of mates over later for drinks. Dan said he'd pop in at some point,' she adds finally, breaking the unbearable silence. She puts the cup of herbal tea carefully into his hands. 'So it won't just be me and you.'

Nik looks at her and can see an uncharacteristic apprehension in her gaze. It's just friendly, he tells himself. It'll be fine. 'Yeah, that would be cool,' he says, 'if that's all right.'

'Of course it is,' she says, moving into the lounge and settling onto the sofa. 'It'll be pretty low-key. You can finally meet my old schoolmates. Why don't you invite your buddy, Teo, too?'

'Teo? Are you sure?'

'Yes,' she says, flicking through Netflix. 'And the other one – the blond guy – Will. The more the merrier.'

25

June 1995

'Are you having a laugh?

'Excuse me, madam?'

'You heard me. Who gave you this number?' Avani glanced down into the courtyard to check her father and fiancé weren't within earshot. They were just as she left them; side by side on fading deckchairs, cups of chai close to their chests, deep in conversation. The sun fell over them before moving behind a cloud. Her father chuckled. Avani pressed the phone closer to her ear to listen to the stranger shuffling through some papers.

'Agniben Rigvedi. She is your mother, no?'

Avani exhaled loudly. She bit her bottom lip in frustration. 'She's insane. I'm already engaged. Do not call this number again.' She slammed the receiver onto the cradle and walked into the kitchen, rubbing her forehead, trying to push her mother out of her mind. It was the third call that afternoon. She'd written the first off as a mistake. The second had worried her. Now that she knew they were her mother's doing, she was enraged. She glanced out of the window again, anxious to join her father and Elliot in case another phone call came through. She wondered if she should disconnect the line altogether, but they were still waiting to hear back from the registrar and florist. The estate agent also said he'd call about the flat in Kingsbury they'd put an offer on. She was determined to move from the mouldy one-bed they'd been renting in Neasden since their graduation but knew it would be at least another year until they could really afford it. Elliot had told her to wait; they were about to get married, they already had so much on their plates. But Avani wanted to move as soon as possible. She wanted to get him out of Neasden. Twice this week, in the days after the social worker told them he'd reached a dead end, she'd woken in the night to find herself alone. When her fiancé couldn't sleep, he'd been walking across the dual carriageway and down towards St Raph's, the estate just a stone's throw away from their flat. It was where he lived with his parents in the years after they left Harrow, where he'd looked after his brother, for those two small weeks. He was going over there when he couldn't sleep, sitting on the bench opposite his old block of flats in the dark, staring up at the window that used to be his bedroom, as though he was waiting for someone, as though trying to convince himself he hadn't imagined it all.

Avani had taken to double-locking their front door before bed, then hiding both sets of keys in a saucepan.

She glanced outside again. Elliot was showing her father a plastic tray of ivy cuttings. He was attempting to propagate some crawlers to make their dull, communal courtyard a little brighter. As she watched him, her gaze running over his chocolate curls, his broad shoulders, she filled slowly with fear. What if something happened to him? What if her mother did something horrific to stop them marrying? How far would she go to stop Avani *bringing shame* onto their family? Avani watched Elliot, in that grey T-shirt she loved, so enthusiastic about those little plants. He lifted an arm to point to the fence beside him and she thought then of what was hidden about an inch above the hem of his sleeve. Neat lines of raised scar tissue. Scars that belonged to a teenager from so long ago, one who had grown into a man and had finally found the joy in life again. But it felt as though he was slipping backwards and she wanted so desperately to stop him, to beckon him towards her, or else twist herself around him to cushion his fall.

Elliot was everything to her; the part of her life she cherished the most. She couldn't fathom how her mother could want to separate them. Earlier that afternoon, her father had come over unexpectedly, peering up the stairs when Avani opened the door, relaying to her in a quick whisper of Gujarati that none of her mother's family would be attending their wedding in three days' time, that her mother, too, was threatening not to come. He apologised, his eyes full of sadness, of hopelessness, of resignation. They brightened and a smile lit his face when Elliot hopped down the stairs.

'Oh hey, Rohan!' Elliot called. 'Come in. I'll pop some chai on.'

'Hello, beta. Only if you're not too busy.'

'Course not. Tame kem cho?'

'Majama, beta,' her father had replied, a hand on Elliot's back.

Once inside, her father had seemed uncharacteristically nervous, shooting glances at the telephone and out of the window. He'd insisted the three of them sit outside, mumbling something about fresh air and sunlight. Elliot had dutifully borrowed a few rusting deckchairs from the students who lived in the flat below, placing them in the pool of light filling the courtyard.

Now, Avani watched her father pointing to a dapple of green moving in their neighbour's cherry tree, a group of parakeets dancing and chirping loudly among the branches. She'd only seen them a handful of times before, this mythical chatter that dashed around north-west London. They rose together amid a flurry of song, swooping up and flying out of sight. Avani sighed, chewing on her bottom lip, then picked up the phone again and dialled Chand's number. There was no answer, so she pressed the switch hook and called again and again.

On the fourth try, she heard a crackle and then a breathless: 'Hello?'

'Rukmani? Hi, it's me. How're you doing?'

'Hey, bhabhi. I'm okay. Feet are the size of little boats though.' Rukmani was heavily pregnant with twins, edging ever closer to her due date.

'Can I bring you anything?'

'We're okay for now. How are wedding preparations going?'

Avani sighed. 'Not great. Actually, wondering if I could speak to Chand.'

'Ha, bhabhi. He's just unloading the car. Ek minute.'

Avani could make out the theme tune to Rajvi's favourite TV show in the background. It was the one Elliot sang along to whenever they babysat, which seemed to fill little Rajvi with pure joy and always resulted in her falling into a fit of giggles. Avani often caught Elliot whistling the same tune long after they'd dropped Rajvi back home. She picked nervously at the peeling paint on the windowsill until she heard a shuffle and her brother's voice: 'Av.'

'Chand. She's fully lost the plot.'

'Who?'

'Who d'you think? She's had three different blokes call me today. She's trying to set me up.'

'Christ.' She imagined him rubbing a hand through what was left of his hair.

'Has she said anything to you?'

Silence.

'Chand. Tell me.'

'I'll call her.'

'Yes. Tell her to pack it the fuck in. What if Ell picked up? It's bad enough the way she's been treating him since we got engaged, but could you imagine how heartbroken he'd be, knowing she's literally giving random men my number *three* days before our wedding?'

Silence. She twirled her engagement ring around her finger absent-mindedly, her thumb catching on the pink morganite in the centre, then running over the little white diamonds dotting the band. Elliot had slipped it onto her finger in Madeira to the sound of waves curling and crashing against rocks, fireworks lighting the dark sky above them, signalling the turn of a new year. They'd been sitting on a black-sand beach after a day of swimming in the sea and drinking fortified wine, Avani tucked between his knees, her back flush against his torso, her head against his chest, the rest of their lives before them.

Her mother's face had filled with disgust when Avani had come back home and shown her the ring. She'd asked if Elliot had purchased it from Argos.

'Honestly. She's actually mad. Mad.'

Chand sighed. Avani glanced out of the window again. 'Do you reckon Dad knows what she's up to?'

'No,' Chand said. 'Well, yes.'

'Chand. Tell me what you know.'

A groan. Then: 'Look, when I was over last weekend she was going on for hours about how she didn't actually think this wedding would happen and how, now that it's just days away, she can't let it go ahead. So, yeah, you're right. I think she has lost it a bit.'

'I don't get it. She was finally just about fine with us being together.'

'Yeah, until you got formally engaged. I think she genuinely thought it was a phase. That you'd see the light and eventually settle with a Gujju boy.'

Avani shook her head as he spoke, warm with anger. A phase. The word shone red. They'd been together for five years. A *phase.*

'And what did you say to that?' Avani asked. There was a moment of silence before Chand spoke. In it, Avani thought of what he would do if he were in her situation. She thought of how he'd dated all manner of women before eventually settling with Poppy, the bright, extrovert brunette Avani was sure he'd be with forever. He'd left her, one cold morning in November, to marry Rukmani. She was a few years older than him, a dentist, and the daughter of someone their mother knew from her temple. When Avani had questioned him about the sudden change, he'd told her it was for the best, and that was that.

There was no doubt in Avani's mind that he was happy – that he adored Rukmani and Rajvi – but now she wondered if some part of him expected her to do the same, to eventually forsake Elliot and settle down with a more suitable match. Surely not.

She was hot with these thoughts when he said: 'I told her to drop it, obviously. Puppa tried to put her to rights, too. You know we think the world of Ell.'

Avani sat down. She thought back to Chand's wedding a couple of years earlier, during their final year of university. Her mother had called when they were writing up the invites and told her she wasn't to bring Elliot. She wasn't to embarrass her mother in front of her new vevai. Chand had put his foot down and insisted that Elliot be there, promoting him instantly to one of his groomsmen.

Avani's voice was low when she spoke again: 'So what's happening then – is she going to be there or not?'

'I really don't know, Av. Probably best to expect that she won't come, yeah?'

'Well. It's easier that way, anyway.' Avani heard the sound of Rajvi crying in the background.

'I'll go home tomorrow. Try and smooth things over,' Chand told her.

'Okay.'

'It'll be fine. Dad and I will manage it. Is Ell about?'

'He's outside with Puppa.'

'Tell him to call me later. Arsenal have just signed a Dutch chap from Inter and I –'

'Yes, all right, I'll tell him.' She tutted and put the phone down. Without thinking about it, she yanked the wire from the socket. The florist and registrar could wait. So could the estate agent. She wasn't going to be held hostage by her own mother.

She pressed her hands onto the windowsill, feeling the peeling paint under her fingers, resting her forehead gently against the glass, letting it cool her. Below, her father patted Elliot on the back then turned towards the flat to look up at Avani. Their eyes met through the glass and his face softened. There was an apology etched into his gaze, in the creases across his forehead, in the worry parting his lips. Something clicked into place. This is why her father came today, she realised, to keep Elliot outside and away from the phone, away from the mess of his soon-to-be mother-in-law, away from the pain that her father knew only Avani could bear.

26

December 2017

Avani parks up at work and unbuckles her seat belt, her mind full of her son. They rowed again this morning and she has spent the entire journey on mental autopilot, replaying shouted words, searching the spaces between them for a resolution, for an explanation of how the strength of their bond could have shattered so. She regrets telling him about Paul the way she did, using it as a weapon to shock him into submission. A flawed part of her expected him to fall back into line, for his hostility to ease as she showed him just a glimmer into the dark world that lay under the surface of it all, the surface she tried her best to keep smooth and palatable for him. Instead, he'd turned up on the first Sunday morning of the Christmas break, a full day later than expected, very hung-over, and in the worst mood she'd ever seen him in.

He'd dumped his bags in the hallway without greeting her, then stormed upstairs with Rani at his heels, before slamming his bedroom door shut. Avani waited downstairs, wondering if this animosity was directed at her. She gave him an hour, then carefully padded upstairs with a mug of chai, leaning against his door frame, half in and half out, staring around his room while telling him that she'd be spending most of Christmas in the Cotswolds with friends, *they've hired a cottage, you see.*

Right, he said. He was lying in bed, the mug he'd snatched from her hands now perched on his chest. Rani had settled into the space between his shins, her tail thumping. A pack of cigarettes and a lighter were perched on the windowsill. He wasn't bothering to hide it any more, then.

So you'll have the house to yourself, she told him, still taking in the cigarettes, expecting him to be quietly delighted by this news. Instead he'd asked if that was it, and if she *could leave, yeah.* She had frozen, his words prickling at her skin and then her eyes. She watched him, gripping the door frame just for something to do. His stare was fixed on her hand. She saw herself through his gaze – a trembling mother holding on to the wall for support. She dropped her hand.

The words whipped out of her before she could stop herself: *I hope you didn't drive this hung-over all the way from university. I can still smell the alcohol on you.* Her stomach had wrung as she heard them back – these words that were borrowed from her own mother – and for a small moment she stepped out of herself to wonder how it had come to this.

No, man. I drove back yesterday.

Oh, did you spend the night with Layla again? she asked, before she could help herself.

He exhaled loudly, impatiently, annoyance flashing across his eyes. *Nah.*

Where were you?

Nothing.

Nikhil?

Alice's. All right?

Silence. Then: *Goodness. Are you messing those poor girls around? I didn't bring you up to behave –*

Fuck's sake, no, man.

Don't use that language with me.

Well, stop making shit up in your own head. Now can you please piss off and let me sleep?

He placed the cup of chai on the floor and turned over in his bed, pulling the covers all the way up to his ears. His words stung her. Layla and Alice. After what she'd told him about Paul . . . she shook her head, stifling the urge to cry. Who was this man? Where was her kind, loving son?

They'd barely been in the house at the same time after that first morning, and they hadn't spoken again properly until today, when she caught him smoking out of his bedroom window, which ended in him storming off to Will's. She's driving to the Cotswolds this evening and will not return until New Year's Day. Part of her is desperate to drive back home, to talk it all out, but the other part is so full of pride and shame and anger that it fries all of her best intentions into hot, sizzling dust.

She takes a deep breath of winter air as she locks her car and walks into the office, trying to leave these thoughts outside, replacing them with fresh worries about the back-to-back meetings she has today and the end-of-year reports that she knows still need looking over. She is already late for her 9am with Legal, so her voice is tight when Francesca meets her in the hall and says, pointedly: 'There's someone waiting to see you.'

'Yes, thank you.' Avani runs a hand through her ponytail

as she strides into her office. 'Sorry I'm late, Lily, there was a crash on the North Circ so traffic was –'

But it is not Lily from Legal sitting in the chair across from her desk. Paul smiles up at her and says, 'Well, hello, you,' in a manner that suggests he's surprised to see her, as if it's she who has walked into his office.

'Hi,' Avani says, reaching for a strand of hair to tuck behind her ear, one she does not find.

'What time d'you call this, eh?' he says, rising to give her a peck on the cheek. He smells of the Hermès cologne that used to sit next to her perfume on the chest of drawers they shared. But there is another scent underneath it, a scent that makes her think of the taste of his neck when he would come to bed hours later than he'd promised and the unfamiliar, floral musk that lingered around his car when he'd been away for work.

'How're you holding up?' Paul asks, his eyes running across her face in a way that feels too intimate for this hour in the morning. She realises, then, that she has not put any mascara on today.

'Paul,' she says. 'What do you want? What're you doing here?' She notices her favourite mug in his hands, an inch of black coffee resting at the bottom of it. She wonders how long he's been waiting for her.

'I had an early meeting with one of the chaps downstairs,' he says. 'Part of their finance division is in New Zealand so we were at it at the crack of dawn. They were talking me through all the other offices in this building and when they stopped on yours, I thought: Avani Harrison, there's someone I'd love to drop in on.'

'Right,' she says, not believing a word. She thinks of

how he'd once described her job, Chief Finance Officer for a tech firm, as a *fun little job to keep her out of trouble.* She'd been in her early thirties and the only female on the company's C-suite. Anger sweeps across her temple. She turns away from him to push her window open.

Francesca pops in and says, 'Lily's stuck on the Tube. Signal failure at Blackfriars. She said she'll be here as quick as she can. I've moved your 9am over to midday.' She looks as though she is especially pleased with herself, her eyes flicking back to Paul. 'Can I get you another coffee?'

'Oh, how could I possibly refuse?'

Francesca's face splits into a smile, her cheeks flushed. She seems to have forgotten how to draw breath and makes a sound Avani has never heard from her before – a sort of half-giggle – as she takes the mug from him. When Avani looks at her, she's struck by a sense of déjà vu, as though she is watching her younger self – who, like Francesca, would so easily melt under Paul's synthetic, mass-produced charm.

When Francesca leaves, Avani's eyes fall back on Paul, who's watching the door. She sits down and asks: 'What d'you want, Paul?'

'I just thought I'd check in,' he says, drumming his fingers on her table. He slouches slightly in his chair.

'On what?'

'You.'

She shakes her head.

'How's the kid holding up?'

This feels like a deliberate jab, like some sort of boastful power play. 'You should know,' she says.

For a brief moment, his bravado falls away. 'I don't, actually.' They watch each other. He continues: 'This is partly why I thought I should drop in. Nik and I were meant to go to a Gunners game last month, and he didn't turn up. I didn't know if he'd just decided he wasn't up for it or if something else is going on with him.'

Avani stares at her blank laptop screen as Paul speaks, pretending to be engrossed in an email. Relief colours her thoughts. This small act on her son's part reminds her of a similar incident with Chand in the week following their mother's death. Avani and Chand had rowed horrifically after the cremation, a hot fog of hostility clinging to her skin whenever she found herself near him. Then, when she'd crumpled to confused tears after someone had mentioned Elliot at a family dinner, Chand had passed her a tissue under the table, even though they were still in the thick of a row. That silent gesture, handing her a piece of kitchen roll to catch her tears, had meant so much. Her son's movements around Paul feel the same, as though their anger towards each other is not so thick that it supersedes the bigger picture. There is still some sense of allyship.

'Has he been holding up okay?' Paul asks.

'He's totally fine.'

'Oh, I don't know about that.'

'Paul. Did you come here to check in on me, or Nikhil? He's not a child. Just call him if you're so desperate to get hold of him.'

The silence that follows is so rich with pride that Avani can feel it pressing against her, making it hard to breathe.

When he speaks again, his words surprise her. 'Listen, Av. Why don't I take you out for lunch?'

'Certainly bloody not.'

'Why?'

'It's nine thirty, Paul.'

'Is there anyone else on the scene?'

'No,' she says, without a beat. There is a sense of complacency wrapped around this short sharp word; she doesn't need to search for herself in the arms of someone else, like he always has.

'So what's the problem?'

'The problem,' she says, his persistence suffocating her, 'is that we made space for you in our lives and then you went and slept with half of south London. That hasn't all just gone away, Paul.' She doesn't blink as she says this, her voice low and controlled, her face set, so that if her colleagues watched her through the glass walls of her office they'd think she was simply pointing out a discrepancy in their latest quarterly reports. Now that he's finally come back, the way she hoped he would, she realises that she doesn't want him at all. She sees him as he truly is, in all of his messiness, as opposed to the smooth, convenient image of him she'd constructed in her mind. Watching him charm Francesca has reminded her of how much she's grown in the time since they parted, of why they broke what they had back into two and walked away from the pieces left behind.

She takes a sip of warm water from the glass still on her desk from yesterday, then says: 'So, do excuse me if I don't want to have a cosy lunch with you. I couldn't think of a worse way to spend my afternoon.'

'Avani.' The friendliness has totally seeped from his voice now. His eyes are dark, flat, like midnight ice over a lake. 'You're the one who called me last summer.'

'Yes,' she says. 'Correct. I called to invite you to my father's funeral, so you could say goodbye. I didn't call to invite you back into my life.'

Hurt flicks across his face. She looks past him to see Francesca strutting towards them. Avani stands up. She plucks the cup of coffee straight from Francesca's hands as she passes, then holds the door open and says to Paul, 'You can leave, now.' She takes a sip of the coffee as he rises to his feet. 'Off you go.'

Somewhere outside, a car door slams shut. Nik looks up from the spliff he's assembling, his eyes frozen on Will's. *Fuck*, he mouths. Will hastily stuffs the weed into his jeans, racing against the sound of keys turning. Rani scrambles over to the lounge entrance, where Nik's mother appears a few moments later. She bends down to let Rani lick her chin, calling a warm hello to Will then simply nodding at Nik. Despite the wordless greeting, Nik can see from her face that she's calmed down since their argument this morning. She even surprises him with a fleeting, thin-lipped smile. Must have been a good last day at work. Rani follows his mother up the stairs and Nik watches her scruffy grey legs trotting away. He's grown incredibly fond of Rani over the break, and even though he and his mother have barely spoken, arguing whenever they do, having the dog around has meant that the tension is diffused quicker than expected, as if she's some sort of neutral safe space between them. He's looking forward to having the house to himself but is gutted that his mother is taking Rani to the Cotswolds with her.

Beside him, Will scrolls through Netflix. He's looking for the latest episode of *Breaking Bad*, which they are binging over the Christmas holiday. Nik grunts noncommittally when Will asks if he fancies hitting the pub later, his mind elsewhere. As his mother comes back downstairs with her suitcase, he swallows his pride and calls through the lounge: 'Mum?'

'Yes?' She's changed into jeans and a white jumper and sits down beside him to pull on a pair of Converse.

'Do you want to leave Rani with me?'

She turns to look at him, then back at Rani, who is by her side, her favourite bear in her mouth, her tail wagging. Abandoning her shoelaces, she puts her hands either side of the dog's face, stroking behind her ears. 'I was planning on taking her with me.'

'You can leave her here,' he says sheepishly, 'if you want.'

His mother watches him, and he knows she sees right past his words to the question sitting reticently between them.

'Would you like her to stay with you instead?' she asks, her eyes softer now.

'Yeah, if you want.'

His mother laughs – which he doesn't expect – and bends down to give Rani a kiss between the eyes. She ties her shoelaces, sighs, then says, 'I mean you've pretty much looked after her yourself since you've been back so I don't see why not.'

Warmth flowers in Nik and he pats the sofa behind

him. Rani jumps up and nudges his hand with her wet nose. Her infallible, constant love has been the highlight of his return home.

'What's Teo up to?' Nik's mother asks, putting on her coat. 'I haven't seen him in a while.'

Will sniggers and says, 'Probs at Alice's.'

Her fingers slip on the buttons she's fastening. Nik picks up the remote again. He can feel his mother's eyes searching for his, calling out to him, trying to reach him. When she doesn't say anything, he glances reluctantly up at her. 'See you then,' he says.

To Nik's relief, she seems to decide against asking any more questions. 'I'll be back on New Year's Day. Have a good Christmas, boys,' she says, standing up. 'And behave yourselves.'

'Always,' Will grins from the other end of the sofa. 'Merry Christmas.'

It's almost midnight when Nik drops Will back home. As soon as Will has given Nik a fist bump and hurried down the driveway into his home, Rani hops into his seat from the back of the car and folds herself into a scruffy ball. Nik strokes her back as he drives. Without being fully conscious of what he's heading towards, he finds himself turning down the road that leads to the cul-de-sac of his childhood, his grandfather's old home tucked within it. This has become a bit of a habit over the break; it's as though the Beemer has a hidden compass inside it, drawing him towards his grandfather's home. This time, he knows that something's different before he parks up. A dim, yellow light falls through the lounge windows, stretching its way across the front lawn. An old Mazda sits on his grandfather's driveway. Nik parks by the kerb and looks up at the face of the house.

Through the window, Nik can see two figures moving within. He recently overheard his mother saying the probate had been sorted and the house sale would be completing any day now. In this moment, he realises that this is what he's been waiting for. He's been driving past silently, watching, waiting, daring them to move in. Now, finally, here they are.

Something that's been spinning silently inside of Nik for months seems to slow, then stop. He finds himself holding his breath as a young couple move into view. They haven't yet drawn the curtains. The woman is dressed in a pair of red dungarees and the man in a dark tracksuit. He's on a stepladder, reaching up to put a shade over the exposed bulb that hangs from the centre of the ceiling. She's nudging items around in a cardboard box that's pressed against the lounge window. A Christmas tree has been hastily stuffed into the corner where Nik's grandfather's favourite armchair used to be.

Nik's gaze moves to the exterior walls. The thick branches of roses and wisteria that wound around the outside of the house are gone. They've been messily hacked off. Nik counts a dozen black bags next to the overfilled bins at the front of the drive, the remnants of the plants that his grandfather had spent years growing now spilling out over the path.

Nik thinks back to the morning that he and his mother had bought the wisteria. It had been Father's Day and he'd visited a garden centre near the Welsh Harp with his mother and Paul to pick out a present. Nik had sat in the middle of the Volvo with two young plants strapped to the seats either side of him as they drove to his grandfather's home. Paul had drilled two trellis fences into the bricks above the front windows. His mother had delicately trained the existing roses around them while Nik helped his grandfather plant the wisteria into the earth. He thinks back to how it took three summers for them to flower, how excited his grandfather had been when he spotted those very first lilac droplets forming among the thick green leaves. How, after Paul left, Nik took over the job of climbing up a rusty ladder every summer, held firmly in place by his grandfather, to trim them back, being careful not to disturb the family of birds he cannot name that made their nest among the winding branches each spring.

A sense of finality sweeps over him. The building has shed a layer of skin. Everything is moving on. He closes his eyes and thinks of his grandfather's sweet haven as he wants to remember it – the neat green lawn, the roses and lilac wisteria dressing the terraced house. He thinks of how, during the summer, he'd often see people stop to admire the little home brimming with colour. A fairy-tale cottage in the middle of Harrow. Then he opens his eyes to the reality waiting in front of him – the barren building engulfed in shadow. Violated. Bare. Exposed. It contrasts so perversely with the image he remembers that it makes him suddenly livid. It's as though the final, tangible piece of his grandfather has been taken. He shakes his head, starts the car, and pulls away from this small piece of home for what he knows will be the last time.

The next morning, Nik swallows down discomfort as he stands on Teo's doorstep, his finger an inch from the bell. Alice's house party the day they'd driven back to London is still vivid in his mind – the party which had ended with Alice and Teo hooking up. Nik had downed too much rum to drive home that night, so ended up sleeping on Alice's sofa, Will snoring a few metres away, while Teo was up in her bedroom. They'd been inseparable almost immediately after he introduced them; he'd seen an uncharacteristic softness in Teo's gaze that had reminded him of his parents in that graduation photo. Nik had driven home wrapped in an anger he didn't want to confront as soon as dawn broke. According to Will, he'd missed the glaringly obvious signs that Teo and Alice liked the look of each other and were simply waiting for him to introduce them, a realisation which only pissed Nik off further still. Nik had tried to bring it up again with Will one evening at their favourite shisha bar, but Will's face had crumpled into a frown as he asked: *Hold on, aren't you into Layla?*

Yeah, of course, man.

And you and Alice are just mates?

Nik nodded slowly.

And nothing's ever happened between you lots?

He thought of the night they'd almost kissed. *Nah.*

Then what's up, broski?

Allow it, he'd said, busying himself with a long drag of minty, bubbling smoke.

He'd just about accepted that it was Layla he really liked, but then seeing Teo with Alice seemed to throw the whole thing into a confused tangle again. He tries hard now, as he stands on Teo's doorstep, to settle on how he actually feels about it all. It's Layla he wants to be with, it's definitely Layla. Alice and him would never work. He knows this, but thinking of Alice falling into something with one of his boys makes him feel so many different emotions at the same time that he can't pin them down to look at them properly. There's resentment in there, protectiveness, something that feels a little like jealously too. Why did she have to pick his best mate?

Once he grows tired of spinning around in the midst of these thoughts, he decides to simply go home, order a Domino's and spend Christmas Day with Rani instead. He's walking back towards the Beemer when Teo's grandmother appears from an Uber, pulling him into a soft hug. He sighs and follows her in, his worry dissolving when Teo runs down the stairs, claps him on the back and leads him into the kitchen. The day passes in a blur of rum and music and the most delicious food; warming egusi soup with pounded yam, spicy jollof, hearty tomato stew. Nik finds his eyes following Teo when he rises from the table halfway through dinner, his phone buzzing in his hand. Nik tunes out of the conversation thereafter, shooting glances at the ceiling in between mouthfuls of puff-puff, wondering if it's Alice who called and what they might be talking about up there. Teo surprises him by coming back downstairs forty minutes later and handing Nik his phone. Alice appears on the screen in red lipstick, reindeer antlers and a tight green jumper. 'All right?' Nik says, his mouth full.

'Merry Christmas,' she says, waving.

He waves back, chewing as fast as he can.

'Ah, so you do still have thumbs then. They've not been sawed off.'

He covers his mouth and says: 'Huh?'

'Just wondering why you've been ignoring all my messages. Assumed your thumbs must have fallen victim to frostbite, or gout, perhaps.'

'You can only get gout in your feet, man.'

'Not true,' she says, taking a sip of red wine. 'You can get gout in any of your joints. Fingers included.'

Nik crumbles reluctantly into a laugh. He looks up to see Teo in the kitchen, helping his sister put cling film over bowls of leftovers.

'How've you been? You doing okay?' Alice asks.

'Yeah, good, man,' he says. She looks really pretty. Part of him pulses with sadness. He's missed her, he realises.

'What've you been up to? We've barely seen you.' She rests her elbow on the arm of her chair as she speaks. Nik watches her. She didn't say 'I', she said 'we'. A lump has formed in his throat. They're proper in something, these two.

'Just chilling, you know.'

'Okay. Will I see you on New Year's then?' she asks, cautious.

'Ah, are you coming too?' The boys are planning a night out in Shoreditch. He didn't realise Teo invited her.

'Yeah.' Of course she bloody is. 'If that's all right?' she adds, her forehead creasing slightly.

'I'll see if Dan's around too,' Nik says, scratching his neck. He hands the phone back to Teo without saying goodbye, then takes a seat between Teo's mother and sister, his eyes firmly fixed on the plate of shuku shuku someone has just placed in front of him, trying his best not to dwell on the memories from that house party at Alice's, the way he'd walked into the garden to see them kissing, her arms around Teo's neck, his around her waist, a spliff hanging limp from his fingers, the sensation that a piece of Nik was twisting and falling from a great height.

He leaves soon after, glad he's got Rani as an excuse to cut early. He spends the days leading up to New Year's Eve playing FIFA with Will and ordering more Deliveroo than they can manage, Kendrick's *DAMN.* blasting through the house as they smoke freely out of the lounge windows. It takes a whole forty-eight hours after Christmas for Nik to register that this is the first year he hasn't received a card from Paul, and the thought comes and goes, as though it is a storm he is watching from afar. Their story has folded quietly, discreetly, and Nik marks it by finally spending the twenty-pound notes that have been tucked into that shoebox all these years, recycling the cards they came in, the envelopes too.

27

December 2017

On the last morning of the year, Nik sits in his car, looking at a photo of Layla that's just been uploaded to Instagram. She's in a pub, fairy lights twinkling above, an untouched pint of Guinness on the wooden table in front of her. Her hair is up and she wears a white top with puffy sleeves. She's glowing. An older man Nik's never seen before sits next to her in a grey fleece, his arm around her shoulders, half of his face covered as he takes a sip of beer, his eyes on the camera. Her father. She barely ever uploads to her grid, so he knows how much it must mean to her to be back in touch with her father after all these years. Nik likes the photo and clicks on the speech bubble to leave a comment. He selects a white heart and the shamrock emoji. Then he DMs her: You look so happy. Hope it's going well x

He locks his phone and lobs it onto the passenger seat next to him, rubbing his face. Papa Burns comes in and out of view across the street, speaking to someone within the garage that Nik can't see. His final job of the year appears to be an MOT on a silver Mercedes. The owner is an elderly kaka who's wrapped up warm and is quick to smile. He waits on the low brick wall adjacent to the garage, legs crossed, reading the *Gujarat Samachar* while Papa Burns finishes up.

When the Mercedes pulls away, the kaka waving back

to Papa Burns before he turns the corner, Nik fires the ignition and crawls into the garage. He spots Will and Teo creasing with laughter by the office. Nik cuts the engine and gets out to greet them.

'Right, son. Where's this scratch?' Papa Burns emerges from his office a moment later, clapping his hands together. Nik heads back to the entrance of the garage, hoping the boys won't follow. They carry on chatting, ambling towards the car behind him. Shit. Since coming back home, he's been careful to hide the damage from the boys. He stands in front of the scratch now to block them out and gestures vaguely to it, Papa Burns crouching down for a better look. He lets out a low whistle and says: 'Looks like a key for sure,' then pauses, taking in the words below it. Nik's insides freeze. He doesn't have the energy for a conversation about this right now.

'Son,' Papa Burns says, standing up now, his grey eyes on Nik. Nik can't bear to meet them. Teo and Will appear to have caught on and their conversation stops abruptly. 'Son, when did this happen?'

Nik shakes his head, wondering why he's struggling to speak. His legs feel like they're not there any more. His breathing is growing shallower, his fingers turning numb. A slow sense of anguish creeps over him like a stifling fog. Fuck's sake. Not this shit again. He tries to breathe through his nose, slowly, like Dan taught him. He's been ignoring the scratches for the last couple of weeks, trying and succeeding not to think about them. But now the weight of those words seems to crush down on him, trapping him. 'At uni,' he says eventually, his voice thin.

Teo pushes past him, scowling at the thick scar and the

small white words beneath it. 'Yo, broski, man,' he murmurs. 'Why didn't you say?' He runs his fingers across the letters, as though he's trying to wipe them away.

'Mate,' says Will. 'Was it that little runt fucker in your halls? The bald one?'

Everything feels so much brighter than it did a few minutes ago. Nik looks between them and says, 'Yeah, look, I don't want to make a big deal –'

'Nah, fuck this shit, man. Listen, lemme come with you when you drive up, yeah? I'll sort that prick out,' Teo tells him, standing up.

'You need to report that, son,' Papa Burns says gently from behind them. 'It's not on.'

'To who, though, Papa B?' Teo asks.

Papa Burns shakes his head, a hand running over his stubble, his eyes on the words. 'I thought we left this rubbish in the eighties.' He sighs, then says once more: 'It's simply not on.' He looks up at Nik, placing a hand on his shoulder. 'Leave her with me, son. I'll have her sorted by the time you head back to university. Leave her with me.'

The fizzing under Nik's skin only subsides after he spends a long hour in the garden nursing a spliff while playing fetch with Rani. When he comes back in to brew a pan of chai, he messages the boys, trying his best to pull out of their New Year's Eve plans, but they aren't having any of it. Teo shows up twenty minutes later and almost forces him out. He seems particularly watchful as they take the Tube across to east London, his eyes finding Nik's more often than usual, making an effort to include him in the chatter unfolding around them. Alice sits beside Teo, her hand intertwined with his, shooting smiles at Nik, which makes him sure that Teo told her about the scratches. Dan meets them in the queue to the club, already very tipsy, along with a couple of randoms he's brought along. Will and Nik cluster together for most of the night, downing Jägers with what's left of their first-term grants, Nik's mind on Layla as midnight approaches.

A bright red countdown timer ticks above the bar. Nik looks around. Will nods to 'Passionfruit', sipping rum and Coke. Dan drunkenly FaceTimes Melanie from the middle of the dance floor, the boys ignoring the fact that he's spent much of the night flirting with a redhead who works behind the bar. Teo and Alice disappeared ages ago, and the rest of their group are scattered throughout the club. With thirty seconds left, Nik turns to his phone. He sees Layla is online.

23:59 Nik: Hey you. Happy new year x

23.59 Layla: You're a bit early babe. Happy new year x

He pushes through the crowd and heads towards the smoking area. A countdown erupts around him, but he ignores it, his thumbs dancing across his phone screen as he types.

00:00 Nik: What can I say, I'm a punctual guy you know (apart from when I'm meant to be driving down to say goodbye before you go to Dublin kmt soz again) x

00:00 Layla: Loool it's calm

00:00 Nik: When are you back?

00:01 Layla: Next week

00:01 Nik: Can we link? Would be good to see you x

00:01 Layla: Yeah I'll let you know. Have a good night yeah x

00:02 Nik: And you x

Nik's only just slipped his phone back into his jeans when it buzzes again. He fishes it out cautiously, suddenly worried that it might be Paul. He's surprised to find himself hoping, with all of his might, that it's not. He sees his mother's name on the screen instead.

00:02 Mum: Happy new year, Nikhu. I hope this year brings you all the happiness in the world, beta. Love, Mum xxx

00:02 Nik: Happy NY Mum. You too x

Avani looks from her phone to the fireworks sparkling above. As it always does on New Year's Eve, her heart sits heavy in her chest, cloaked in the weight of a sadness that always seems to fall upon her on this day. No matter how many years pass, whenever she sees fireworks bursting across the night sky to welcome in a new year, she's taken back to that beach in Madeira, the whole island lighting up around her, whispered words tickling her neck, a ring sliding onto her finger, a rush of pure joy flowing through every inch of her.

'Avani, you okay?'

Avani turns from the window to see Aarav walking from the kitchen towards her, two glasses of cold champagne in his hands. He smiles and offers her a glass. She hadn't realised that he'd hung back too; she thought she'd left him in the garden with the rest of their friends as they counted down to the new year. She thanks him and looks back to the fireworks, surprised to find that her cheeks are slightly flushed, her thoughts suddenly brighter, the mirage of memories ebbing away.

From the moment she arrived at the cottage on Christmas Eve, Avani knew they were setting Aarav aside for her, as such. Every time Richard mentioned his old university friend, how he'd be joining them for New Year's Eve, what a stand-up chap he was indeed, his eyes would flick tellingly to Avani before hurriedly flashing away again. Her insides would squirm every time this happened. She wondered if she could come up with an excuse to head home early and skip meeting this guy. When Aarav arrived, however, Avani found herself slightly disarmed by how handsome he was, by the warmth he brought into the cottage with him. Just a few inches taller than her, he had thick black hair which he wore long, pushed back, resting just behind his ears. His eyes were the colour of chestnuts, and rosy pink cheeks sat high on his face. He'd shaken her hand and kissed her politely before moving towards Maya, who squealed and pulled him into a tight cuddle. Once he'd greeted everyone, three bottles of champagne emerged from his overnight bag. He placed them on the breakfast table and asked if anyone fancied a Mimosa, a question which was met with a loud cheer.

Later, he washed his hands before offering to help make their packed lunches, which Avani found herself pleasantly surprised by, then rolled his sleeves up and got stuck in. He caught up with Maya's brother and sister-in-law while slicing a block of Cheddar into neat sheets, occasionally popping one into his mouth. On the New Year's Eve hike they embarked upon a few hours later, he'd stop to call out the names of birds or trees, eventually falling into step with Avani, which, by that point, she didn't mind at all. She already knew he was a divorced and childless architect who lived in Watford, but she asked anyway, and the idea of him defrosted further still when he delivered a five-minute soliloquy about his beloved Aussie shepherd, Mahadev, who he'd left back in Watford for the night with his nieces.

The acceptance that she wouldn't be wholly averse to getting to know him better appeared slowly, like dappled sunshine through forest trees, between the steps they took around each other as Slad Valley appeared in the distance. It was in the way that when they got to a kissing gate, he'd open it and wait to let her through first, though when they got to a difficult part of the route that required a bit of a scramble, he wouldn't patronise her by pre-emptively putting his hand out or offering to help. He'd let her get on with it, and only when she asked, which she did once just to see what would happen, would he assist her without a hint of pride.

It had solidified, this feeling, when they all stopped by the lake for sandwiches and he'd pulled out a two-litre flask of chai with eight mugs, which he told the group he'd brewed earlier that morning before setting off. Maya had eyed Avani and raised her eyebrows, a loud *told you he was great* communicated in her stare. Instead of scowling and telling Maya to give over, Avani tucked into her sandwich, smiling slightly.

Now she turns to Aarav in the cottage, tilts her glass towards his, and says: 'Happy new year.'

'Happy new year,' he murmurs, green lights from the

fireworks flashing above. He places a hand lightly on her arm as he reaches down to sweep his lips across her cheek. A single peck, his lips soft like petals. She breathes him in, a joyful eddy of tea leaves and spice and champagne, with possibility nestled quietly in its midst too.

Nik's pleased to see that his mother looks surprisingly well rested when she returns to London. She seems calmer, much more chill, and generally in a better mood than he's seen her in for months. He'd been worried about her coming home; she always draws into herself around New Year's. But her return marks another transition: a fresh term at university, which Nik has been thoroughly dreading.

He leaves it until the very last minute to pack, a thorny shallowness in his chest when he bends down to hug Rani goodbye. His mother appears from the kitchen with a large Waitrose bag as he's putting his coat on. He takes a peek inside to find a stack of home-made thepla wrapped in foil, glistening bateta nu shak, samosas so full they're bursting at the seams, fluffy yellow dhokra cut up like pieces of lego. He gives her a hug, tells her he'll be back to visit soon, then ambles with his bags to the car, which he is still parking out of sight round the corner. Papa Burns had worked over New Year's Day to buff the scratches away and spray over the panels, refusing to accept reimbursement. The worry pulsing through Nik slows when he thinks of this, of the kindness afforded to him off the back of something so cruel. It's like it never happened, he thinks, as he reaches the car, running a hand over the fresh paint, his fingers searching for the trauma they cannot find.

Both Dan and Alice are waiting for him on the steps outside Alice's home when Nik pulls up. As they crawl out of London, Nik's thoughts grow faster and louder, pinging around his mind. Everything seems to have gained momentum somehow – the pile-up of assignments he still hasn't completed, the money he doesn't have that's already been spent on fixing up and insuring the car, the fact that he has to force his way through another two whole terms sharing a flat with that prick Simon. Something that has been collecting inside of him for months, dripping slowly and steadily, is finally threatening to spill over. With each mile that sweeps under the bonnet, the realisation that he simply does not want to go back to university grows clearer, ringing through him. A part of him is screaming, telling him to return to the cosiness and comfort of home. The thought of even just another week in that awful little town fills him with dread. If he hadn't offered to give Dan and Alice a lift, he knows he may well have not gone back at all. He tells himself he'll give it a week; if he's still hating it by the time Friday arrives, he'll cut his losses and return to Harrow for good.

'Should we go straight to the pub?' Alice asks, unbuckling her seat belt and stretching as Nik parks up. She takes the words straight from Nik's mouth: 'I genuinely don't think I'm ready to face another term of this.'

'Hell yes. Mel's already saved us a table,' Dan says.

'I'm game,' Nik yawns. 'What're you up to back there?'

He squints at Alice in the rear-view mirror. She's bent double, rummaging around under his seat.

'Bloody phone is stuck,' she says.

'Lemme see,' Dan says, pulling open her door. Nik steps out of the car and peers over Dan's shoulder. The light from his phone cascades down into the footwell. 'Hold on, it's jammed under something,' Dan mutters, resting on his knees and bending over for a better look.

Nik crouches down too, searching for what's stopping Alice's phone from sliding towards the front of the car. There seems to be a black plastic tray, no thicker than a couple of inches, attached to the bottom of the driver's seat. Nik freezes, anticipation flooding through him. He has never noticed it before, even when he gave the insides a quick hoover back at Papa Burns's; it would be almost impossible to spot unless he knew it was there. Just as Dan shouts 'got it', the tray slides forward with a citrusy waft of air. Alice's thanks are muffled, as is the rest of their chatter, because the contents of the tray are now sitting in Nik's footwell. There, lying among several coppers, four sherbet lemons, an old pack of Wrigley's and a tiny white sock, sits a black Moleskine journal.

Nik reaches for the book and flicks through the pages, neat blue ink greeting him on every sheet right until the last. For a moment he feels a wash of déjà vu, a sense of disconnect, as if he is watching himself from above, because the handwriting is identical to his own. He flicks back to the first page.

Jan 1998
Elliot Harrison – Poetry

'Hey, bud, you coming?' Dan asks from somewhere behind him.

'Yeah,' Nik says, his voice barely there. He stuffs the book into his coat pocket with trembling hands and follows them to the pub, his mind racing.

28

May 1998

Avani's eyes flitted from the wet road in front of her to the clock on her dashboard. The red hands stood alert in a line, almost poignant in their straightness, telling her it was five minutes to five. She had spent the afternoon in a senior leadership meeting which had not gone well. Once it was finally over, she'd decided to cut her losses and head straight home, clocking off earlier than usual. The possibilities of what she could do with this stolen hour flirted with each other in her mind. She could finally finish the oil on canvas she'd started a few weeks earlier, of Buttermere at dawn. She could have a bath, or spend an hour stretching the stiffness from her muscles in the garden, watching the sky turn from yellow to pink to orange. She could sense, from the deep glow already dancing behind the clouds, the promise of a rich sunset tonight.

She crawled past her husband's new BMW, sitting proud in the driveway, in her spot, before parking on the kerb behind it. As the front door clicked shut, she called his name, knowing he would be glad that she was home so early, ready to find him in his running clothes at the kitchen table, hunched over a pile of essays that were waiting to be marked. His routine was like clockwork.

She turned the corner into the kitchen but the table was empty. She peered up the stairs, searching their two-up two-down for him.

When he didn't appear, she busied herself by hoovering the floors of their home while still in her work clothes, running a mop over the mud on the wood where indentations of her husband's soles had left their mark. It was a constant battle, trying to get him to remove his shoes when he came through the door. She'd hoped, now they were in a nicer home, one that they owned, that he'd take a little more care. No such luck. She thought about this as she snacked on a portion of pecan nuts while staring out of the front window, wondering where he was. He was usually home by four.

She thought about calling the school, but only got to the third digit before she put the phone back on the cradle. Instead, she stepped out of her clothes and into the bathtub. Now that she was in the safety of her home, she allowed herself to revisit the mess that was her afternoon; how the new finance director had struggled with her name and spoken over her for a full hour while staring at her chest. When she tried to raise it with her boss, he'd used the word 'oversensitive' and told her she needn't be so insecure. She was hoping for a promotion soon but dealing with senior stakeholders and their stale, archaic ways, was proving more difficult than she'd hoped. Avani had been soaking in the bathtub with these thoughts for all of two minutes when the front door slammed shut so hard that she felt it take the breath from her. She tutted, watching the glass of water on the edge of the tub tremble slightly. She already asked him to click it shut quietly – their neighbours had complained about how the noise aggravated their new husky puppy, whose howls now echoed through their house and pressed into the adjoining walls.

'Avani?'

'Up here,' she called, aiming her voice at the hallway. Elliot's footsteps were careful and light on the stairs, and he appeared a moment later in his running clothes, the warm scent of him filling the small bathroom. She could see from his face that it had been a bad day. He gave her a salty kiss on the cheek and then took a seat on the edge of the bathtub. Avani noticed his trainers were still on. Leaves and mud and who knows what else had collected on their soles during his lap around Harrow. She bit her tongue, reminding herself a little dirt was not the end of the world, and instead said, 'Good run? You were out longer than usual.'

'I couldn't stop.'

'What do you mean?' He placed a hand in the tub and moved it to and fro, his eyes following the ripples curling through the water. Avani's leg was just a few inches below his fingers and she waited for his hand to find her shin. It didn't.

'My head was so full. I couldn't stop. I ran twenty K.'

'Whoa, honey. You must be exhausted. Was school okay?'

He took a breath and held it. She thought how sad he looked. The words he'd spoken a few months before came back to her. She had hugged him tight, his tears dripping onto her bare shoulder, as he told her in a whisper: *I'm just overwhelmed all the time. It won't stop. I don't know what to do.*

She could see the shape of similar thoughts behind his eyes now, glinting despite their darkness. He did not meet her eye when he spoke. A student of his, who was in the care system, was being sent to a new family. They were trying to find a way to keep him in the same school despite the new postcode. Avani watched her husband's face as he told her about how awful the beginning of the boy's life had been, the mess he was born into, how the weight of it all was presenting itself in lacerations across his thighs that were spotted in a PE class. She closed her eyes at the words.

'I can't figure out what more I can do to help,' he said, picking at a nail, the sound of it ripping through her. 'There must be something.'

Her gaze fell to his hands. The skin around his nails was raw. The sight of it made her feel slightly nauseous, a metallic taste growing in her mouth. She didn't know what to say to him, and found herself thinking instead of the painting she still hadn't finished, of the fact that evening was approaching and that she hadn't yet managed to catch up with her own day.

'Maybe if I just –'

She reached out a wet hand and bound her steady fingers around his. 'Ell, honey, we've talked about this a thousand times. You need to find a way to do your job without carrying everyone's pain around with you all day.'

'How is that even possible?'

'I don't know, Ell, maybe don't care so much.'

His gaze hurt. She adjusted what was left of the soft, foamy bubbles, pulling them towards her. 'Sorry,' she said. 'You know what I mean. Just do your job but don't soak it all in to the point where it's affecting you like this.'

'But I'm not built like that,' he said.

'You can't save every single child you come across. It's impossible,' she said, hearing the bite in her voice. 'You already make such a huge difference to their lives by just being someone they can open up to. That's enough. You really need to prioritise your own sanity.'

'You're not getting it.'

He said the words gently, without confrontation, but Avani felt them whip across her exposed skin. She drew her knees to her chest and said, 'Look, this is the whole reason why we went to the Lake District – so you could decompress a bit. You've only been back a couple of weeks and you're already miserable again. Have you been writing your poetry like that therapist said? Maybe you should take some time to –'

'Fuck's sake, Av.' He stood abruptly, making her flinch. She watched as he walked out to the hallway.

Avani grumbled, then rose out of the water, the cold air prickling at her, as though it had heard, as though it was judging her. She wrapped herself in his dressing gown, her wet feet padding over the mud Elliot had invited into their home. She knew they were out of step; she was in work mode, looking for quick solutions, while he just wanted to vent, to air his thoughts out with her, with the delicacy and patience he often afforded her when she needed it. But she no longer had space for the same stories, the same pain, relayed over and over. Not today.

She found him downstairs, sitting on the edge of the sofa. She knelt down to untie the laces on his trainers, then remove them one by one. The water clinging onto Avani's hair collected in drops which ran along her back, making her shiver. She was about to apologise, the words growing against her lips, to tell him she just needed half an hour to herself and she'd be fine again, when he took her hand in his and said: 'I'll try and remember about my shoes.' Then, in the same breath: 'Have you taken a test today?'

She sighed and watched her impatience reflected back in his face. Tugging her hand from his, she stood up and walked into the kitchen. 'I don't need to do one every day, Ell. It's just a constant reminder that something's wrong with me.'

'You don't know it's you,' he said. 'It could be me.'

'Oh, it's definitely me,' she said, drinking water straight from the tap, then splashing more of it around her face. She filled a glass. The heat from her bath was drawing a headache towards her temples. 'I get like six periods a year,' she told him, but he already knew this; she could not count the number of conversations they had had about her fertility since they bought their first home together. Everything else had been ticked off their list, apart from this one final, seemingly unattainable, task. She would never tell him this, but each time she'd been met with crimson over the past year, she'd stare at it, waiting for devastation to flood her, disappointment even. Instead: a moment of ambivalence, quiet relief in its wake. It was not yet time. She was not ready for a child.

Elliot walked into the kitchen behind her and she

felt her shoulders relax slightly, knowing she would, in a moment, feel his arms wrap around her waist, his head stooping to nuzzle her neck, an embrace to break this cycle of sharp words they did not mean. Instead, she turned to see him leaning against the door, running a hand through his hair.

'Maybe you should take it easy with work,' he said, looking out at their garden, where tulips were swaying in the breeze. 'This promotion just isn't worth what they're putting you through. Stress can impact your cycle, right?'

Avani closed her eyes. She wanted to be soaking in the bath, not standing in the kitchen, growing colder, angrier, traipsing round in this endless circle yet again. She could feel the space between them stretch another degree further, like a pocket of icy mist. 'Christ, Elliot. Can we please not do this right now?'

'Avani.' He turned to face her. 'Do you want a child with me? Do you actually?'

She groaned and lifted the glass of water to her temple, feeling the coolness of it against her skin. 'Yes, Elliot. I want a baby with you. But I'm trying really hard for this promotion, and you're struggling with your head right now, and I think if it's not happening then let's not force it. Let's just take it steady and take the pressure off. It's obviously not meant for us right now.' Silence. 'I can't keep constantly reassuring you, it's exhausting.'

'Understood,' he said, but something had moved behind his eyes, she had seen it. She had never heard him say that word before. It didn't sound like a something that belonged in his vocabulary. It was so curt. So cold. So distant. Then: 'Do you mind if I have a quick shower?'

'Can't you wait until I'm done?'

'I need to get back to school. Parents' evening.'

'Honestly,' Avani muttered, irritation rising in her again. 'Go, then.'

Avani propped herself up on the kitchen worktop while her husband washed the day away. She was wrong about the sunset. The sky folded to grey unceremoniously, the sun moving behind a blanket of clouds, like it couldn't be bothered to say goodbye. She watched it nonetheless, dipping dried, sticky prunes into a jar of smooth peanut butter before popping them into her mouth whole. Something had gone very wrong in the last six months. They had everything, the two of them, yet they were moving to different beats, as if the rhythm of their hearts had fallen out of sync.

She'd noticed an edge to her husband over the last few months, ever since the social worker confirmed that they had no record of his lost little brother, or anyone who they thought could plausibly be him. It was the second time they'd tried and failed to find him. She had felt Elliot's hand growing firmer in hers, then limp, as if the hope was seeping from him, as the social worker told them: *He wasn't registered within six weeks of his birth, as legally required by his parents. So there's no paper trail, unfortunately, no follow-through from foundling to adopted child. In fact, none of the foundlings registered in the months that followed match his description. Even if he was adopted, he's not yet eighteen, so it would be incredibly difficult to instigate contact, especially without his birth parents leading the search. Your best bet is to wait. To see if he searches for you once he comes of age.*

A few days later, Avani had asked Elliot about his parents, if writing to them was an option. She'd already drafted a carefully worded letter explaining they wouldn't cause any trouble, they wouldn't go to the authorities, they just wanted to know where little Nick had been left, that was all. Elliot's eyes had flicked silently over her words. She'd asked him if he knew where his parents lived, but he'd sighed, pushing the letter back into her hands: *I have no idea, Av. It took everything I had to leave them. I couldn't bear to see them, to speak to them again.*

Well, what else could we do?

I honestly don't know.

We could save for a private search.

What's the point? He got to his feet, making her flinch. *He's dead, Avani. He's dead. Can't you see? He wasn't a foundling and he wasn't given up for adoption. We'd have found him by now if he was. He's gone. And it's better he is, than for him to ever know the hate he was born into.*

Elliot. Don't say that. Don't say those things.

The pain of this finality revealed itself in small ways; in silences that grew deeper, in the weight that was dropping off him, in the way that, when she'd stir in the night for the bathroom, she'd hear the sound of Leonard Cohen playing in their lounge. She'd pad downstairs to find her husband on his own, staring into nothing, trapped by the weight of his own thoughts. When she'd wake to silence, she'd turn to find him lying next to her, his gaze fixed on the ceiling, as if watching his thoughts grow into tangles before his eyes. But alongside him, Avani was growing tired too, unable to manage her own lot, tired of holding back how the old boys' club at work was making her feel, tired of casting it all aside and cracking on, because she did not want to bring her husband down further.

She was taught to simply work twice as hard, to adjust, to crack on. She had watched her parents' generation do the same, she knew the rules; to achieve, to be humble, to never yield to sentimentality or emotion, to never complain, even in the face of hardship. She understood she must demonstrate her malleability, her affability, her capability, and to be grateful, so incredibly grateful. She would do this, all of this, always, and one day, maybe they would come to respect her, just a little. These were the rules and she'd followed all of them; spending years biting her tongue, turning a blind eye, accepting more than she could reasonably manage. She was now just two steps away from Chief Finance Officer and convinced herself that if she just held everything together for a little longer, she'd make it. So she had lied, when her husband asked if she'd taken a test recently; she hadn't taken a pregnancy test for weeks because she simply wasn't ready for even the thought of a child. What she wanted was that promotion and the pay rise which would mean they could take another big chunk out of their mortgage each month, the pay rise that might even allow them to, one day, when they found the strength, start a third, fresh search for his lost little brother, privately this time.

When all the prunes were gone, she headed back upstairs to fill the tub again. Pink Floyd's 'Wish You Were Here' seeped gently from the record player. She found her husband standing in the hall, rubbing a towel through his hair. He was naked, his skin slightly pink from the heat of the shower. Avani ran her hand along his torso as she passed him. That moment would stay with her, she would always hold it tight, the warmth she'd felt under his skin. It would return to her in the days, months, years, that unfold after this one, like an orchid blooming and blooming and blooming from a single seed.

She immersed herself back into the steaming tub ten minutes later, breathing deep, doing her best to relax. She was enjoying the Pink Floyd vinyl and the way their psychedelic sound drew colourful shapes behind her eyes, so she tutted when her husband changed the album over to Patricia Kaas's *Je Te Dis Vous*. It was a gift from that French teacher he worked with. Elliot seemed to love it, but Avani wasn't as fond. The first song on the album made Avani think of a nursery rhyme, or a children's lullaby, of the child they still did not have, of the one they had failed to find.

She thought about what would make her feel better, and the answer came to her almost immediately: finishing that oil on canvas she hadn't had the time to work on for weeks. She was far away, wrapped up in how she could build up the texture of Fleetwith Pike behind the lake, her mind full of Prussian blue and burnt sienna and viridian green, when there was a careful knock on the bathroom door. She took a deep breath, forcing the annoyance out of her voice, as she called: 'What now?'

'Av, honey, your car is blocking me in.'

She gritted her teeth. The image of the BMW in the driveway pressed against the dark of her eyelids. The one they'd rowed at length about when he'd surprised her with it, the one he'd insured with the money they'd saved to replace their mouldy roof, the one that absolutely inhaled fuel. That bloody car.

'Elliot, I'm trying my very best not to kick off. If you knew you needed to head out again tonight why didn't you park on the street?'

'Where are your keys?' His voice was broken when it reached her, as if he had given up. 'I can move it.'

'Check my handbag.'

'I have, Av, they're not in there.'

Silence. Avani closed her eyes.

'It's okay, sweetheart,' he said. She imagined his temple tilting lightly against the door as he spoke, his fingers on the handle. 'I'll walk.'

29

January 2018

Nik sits in a corner of the bar at Goldsmiths, sipping a pint of beer. Condensation drips from the windows. A group of students sprawled across the other end of the table exclaim loudly and often, one of them punctuating their hollering by thumping a large hand on the wood. Nik winces every time the table moves under him, clenching his jaw. A game of pool has just started nearby, a girl with a northern accent explaining the rules to her friends. Nik checks his phone for the time, then looks up to see Layla walking in, dressed in a dark puffer jacket. Her hair spills out from under a lilac beanie hat. She blows into her hands as she circles the bar, looking for Nik.

'Hey, you,' she says soberly, once she finds him.

Fuck, Nik thinks, *it's bad.*

'Sorry I'm late, class overran. Did you find it all right?' she asks.

'Yeah.'

'Is this for me?' She points to the pint of cider resting next to him.

He nods.

'Ah, thanks, babe.' She removes her coat and just the scent of her is like a hug. A pair of Beats rest around her collarbone, a bass line slapping through them.

Layla takes the black Moleskine journal out of her bag, holding it in her hands for a moment, before resting it on the table in front of him. When Nik reaches for it, he feels the warmth of her skin lingering on the leather.

He had tried his very best to decipher what the poems meant, using what he could remember from his A level in English, trying to look at the words, then the spaces between them, what was left in the unsaid. He read every one of the eighteen poems his father had drafted in the months leading up to his death, over and over again, spending so long with the journal in his hands that when he finally parted with it to give it to Layla, he'd been surprised that the soft cover hadn't melted and settled into the spaces between his fingers.

'Nikhil,' she says. 'They're really beautiful' – he can feel her leading up to it, trying to find the gentlest way in – 'but you were definitely right. They do get darker and darker.'

'Yeah, I'd figured that one out myself.'

There's a moment of silence. She glares at him.

'Sorry.'

'Do you want my help or not?'

'I do. I do. My bad, man.'

She opens the book and flicks through it carefully. 'There's this one, actually, near the end.' When she finds the page she's looking for, she caresses it with her hand, as if trying to push out a crease. Nik stares down at the poem that's tucked itself into his mind like an unruly weed, refusing to be uprooted. He's dreamt about it every night since he found the journal. He focuses on the words in front of him, in the spiky hand that could be his own.

The final stanza stands out to him, almost as if it is rising from the page.

To be released simply by putting
One foot –
In front –
Of the other –
To walk blind
To let fate play her part.

'It obviously, like, could tie in with what you said about his death,' Layla says, 'but that's just one interpretation,' she adds quickly, when Nik runs both his hands through his hair and looks down at his chest. Layla puts her arm across his back and her hand finds his shoulder. 'It could be about walking, like, down the aisle or something, or like, it could just be about faith, you know, about just trusting as you move into the next stage of life –'

He zones out and downs his pint, which makes the shallowness in his chest worse. The bar seems to have grown much louder, the colours of the walls brighter, the air muggier. His hands go numb. He wants to run. Against the black of his mind, he sees his father closing his eyes, taking a step onto the road in front of him. For a moment, Nik is left with nothing, but for the irrefutable urge to cry.

Layla's voice comes back into focus: 'There's loads in here about darkness and loneliness and pain, but also moments of light. You want to read this poem by my boy Keats.' Nik looks up at her. 'It's peng. About the transience and interconnectedness of both joy and sadness –'

'Layla, man. I really don't care.'

Her lips press into a hard line. 'I swear down if you keep snapping –'

'Nah, I'm sorry.' He reaches for her gaze. She looks away. 'I'm being a dick. I'm sorry.'

The hand that's still resting on his shoulder moves back and forth slightly, creating warmth in the layers under his coat.

'I don't know how to process this, man,' he mutters.

'It's a lot.' There's a gentleness, a kindness, in her voice that he knows he does not deserve. 'Nikhil . . . you know I'm here, yeah? I'm always here.'

Nik turns his face from her so she doesn't see the tears her words have summoned. She rarely says his name, but when she does it's always Nikhil – never Nik – as though she is there for all of him. He thinks back to their first day at college: a free period, September sunshine falling through the canteen windows, Bashment playing from a mini speaker someone had placed on a nearby table, Nik and Layla catching each other's gaze across a group of mutual friends, until he'd cut across to her, introduced himself as Nik. She'd leaned over to inspect the ID card hanging from his lanyard, the sweet scent of her dancing towards him, her dark eyes flashing back to his as she said: *Yeah, I'm not calling you that. It's Nikhil.*

Now, he clears his throat and says: 'Tell me again about Dublin. I was thinking of you, you know, over Christmas.'

'It was good, babe,' is all she offers, both now and the first time he asked her. He can tell by the lightness in her voice that it was better than good, that perhaps she managed to fix whatever her father broke in her when he left all those years ago. Nik is grateful to her for holding this back for now.

She takes a sip of cider. 'I forgot to say, but I saw your mum just before I went to Ireland,' she tells him, a finger following a line of condensation down her pint glass.

'What? Where?'

'Some art gallery just up the road.'

'What, in these ends? Who was she with?'

'Dunno.' She shrugs. 'Some old white dude.'

Surely not, Nik thinks. Surely not Paul.

'She looked really nice.'

'Like she was on a date?'

'Maybe. Dude was fully punching if so.'

Nik tuts and scratches his neck.

'Did you see the other bit in there by the way?' Layla asks, tapping a finger on the journal. Her nails are bitten and what's left is painted turquoise.

Nik knows exactly what she's talking about and flicks to the very last page. 'About Nick with a c?'

Her eyes narrow slightly. 'Yeah. Who is that?'

Nik shakes his head and looks down to the list scratched into the back cover. It reads:

1. For Av
2. For the children at school
3. For squash on Thursdays with Gopal and the boys

4. To watch Rajvi and the girls grow up
5. To have my own children, two boys and a girl
6. The possibility of, one day, finding little Nick

'Nick with a c,' he repeats. 'Who is that, man?' His hand runs over the words as he thinks.

'What do you think this list is?' Layla murmurs, tilting her head to read it again. Her expression tenses then clears, almost as though she's found the answer to her own question. She blinks. Before Nik has a chance to turn back to the page, she closes the journal and puts her hands over it, like she's hiding something. 'Why don't you come back to mine for a bit? I can make us some dinner.'

'I'd really like that,' Nik says, tired suddenly, wishing he could. He sighs, rubbing his face. 'How about tomorrow night? I need to get to the bottom of this first.'

Nik crunches through a packet of crisps, not tasting anything. His eyes are sore and red. He squints as he watches lorries shooting up the M1. He hasn't looked at his phone – which has been resting in his jacket pocket, on silent – since leaving Layla's university several hours ago. He has eighteen missed calls and a number of messages.

21:36 Alice: Nik. Open the door

21:49 Alice: Where the actual fuck are you?

21:52 Alice: I will literally break this door.

22:11 Dan: Bud, you okay? Alice says we should call security soon to check if you're in your room but your car isn't here so I'm assuming you've gone back to Lon—

Nik scrolls past.

22:18 Teo: Oi Nik man. Alice says she hasn't seen you for a couple of days. Where you at fam?

22:40 Rajvi: Hey broski. That nutter Teo keeps sending me messages on Snap asking if you're at ours?? He's proper begging it lol. You okay yeah?

23:07 Will: Nik man, you alright yeh? I know stuff is proper shit right now, but you're not alone, mate. Call us, yeh?

23:24 Layla: Babe. Call me x

He calls Dan, who picks up on the first ring. 'Buddy. You okay?'

'Hey, man.' He's surprised by how quiet his voice is. He slumps against the headrest. 'I'm totally fine.'

'Thank fuck. We haven't seen you since yesterday morning, bud, so Alice was freaking out. Ah hold on, she wants to –'

Nik can hear Alice snatching the phone from Dan's hand. 'You scared the shit out of me, Nik. You just disappeared into thin air. Where the hell are you?'

Nik's eyes sting with tiredness. He closes them. 'London.'

'No you're not, Teo said he hasn't seen you since New Year's.'

'I don't really want to do this right now, Alice, all right? I'm totally fine.'

She sighs. 'What's going on with you, Nik? I know you were struggling before Christmas but it's like you've come back broken.' He thinks of the evening they spent in the pub the night he drove back to university, just after he'd found the journal, feeling so much like he was watching them from the other side of a glass wall. He knows he's been like a zombie since, ignoring their messages, pulling the duvet over his head when they knock on his door. He didn't think they'd notice he wasn't in his room.

'I'm fine, stop worrying about me.'

'Nik, is it because of me and Teo? I don't want –'

'Nah, it's not that, man. Honestly.' The version of him that was so consumed by all of that nonsense feels like a boy. It all seems so insignificant compared to the weight of the knowledge he now holds.

'Look . . . I know you've been really down recently, but –'

'Alice, my phone's about to die, man.'

She doesn't respond to this, so Nik assumes she's got the message. But then she adds, 'You need to speak to someone, Nik.'

'Piss off,' he says, scowling.

'Talking therapy is –'

'– a white woman luxury, man. I'm brown, we just block that shit out and crack on.'

'Yeah, that really seems to be doing the trick, doesn't it?'

Nik rubs his eyes. It's a fair point. He can hear Dan speaking in the background, his voice low. There's a muffled noise, followed by Dan's voice: 'Buddy. We're just glad you're all right. The car was gone and we couldn't find you or get through to you and we thought you'd been in an accident or something. We'll message your London mates to let them know, yeah?'

'Sorry, man. Yeah, that would help me out, my battery's on like three per cent.'

'When are you back?'

Nik thinks about this and his mouth dries up. He switches the phone to his other ear. 'Mate. I dunno.'

'Listen,' Dan says, his voice growing gentler still. 'I know last term was a pile of shit, but you can like . . . take some time off or switch courses, maybe.'

'Yeah, maybe,' Nik tells him. He is hungry and exhausted and has no space to think about university.

'Alice and I are back in London this weekend,' Dan says. 'We'll come and see you, bud.'

'Yeah,' Nik says. 'Yeah, sounds good.'

Nik downs a can of Coke in one go once he's off the phone. The cold seems to momentarily numb the jitters in his chest, but then they rise once more with such force that he finds himself shivering. His phone lights up and he looks down to see Layla's name silently filling the screen. He feels, for a moment, overwhelmed to the point of tears.

'Hello,' he says.

'Babe, you okay, yeah?' Her words are patient, calm, as if she's just seen him buckle on the street but doesn't want to draw too much attention to it. Somewhere behind her, music plays, a voice saying it'll trade broken wings. She doesn't turn it down, doesn't raise her voice to stop it from drowning against the melody swaying around her. Nik realises, then, that in his mind the shape of her is synonymous with song. She is always humming, singing, whistling, music playing from a loose headphone hanging against her collarbone. It is forever around her.

'Yeah, sorry, my uni lot were on a mad one thinking I'd been run over or something.'

In the moment that follows he hears what she does.

'Have you reached yet?'

'Nah. I'm tired . . . I pulled into a service station.'

'It's late,' she says. 'It's almost midnight.'

He blinks sleepily, watching cars shooting past.

'I would have come with you,' she tells him. Her words sit flush against others, others that themselves are tucked between strings and horns and, when the bass falls, a sound Nik can only describe as sunshine. He recognises the song playing now: Beyoncé's 'All Night'.

He clears his throat to speak, but he knows his voice will betray him. The silence between them is comfortable; there's a quality to it that reminds him of her warm palms against his skin, her fingers trailing along his back.

'Do what you need to do, then come straight back to London,' Layla says, as if this thought only just occurred to her, as if it's the simplest thing in the world. 'Just write off this year and start somewhere new in September.'

Nik closes his eyes, breathing in her voice.

'I'm going to call Will and Teo to let them know you're all good, yeah?' she says. 'Bell me in the morning.'

'I will,' Nik whispers.

He puts the phone down and rubs his face. Time has stretched and skewed itself, and the last twenty-four hours feel more like a week. He is embarrassed that his friends were so worried about him, annoyed that he's made such a mess of university and has fallen apart this way. He thinks about Layla telling him to move back as he pulls out of the service station and drives up the M1. It would be the easy route. But maybe that's what he needs right now, a voice tells him. Maybe a clean break is the answer out of this fog. The other option – going back to university, actually completing the assignments that were due weeks ago and getting through the next three years – feels so impossible that the thought of it brings with it the sensation of darkness closing over him.

He takes the next exit and crawls towards the lights of the city. He can think about university tomorrow. First, he needs to find the courage to close a more pressing chapter. He needs to figure out exactly what happened to his father. And there is only one person left who might tell him, one last possibility.

30

June 1998

On the afternoon that her mother breathed her last, Avani sat in her car for a full hour after her father called with the news. She turned off the radio and closed her eyes, recalling the tremble in his voice, the silence that followed – where she was sure tears dripped from his chin onto the receiver – doing her utmost to respond to this news, to meet him in his grief. Her mother was dead. She expected the depth of this loss to hit her, she braced herself for it, ready to wince. But it did not come. Five minutes grew to fifty.

It seemed she had nothing left in her since Elliot's death five weeks prior; after over a month of not being able to move, of pillows and bedding growing salty with her tears, this news had finally stopped the flow. Until her mother's death, she would open her eyes each day and be met with a short, soft moment that she would mistake for peace. Then the weight of her thoughts would catch up with her, anchoring her to bed. She would realise this particular brand of silence was not peace, it was emptiness.

After her father's phone call, the only thing she felt was a chilling stillness, as though she was stuck in the middle of a calm sea. There was no tide. There were no waves. The water only came to her hips. Although there was no immediate danger, there was also no respite; she could not see land. She simply existed, waiting for something a quiet part of her knew was coming, something she couldn't yet see the shape of.

She recalled how her mother had asked her to come to the hospital just the previous evening. When Avani made an excuse and called to speak to her instead of visiting, she'd heard her mother in the background, asking Chand, who held the phone: *Oli kya che?*

Avani thought of how she'd have translated it for Elliot: 'Where's *that one*'. Not 'my daughter'. Not 'Avani'. *Oli. That one.* The word was a jab, pushing Avani out of her mother's family of three.

Avani sat with these thoughts in the privacy of her car, accepting defeat when the tears she summoned did not come, eventually walking back into the office in a daze.

'Charles.' She knocked on her boss's door. He pointed to the empty chair opposite him without a glance up.

'I think I need some more time off, please,' she said, her mouth dry. She smoothed her hands over her skirt as she sat down. The material tugged angrily around her stomach and she couldn't understand how she had possibly put on weight in the last month, despite barely eating, despite waking up every day ripped apart by an emptiness so deep it was making her physically sick.

'Avani.' He sighed her name. She looked up and regretted it immediately. He'd removed his glasses. There was so much pity. She did not want pity.

'Listen, we're delighted to have you back so soon, but I think this is a good decision. A month simply isn't enough. I'll sign you off for another. Let's touch base again in –'

Avani zoned out, tasting the unspoken words resting against her tongue: *Actually, my mother just died.* She swallowed them down, nodding as her boss thumped out an email to HR.

'Hurry along,' he said, pointing at the door. 'Just head straight home and rest up.'

Avani's brow furrowed slightly at this comment, as if he thought she had a particularly nasty bout of flu. She opened her mouth, then decided against it, instead gathering up her belongings and leaving before her colleagues could ask where she was going.

Three days later, on the eve of her mother's cremation, she sat in her old bedroom, leaning against the wall, looking at the window behind her bed, her eyes taking in the vacant space where Elliot would appear each morning for chai.

The sound of someone on the stairs made her turn. The door inched open a sliver. Chand looked surprised to find her on the floor, but then crossed his legs and sank into the carpet opposite her. His hair was thinning and there was a fullness to his stomach that had grown steadily in the months after his thirtieth birthday. An open suitcase lay on the carpet between them, filled with a sea of white cotton.

Their eyes met. For a moment, it was like they were teenagers again. She could not recall the last time they were alone, the last time he didn't have his toddler daughters climbing his legs or his wife by his side. A crack had appeared between brother and sister over the last few years, eventually splitting them clean in two. The fissures were small at first. She noticed he began to cut her off when she spoke, that he had a sudden lack of patience with her open-mindedness, that his language became peppered with phrases such as 'rather displeasing', 'how ghastly' and 'I do suppose', which made Avani think not of her brother, but of all the people behind him, the people he surrounded himself with, who, until now, he'd always watched from the outside. His curiosity and appetite for life had succumbed to an apathy so dry it bordered on hostility.

Avani had tried her best to convince herself that this was simply some sort of phase or performance brought about by fatherhood and corporate climbing, and that the laid-back brother of her childhood would knock on her door again one day in a faded band T-shirt and cut-off shorts, and say, 'I'm done being a boring bugger. Let's go to the pub.' But it never happened, and the space growing between them had been accentuated further when he moved up to Leicester last summer, and then again in the weeks since Elliot's death. He'd barely looked her in the eye since her husband died, and a devastated part of her whispered that perhaps he blamed her.

The only time she saw a flicker of the old Chand was when Maya was around. Not in him, but in her; despite everything, Maya's smile for him was still as warm as it had been when they were kids. She, being one step removed, seemed to still find the Chand of their childhood, the Chand Avani had adored, in the face of the balding, miserable man Avani could no longer recognise.

Chand and Maya were the only people Avani had been able to trust with the truth. They'd grown up with Elliot.

They saw more of him than anyone else had, apart from her. Instead of shock, horror, anguish – any of these reactions would have done – they each told her, with utter confidence, as if they themselves had been there, that she was wrong, that perhaps this was a coping mechanism. It was her mind trying to apply a level of control, and therefore clarity, to the freak accident that claimed her husband's life. Instead of taking comfort in this, Avani had been filled with silent frustration. Together, they had made her feel even more alone. They just wanted to believe what was convenient, she told herself. They did not know him like she did. They did not know what it had felt like to watch the life threaten to leave his body once before, wet and limp, its weight almost pulling her with it. She had ignored their calls thereafter, instead cocooning herself in the comfort of bed, shutting out the pity she did not deserve.

'Are the girls asleep?' Avani was the first to break the silence.

'Rukmani's just tucked them in.'

'How's Puppa doing?'

His gaze found hers, puffy and red. He shook his head. 'He's never lived alone. I'm going to speak to work again about that transfer back to London.'

'There's no need,' Avani said. 'I'm just up the road.'

Chand didn't respond. He tilted his head back to rest it on the edge of Avani's bed and closed his eyes. She could see a patch under his neck which remained smooth despite dark flecks of three-day stubble growing fiercely around it. It felt as though staring at this little circle of smooth skin was some form of trespassing, that he would be embarrassed if he knew it were there, but Avani could not look away.

'And how are you?' The words were light on his breath.

'Chand,' Avani said, watching him, 'I haven't cried.' It flew from her lips, smooth, as if it had been pulled out of her by a string.

He looked at her and she could see him flicking through the last few days as if they were a catalogue of photos, searching for a reason to contradict her.

'You miss her though, don't you?' he asked, a warning in his voice.

She opened her mouth but words did not come. She wanted to tell him how disgusted she was with herself for failing to respond to her mother's death. Instead, she felt relief – as though a thorn had been plucked from her heart – and she hated herself for it. Avani opened her mouth, then closed it again and watched the swaying branches of the eucalyptus tree outside her window. 'Of course,' she said finally, hoping it was true. 'I'm just numb. Maybe I'm not registering it or something.'

'Don't give yourself too much of a hard time, ben,' he said. She hated him calling her this; it made her feel old. He licked his lips, and Avani could sense him searching for a way to go on. 'I know you and Mumma had a difficult relationship, and I suppose sometimes regrets can make one feel rather . . .' He trailed off when he caught Avani's expression.

'Regret? On my part?'

Chand sighed. 'Maybe that's not the right word. I just meant that, perhaps, now you're an adult, you can see that you were both just as culpable as one another.'

'Have you lost the bloody plot? She was *cruel,* Chand.'

'You exaggerate,' he said, shaking his head. 'The two of you simply didn't see eye to eye. You were too similar.'

She looked up at him, but could not find her brother in the face of this cold, pompous stranger, so utterly divorced from reality. 'I'm *nothing* like her.'

'I think you're rather more alike than you think, ben.'

'You think I'd lock one of your girls in their room all day?'

'What're you on about?'

She tucked her hair behind her ears and stuttered: 'The day you came back to visit and she'd – I was locked in my room – the Ganapati puja . . .'

Confusion rippled across his face. Then, it cleared and he said: 'You had a headache.'

His words suffocated her; the pain of that day almost overshadowed by this fresh reminder that her voice held no weight. It was easier for her brother to believe a lie, one so palatable it usurped the truth.

A deep loneliness washed over her. She shook her head, a stinging behind her eyes. This was a conversation she would have taken to Elliot – depositing it on their kitchen table, dissecting it over a glass of wine and sharing the shock of how unfair this was. But she no longer had anyone to take this to, no one to sense check it with. Tears fell onto her lap.

'What the fuck happened to you?' Her voice was thick with emotion. She looked straight at him, her heart pleading. Where was her loving, kind, generous brother? The one who always had her back, who'd been her first best friend, before Maya and then Elliot came along. They'd once been like pillars, the four of them, and she couldn't bear to think of how now it was only Maya that was left standing beside her. She swallowed her pride and searched for an explanation, a way to understand. 'You know I adore Rukmani and the girls, but I just don't recognise you any more.'

'I know you think I've turned into a bore, Avani, but one of us had to grow up,' Chand said, his voice dry.

'What does that mean?'

'We couldn't both break Mumma's heart. It would have killed her. I married Rukmani so you could have Elliot. I veered from my own path so you could follow yours.'

He delivered the words plainly, but the force of them cut through her. It was as though he were talking about holiday destinations or wedding venues or dinner reservations instead of love, of marriage, of life. It couldn't be true. It couldn't have been that simple for him. She thought of Poppy, of how besotted he'd been, of how he'd cut things off just as Avani expected him to propose, how he'd got engaged to Rukmani within months. The weight of his words sank the hope in her, telling her that what she feared most was true; that she alone was the source of his resentment.

'It's okay, ben,' he said, reaching out to put a hand on her shoulder. Again, he had misunderstood her silence. 'Look, we've all said and done things we regret. Mumma would have forgiven you.' His grip tightened.

She did not have the strength to brush him away.

31

January 2018

Nik is still half asleep, his neck incredibly sore, when he becomes aware of a balmy slice of sun reaching down towards him, caressing his face like the curl of a hand. He has been dreaming of his grandfather and nestles into the small ray of warmth, searching once more for sleep. Then the sound of nails tapping on glass tugs him away. He wonders if this is Alice again, pestering him to get up for seminars. But something is wrong; there is no duvet over him, no pillow under his head. Despite that yellow sliver of comfort, the air around him sits thin and frosty, the sort that lingers in old derelict buildings, with a bite in it that suggests it has never known the touch of central heating. He opens his eyes to see Rukmani pressing her fingers against the window next to him, her brow full of worry.

'Nikhil, beta,' she says, as he pushes the car door open. 'Are you okay?'

'Hey, Mami,' he says, stretching. His body is stiff from the draught that laced its way around his limbs and towards his torso during the night. He notices puffs of white leaving his mouth when he breathes. The street he parked up on in the small hours is now covered in a blanket of ice. The sky is bright, the day cold.

'Beta, what're you doing here?' she asks, looking from him to the car. She seems to be on her way to the surgery; she clutches a silver flask and is dressed in a pencil skirt, heels and a long black coat. 'You didn't sleep out here all night, did you?'

'I didn't want to disturb you.'

'Don't be silly. You're always welcome, beta. Was it Rajvi you're after? She's gone back to university for the new term.'

Nik rubs his eyes. 'Chand.'

Her forehead creases. 'Is your mum okay?'

'Yeah,' Nik says, though he actually hasn't checked in on her since he found the journal.

'Come in.' She turns towards the house. 'I just brewed a pan of chai.'

'Honestly, Mami. I don't want to hold you up.'

She waves his reticence away and strides back to the house. Gravel crunches under their feet as they approach and the noise is amplified against the silence of the street. There is movement by the front bay window; a large hand flails around the net curtains and Chand appears, buttoning his collar. He stares sternly past Nik and at the Beemer parked outside, his mouth parting. When Rukmani pushes the front door open and Chand walks into the hallway, they simply watch each other. Nik knows what his uncle must be thinking: *Here he is, he's finally got some girl pregnant or has the police after him, just as I expected, crawling to the patriarch for atonement.*

'No,' Nik says, aloud. His cheeks grow hot as he hears the word back.

'What?' Chand spits, screwing up his face, looking from

Rukmani to Nik. 'What on earth is going on? Where's your mother? What are you doing with that car?'

'Tell me how he died,' Nik says. 'I need to know.'

The hardness in his uncle's face falls away. A dove begins to coo from the bare cherry blossom tree on the driveway. Nik can feel the warmth of the house spilling out and washing onto his chest. A winter chill presses against his back.

'Chalo, come inside,' Chand mutters eventually. He nods at Rukmani as if to say *I'll deal with this*. She gives Nik's shoulder a light pat, then leaves them.

Nik steps into the hallway, where the carpet is soft and deep red, the walls lined with Rajput paintings and textiles of Hindu deities. He realises that he hasn't been back here since he was sixteen, when he and his uncle got into a heated discussion about *To Pimp a Butterfly* that resulted in Chand telling Nik to *turn off this nonsense shouting*. Rajvi had, later that evening, driven Nik back to London, several days earlier than planned. Now Chand motions for Nik to go through to the lounge as he lifts his phone to his ear. This was such a stupid idea, Nik thinks, sinking into a chair, the dumbass is probably calling his mother.

He hears Chand through the hallway: 'Hello. Yes, it's me. I'm going to be late, not sure quite how long. Reschedule my morning meetings, will you?'

Nik exhales and slumps deeper into the chair, his hands still in his pockets. Across the room, an antique clock ticks, punctuating the silence. Chand reappears a moment later to hand him a rubbery hot-water bottle. He places a steel tray on the table in front of Nik, holding a cup of chai and three small bowls of naasto. Nik is too distraught for any of it, even the chai.

'Chalo. What's happened?' Chand asks, hitching his chair under the mahogany dining table with short puffs. Nik's gaze is set just above his uncle's left ear, on graduation portraits of the twins, Sarita and Priya. When Rajvi finally graduates from medical school this summer, he'll have the complete set.

'You heard me,' Nik says, focusing on his uncle again. 'Mum won't talk to me about it. I need to know what happened. Everything.'

Chand closes his eyes and rests a thumb in the space between them. 'I always thought Puppa would be the one having this conversation with you,' he murmurs, as if to himself. Nik thinks of his grandfather, of the whisper that day in hospital: *Chand will be able to tell you more than I can.*

'Tell me,' Nik says.

'There is nothing to tell.' He presses a carefully folded handkerchief against his forehead, where beads of sweat are collecting. 'It was a hit-and-run. It was an accident.'

Nik shakes his head. 'There's more. Does my mum believe he walked out onto that road on purpose?'

Chand rests his head in his hands, as if defeated. He takes a deep breath, then rubs his forehead. His words are slightly muffled when he says: 'Look, beta –' the word takes Nik by surprise, he can't remember the last time his uncle called him this – 'when they arrested the . . . deplorable . . . who ran your father over, his defence was that Elliot deliberately stepped out onto the road.'

Nik sits very still, not daring to move. He is sure he is moments from being sick.

'It was a load of utter nonsense, of course. The driver was way over the legal limit, Nikhil. He'd been drinking.'

Nik clenches his jaw, biting back emotion. He is cold to the bone and his vision begins to blur, his eyes filling with tears. He whispers: 'What do you think happened?' He is surprised to find that this matters to him.

'Doesn't make a difference.'

'Of course it does. You were friends. You knew him. Tell me.'

'You know what I think, Nikhil.'

Nik leans back in his chair, crosses his arms, and watches Chand closely. Neither speaks for a while. Instinct tells Nik to wait, to let Chand come to him. The sound of the ticking clock on the mantel seems suddenly overwhelming. When Chand eventually meets his gaze, Nik senses that his uncle sees a man sitting in front of him, an equal, not a child.

'I know this may sound unlikely –' Chand pauses, and Nik thinks he can see emotion tugging at his face – 'but you're right, we were good friends, your father and I. Very good friends. He grew up just a few streets down from us.' He points out of the window as if they are in Harrow. 'He was so wonderful with the girls. Would write them a poem every year for their birthdays. Your mother would paint a canvas to go with it. They were like a little double act. Rajvi absolutely adored him.' He says this without a trace of resentment. Nik thinks he can even hear pride tucked in the spaces between his uncle's words. 'Has your mother told you much about his family?'

Nik shakes his head. He tried hard, over the years, asking after the uncles, aunts, cousins on his father's side, and especially after his 'other grandparents' – his friends all seemed to have four yet Nik had just the one. The response had always been 'there's no one' then a change in topic when his mother was in a good mood and a hostile silence when she was not, one that made it very clear that he was trespassing.

'He was an only child, beta, and he didn't have a good relationship at all with his parents. To say they were neglectful would be a gross understatement. When he was seventeen or so, there was some sort of physical altercation involving a flight of stairs. His father was involved. Elliot ended up in hospital.'

Nik finds he is holding in a breath, too scared to breathe, to move, to interrupt his uncle in any way.

'It was touch and go. When he recovered, he cut ties with them for good. Stayed with friends, even with me for a few weeks. He did well, beta; he managed to finish his A levels and went on to university with your mother and Maya Masi. He got better, then, he rather grew into himself. He was so tall, like you –' brightness is returning to Chand's face now, there is the beginning of a smile growing around his lips – 'and had this huge personality when he felt safe and came out of his shell. His humour was so dry and quick and . . . God, nobody could make me laugh like he did.'

There is nothing then, but for the resolute ticking of the clock. Their eyes meet for a moment before flashing away.

When Chand speaks again, his voice is lower, his words careful. 'But then, other times, there would be this part of him that was constantly in a state of apology, as if he believed he was taking up space, as if he felt safest when he went unnoticed.'

Sadness grips Nik's throat. He cannot find his voice.

'He struggled, beta,' Chand says, and Nik knows this is what he was leading up to, as if he had to warm himself up before he got here. 'I don't know how bad it was but we could see he had these bouts where there was no light in his eyes. Something was eating away at him. Something he never articulated to me, but I could feel it.'

'What do you think happened, Mama?' The word comes automatically, even though Nik hasn't called Chand this since he was a young child. Something is shifting between them, still oscillating, like scales that haven't yet set.

This time, Chand takes a moment before answering. 'It was an accident, beta,' he says, almost pleading. 'That's all it was.'

This is what Nik wanted to hear, but now he has, his mind is filled with those short, sharp, spiky letters, the final stanza of that poem. He thinks back to that list he and Layla spoke about, scratched into the last page of the journal. It makes sense now. A list of reasons to stay. 'You can't know that, though.'

'No, I can't. There were no dash cams back then, no street cameras on that road, no footage of what happened. No one can know for sure.'

Nik's mind races. He tries his best to follow the thoughts whipping through him. Just because his father wrote that poem, it doesn't mean he necessarily took his own life. Nik knows that the space between wanting to no longer be here and actually acting on it could stretch for aeons.

Maybe he just wrote the poetry to process everything, to let it all out. Maybe his death was genuinely an accident. Uncertainty fills him once more, like slow, dark poison.

'What did Bapu think?'

'It doesn't matter,' Chand says, almost impatiently.

'What about Maya Masi? She knew him too, right?' As a child, whenever he tried to ask Maya about his father, her gaze would skip to Nik's mother. If she was within earshot, Maya would shake her head slightly, an apology in her eyes. If his mother wasn't nearby, Maya would smile and say something sweet, sentimental and unspecific, like: 'Elliot was the best. He'd have loved you so much, honey.' Nik learned from a young age that she would always remain loyal to his mother, following her lead.

Chand is still shaking his head when he says: 'She thinks the same as me, beta. But it doesn't matter. Nobody's particular theories should matter. No one could know for sure.'

'Well, that's not good enough.'

'It has to be. We have to simply live with not knowing. There is no other option. Whichever route you choose, the outcome is the same. He's gone.'

Nik runs his hand through his hair. 'That's not true at all. Of course how he died matters. Maybe if I just –'

'You won't be able to have a conversation with her,' Chand says. 'It's not going to happen, Nikhil. I've tried for years, believe me.' Nik can hear empathy padded between the words; there is a new patience to his uncle's voice. Nik shakes his head. A large, warm hand fills the space between his shoulder blades. Tears fall onto his lap.

It's then that something overwhelming in its magnitude

crushes down on Nik, silencing the loop of questions circling his mind: the possibility that he may well never find out what happened will continue to chip and crack and eat away at him, forever. The nightmares of watching his father closing his eyes and stepping onto an empty road may never cease. It's like a seed has been planted and it's too late to stop it taking root. He understands now why his mother never wanted him to know. He can't even begin to understand how anyone might process the sheer weight of this unrelenting uncertainty, let alone ever lay it to rest.

'She threw her grief inwards,' Chand tells him. 'There is an impenetrable wall around her when it comes to this. Your mother,' he says, stumbling through, 'your mother, she will always believe –' he exhales, searching for the end of this sentence. He appears to find it after closing his eyes for a moment – 'that he walked out in front of that lorry, that he took his own life.'

Nik rests his elbows on the table, his forehead cupped in his palms. He pushes his hands through his hair, gripping the ends, tears meandering down his nose and onto the cotton runner beneath.

'I won't believe it. In my mind, it was an accident,' Chand tells him. 'He was just at the start of his life. There was so much to live for.'

Nik can see now that Chand, Maya and his mother each seem to hold a slightly different version of his father in their memories, a different iteration of what may have happened that night. Nik thinks about that one poem, and the others too, in the journal which sits now in his coat pocket. He knows that he will never show them to anyone; the thoughts in that journal were never meant to be shared. He'll hold them with him, silently, forever. No one but he and Layla, and perhaps his grandfather, will ever have to bear the burden of them.

'Your mother and I had been growing apart for years –'

'Why?' Nik's head shoots up at the mention of his mother. She and Chand are, quite plainly, the opposite of one another. One is the earth, the other the moon. Nik can't imagine them having ever been close. 'What happened with you two?'

Chand sighs, removing his glasses. 'She has her version and I have mine.'

'What does that mean?'

'From my perspective . . . it was not one particular event or moment, but the weight of many small ones. By the time your father died, what we had left was so delicate. His death sent us in two very different directions,' Chand murmurs, cutting through Nik's thoughts. He adds, quietly, in Gujarati: 'And I shouldn't have let it.'

Nik looks up, his eyes resting on his uncle's. They're so similar to his mother's, he realises, now that his uncle has removed his thick black frames.

A little while passes until Chand says, 'I helped him pick that car.' He nods to the bay window at the front of his living room. 'I drove him down to Brighton to pick it up and we drove back in convoy. It was his pride and joy. Whenever I see a green car in my rear-view mirror, I find myself looking for him in the face of the driver.

'I wish I'd spoken to him,' Chand murmurs, pressing his lips together, his eyes shining. His voice is broken when he says: 'The day we drove to get it, I could see something was wrong, that he was in pain. I didn't know how to start the conversation. I've spent so much time, since his death, telling myself I should have found a way to talk to him, to let him know I was there, that I would always be there, no matter what.'

He sobs silently into his handkerchief, his glasses lying on the table between them. Nik watches him, fresh tears rising in him. The way Chand speaks, the pain in his voice, tells Nik that his uncle has been holding these words in for years. He can't recall seeing Chand cry before, not even at his grandfather's funeral. Without thinking about it, Nik reaches over to put a hand on his uncle's shoulder. Chand surprises Nik by pulling him into a hug. He has never been held by his uncle, and the firmness of his arms, the clean scent of him, the way his hands wrap around Nik's back, makes a tightness that has gripped Nik for months ease just a fraction, as though he is letting out a breath he didn't realise he was holding in.

'You can always come to me, beta,' Chand murmurs into his shoulder. 'Especially now Puppa is gone.' The words echo others, ones that were overheard last summer: *Now that Puppa is gone, I feel I have a duty of –*

A duty of care. It's the duty of care Chand thought he was practising when he was trying to tell Nik's mother that he needed to 'be careful' with dating Layla. That he shouldn't be wasting his time studying History. Nik never for a moment thought those prejudiced, pushy words had come from a place of care, of love, of protection, however misplaced they may have been.

The clock continues to tick in the background, Nik trying to focus on the steadiness of it as he swallows down a sip of cold chai and wipes his face. Chand places a hand on the table as he stands. 'Listen, I have some of Elliot's things – poems, photos, some letters his pupils sent your mother when he died. They're in my office.'

Nik watches him, thinking back to when his grandfather first told him about the key, that summer day that feels like years ago, and how he'd immediately assumed it would unlock a box of his father's old things. Here it is, at last.

'Can I see them?'

'Of course,' Chand says. 'They're yours, beta.'

When Nik heads back to London that evening, he drives with all the windows down, feeling as though the air that flicks past his skin, that drums against the shape of the car, pounding at his ears, is lifting parts of him away, revealing something new underneath. Before he left, he charged his phone and sent his mother a message. It was short, telling her everything he needed to in just two lines:

Mum, I get it now.
I am with you x

He cannot begin to fathom her pain. It comes to him, as he drives, that the territorial nature of his mother's grief, the reason why she will not speak about his father's death is the very same reason she did not want him to know about Paul's affairs. To protect him from the pain lying in truth's wake. He thinks back to when she took that photo from his room, the first one he'd ever had of his father, and placed it on her dressing table instead. *This is not your pain, it is mine.*

Nik had meant it, when he texted her, accepting, finally, that she may never be able to talk about this, that he may never be able to fully interrogate it, to find out what really happened; if his father had deliberately stepped onto that street that night, if it was an accident, or if it was something between the two. Either way, he will never know, and now, as he drives back towards her, he tells himself all that's left is for him not to let them consume him, these lost things, like they did his mother. He must find peace in the space between the two possibilities and accept that no one holds all the answers. Some things are simply better left with the wind.

He silences all the questions he once had for his mother, all but one. It's one that he'll keep aside for much later, he will allow it to bud in him, and bloom, perhaps. Maybe, he will even let it wilt, and the words will never reach his lips. He knows something has changed for him to hold such patience, for him not to need the answer right away. So he tucks the question away, with his intuition telling him that whatever the answer is, the journey of finding out may one day bring him and his mother closer still: *Who was little Nick and how can we find him?*

32

January 2018

Evening has fallen over Harrow, the sky growing dark as night approaches. The day will soon be over. When Avani closes her eyes, she thinks of how the sound of passing cars in the distance could almost be mistaken for rolling waves.

Earlier that evening, she finally found the courage to retrieve her half-finished canvases from the old cardboard box that once lived in her father's loft. As she did so, a flash of green had appeared against the window, swooping over her home. She'd rushed to the other side of the house to watch the flock of parakeets that she'd seen only a handful of times before, the wild ones that graced unsuspecting Londoners with their presence every now and again. The week after her father's death, she'd spotted a pair in her garden, watching her silently from the branch of an acer tree.

Now, a dunnock sings as Avani picks up a dollop of brilliant white on a clean brush and dabs it into the edges of the clouds that line her sky. It has taken her close to two decades, but she's finally just an hour or so away from recreating Buttermere at dawn.

After the call from her brother earlier that day, then the text from her son, Avani had sat on the bottom step of her staircase, Rani by her feet, and she had let it come. The memories had hit her like an aggressive tide, their force pulling her under. She allowed herself, for the first time in years, to fully go back to what it was like to lie that final night, looking at the cold space in the bed beside her, picking the paint that was stuck to her fingernails, thinking of the canvas she'd been working on after her bath, secretly glad for the quiet, for the emptiness of the house. But the quiet and emptiness had stayed too long. She'd assumed that Elliot had stayed at school a little later to get some extra marking done, or perhaps gone to the pub with his colleagues. But she knew something was wrong when the clock on the bedroom wall crept towards ten, when the sound of her husband's keys in the door never came. She had called her father, who accompanied her to her husband's school where, on the way, flashing blue lights drew the breath from her, broken glass glittering across the tarmac, people in uniforms holding her back, telling her things she did not want to hear.

She knows that she is out of time. She must find a way to create space for her son to join her. Rani finds Avani's hand, limp by her hip, and nuzzles into it. Avani reaches for the spot behind Rani's ears and strokes her, staring at the photo of her father just beside her easel, hearing all of the words she knows he would be murmuring to her if he were here now, words of strength, of looking inwards to find a bravery he knows is in her.

She glances back at the canvas, admiring the colour, the depth, the pureness of it. There has been such a change to her style since she last painted. She thinks of the careful, controlled impasto brushstrokes of her past, thick with layers of oil paint, congested and congealing. Now, her strokes are light, the paint heavy with water, the colours soft, practically translucent, so the white cotton of the canvas presses through.

When night falls over Harrow, it brings rain with it, rain that starts as a soft mist but soon graduates to thick sheets, cleaning the streets. The hiss of tyres on the wet road continues to rise and fall as cars pass Avani's open window.

She is painting a couple of green birds against the sky, close together, dancing in the wind, when another sound makes her stop. It's the sound of an old engine turning into the road, pulling up outside the house. She puts her brush down, looking at the image in front of her, of the lake she began painting almost two decades ago but did not know how to finish.

A car door slams shut. Her son's steps grow closer. Avani looks away from the lake and rises, Rani like a shadow behind her, to let him in.

Acknowledgements

Endless thanks to everyone in the publishing industry doing the work to foster change and champion novels like this one. Thanks especially to Holly Faulks, who understood my characters better than I could have ever hoped, for seeing them all so clearly, for believing in their story.

I owe a great deal of thanks to everyone at #Merky Books, Cornerstone and Penguin Random House. Thank you to the New Writers' Prize judges who read my entry and saw something in it, to Stormzy for launching such an important imprint, to Tallulah Lyons, Lemara Lindsay-Prince, Helen Conford, Najma Finlay, Natalia Cacciatore, Laurie Ip Fung Chun and all the many people who worked tirelessly behind the scenes.

I would like to thank Batool Raza and Bryony Walsh – words cannot do justice to how much your love and friendship has meant to me over the years, particularly while I was writing this.

Thank you to Elaine Frost and Zainab Omaki who read early drafts of Nik and Avani's story, and who told me to keep going, even when I wasn't sure how. To Jagravi Upadhyay and family for answering all of my many questions and for believing in me from the very start. To Natalie Stubbs and Calum Harris for being my home away from home and for all of the encouragement. To Rajasree Variyar, Tanya Banerjee and Peggy Lee for your invaluable feedback and for always asking to read more.

To the friends who have, in various ways, supported my writing, this novel and my dream to be an author: Charmi Patel, Raheem Williams, Caz Blaxcell, Josie Lister, Cara George, Farah Shahabuddin, Krystle Zara Appiah, Harriet Cummings and Delwar Hussain.

Thank you to my mother for encouraging me to write this, my father for your stories and your music, and Aleksandra for helping me to fall in love with books.

I wouldn't have got here without the teachers and tutors who nudged me along. Thank you to Andrew Cowan for helping me to find my voice and my way with this story. Giles Foden and Trezza Azzopardi for all of your guidance, too. Thank you especially to Colin Wills for telling me I could one day, if I wished, have a future as a writer.

BUSES IN BRITAIN
The 1970s

Stewart J Brown

Capital Transport

Foreword

First published 1999

ISBN 1 85414 217 8

Published by Capital Transport Publishing,
38 Long Elmes, Harrow Weald, Middlesex

Designed by Tim Demuth

Printed by CS Graphics, Singapore

This is the third book in the Buses in Britain series. The first two were contemporary volumes, dealing with the current scene as it was in the 1990s. These are now out of print. This one is different in that it is retrospective, and covers an entire decade: the 1970s.

In keeping with the spirit of the original idea, the bulk of this book is a regional review of who was running what and where, supported by high-quality colour illustrations submitted by a range of photographers. The regional reviews show the picture as it was roughly around 1975 – not long after local government reorganisation and the creation of additional PTEs, when many fleets were adopting new colour schemes to reflect changes in ownership. NBC's corporate colours were widely spread by the mid-1970s, but a few buses were still running in pre-1972 colours, and a selection are shown here.

To set the scene and cover the early part of the decade, there is an introductory section on the pages which follow. And the book finishes with a brief review of events in the late 1970s, when new models were appearing in a number of fleets.

Depending on your age, the 1970s might seem like yesterday or they might seem like ancient history. They were interesting times, despite tight licensing controls and the large measure of public ownership which was then the norm and in consequence was taken for granted.

In keeping with the ethic of the time I have used the term 'one-man-operation' and its abbreviation 'omo' to describe services in which passengers paid the driver. Most bus drivers, certainly at the start of the 1970s, were men and the term 'one-person-operation' was not in widespread use. Similarly, I have been ambivalent about metrication, as was Britain in the 1970s. This is why some vehicle lengths are referred to in metres, others in feet. For example, the length of a PSU3 Leopard could equally easily be described as 36ft or 11m – both expressions were in common use. By contrast Leyland Nationals were always described by their metric length – no one ever referred to a 36ft 9in National.

The spelling of some Welsh place names has undergone change. I have tried to use the spellings which are appropriate to the period, which might not always be those in use 20 years later. The vexed question of apostrophes in operators' names – vexed, at least, for those who worry about such things – is not easily resolved. Generally each operator's own style – Smiths or Smith's – is used, although some small operators were not consistent in their approach.

Thanks must be offered to those photographers who kindly made available valuable, original, and irreplaceable transparencies to illustrate this volume. Their work is individually credited. Colour transparency film was still relatively expensive at the start of the 1970s, and many transport enthusiasts at that time were still working mainly in black-and-white – although that had changed by the end of the decade.

Tribute must also be paid to the work of the PSV Circle and its members, not only in recording vehicles, but in laboriously collating information to produce detailed fleet histories. In addition, a number of people have to be thanked for kindly casting an eye over drafts of the text with the aim of correcting any errors or spotting any major omissions. So thanks, too, to John Aldridge, Michael Fowler, John Jones, Malcolm Keeley, Allan Macfarlane, Iain MacGregor, Roy Marshall, Geoff Mills and Geoff Stainthorpe for their helpful comments. Any errors or omissions are of course mine.

Stewart J Brown, MCIT
Reedley Hallows, 1999

The cover and title page photographs are by Stewart J Brown.

The photographs opposite are by Malcolm King and Paul Caudell.

Contents

The 1970s – opening with change... 4

Scotland 10

North West England 36

North East England... 62

Yorkshire 80

The Midlands... 98

East Anglia 124

South East England 138

South West England 162

Wales 174

End of a decade, end of an era 192

The 1970s – opening with change

WHEN the 1970s opened, the last traditional half-cab double-deckers to enter service in Britain were but a few months old. The world's biggest bus business, the National Bus Company, had been in existence 12 months, but there were few signs of change in the two groups which it had taken over, the state-owned Transport Holding Company and the previously independent British Electric Traction. The four Passenger Transport Executives which served England's biggest conurbations outside London were setting the scene for a brave new world of co-ordinated public transport. And the advanced integral Leyland National was still a hush-hush development project known within Leyland as FPB7 – Forward Project Bus 7.

By the end of the decade half-cab buses were becoming increasingly rare outside London, NBC had a corporate identity, there were seven PTEs including one in Scotland, and – after a sluggish start – the Leyland National could be seen the length and breadth of the country.

One thing above all others shaped the face of Britain's bus industry in the 1970s: the 1968 Transport Act. It was this which led to the creation of the PTEs and NBC, and which saw major change in London, with ownership of London Transport's red and green buses being split between the Greater London Council and NBC respectively, the latter taking control through a new London Country Bus Services subsidiary.

NBC was formed in January 1969, combining the operations of the former THC bus operations in England and Wales with those of the BET group, which had been sold to the THC in 1968. BET feared that the new operating climate envisaged in the Transport Act would not be one in which it could run profitably.

The two groups which formed NBC had quite different vehicle and operating policies. The BET companies had fleets made up largely of AECs, Leylands and – since the introduction of the Fleetline – Daimlers. BET had been an enthusiastic user of rear-engined double-deckers right from the moment the Atlantean appeared, although a number of fleets continued to buy conventional Titans from Leyland and Regents from AEC. The latter, of course, had no rear-engined double-decker on offer.

Left **The formation of the National Bus Company ultimately brought an end to distinctive liveries such as that used by Southdown. This 1967 Leyland Titan PD3 has the final development of Northern Counties' unusual fully-fronted bodywork which Southdown specified, with panoramic windows and a curved front windscreen on the top deck. Southdown had been a BET company.** David Brown

Above **The THC bus operations in England and Wales generally ran highly standardised fleets made up of ECW-bodied Bristols. The Tilling green and red liveries used by the THC companies in England and Wales were replaced by new shades under NBC ownership. Hants & Dorset was unusual in switching from Tilling green to NBC red, as shown by a rare 30ft-long LDL6G Lodekka in Southampton, photographed when a new house could be had for under £9,000. Only six LDLs were built.** Mike Greenwood

Bodies for BET buses came from a wide variety of builders. Alexander, Marshall, Northern Counties, Park Royal, Roe, Weymann and Willowbrook had all been suppliers to BET in the 1960s.

The THC fleets were much more standardised, largely because of their link with Bristol and Eastern Coach Works which, like the THC, were state-owned. Liveries were standardised too – foreshadowing what was coming at NBC – with most fleets being either red or green. Double-deckers were mainly Bristol Lodekkas, although a fair number of the earlier K-series models were still in use. Single-deckers were MWs, LSs and REs, with a few front-engined L-types lingering on, and small numbers of lightweight SCs and SUs on rural routes. The newest models in Bristol's range, the LH and VRT, were beginning to appear in a number of fleets.

Generalisations are always dangerous. Insofar as one can be made about THC and BET operations it is that the latter tended to serve more urban areas, while the former had a higher proportion of rural routes. But that has to be seen as a broad generalisation. While BET was strong in, for example, the Newcastle-upon-Tyne area, Lancashire, the Potteries, the Midlands and parts of Yorkshire and South Wales, it also served rural southern England. Similarly, while THC companies had such unpromising bus-operating territory as Cumberland, Westmoreland, rural Northumberland, East Anglia, North Wales and Cornwall, there were busy urban operations in Bristol, parts of North East England and West Yorkshire. NBC owned 21,760 buses and coaches at the start of the decade.

NBC rationalised parts of its operations in the early 1970s. Some adjacent fleets were put under common management but with little sign of outward change, although others were to disappear. Hants & Dorset took over Wilts & Dorset. Northern General absorbed each of its subsidiaries. Southdown, a former BET company, took over the ex-THC Brighton Hove & District business, operating it briefly as Southdown-BH&D before abandoning the BH&D title. Aldershot & District (an ex-BET company) was merged with neighbouring Thames Valley (ex-THC) to form the Thames Valley & Aldershot Omnibus Co, better known as Alder Valley. There were other amalgamations which joined ex-BET and ex-THC operations. In Wales Rhondda (ex-BET) was absorbed by Western Welsh (also ex-BET), which in turn took control of Red & White (ex-THC). United Welsh, a one-time sister company of Red & White in THC days and earlier, was absorbed by the ex-BET South Wales Transport company. Western National was united with Devon General; the former had been a THC fleet, the latter, BET.

BET subsidiaries in the days before NBC had used a wide range of unrelated liveries and this included some, such as Southdown, which had changed but little over the years. The THC companies' buses by contrast were generally in what was known as Tilling red or Tilling green, with a standardised style of fleetname. There were exceptions – most notably Midland General in blue – but only the fleetname differ-

The colourful MacBrayne livery vanished in the early 1970s as the company's bus operations were absorbed by Highland Omnibuses and Western SMT. Most of MacBrayne's buses were Bedfords, such as this 1966 VAS1 with 28-seat Willowbrook body.
David Brown

entiated between a red Lodekka in Cumberland and a similar bus in Wiltshire.

Initially NBC let this continue, but the arrival of a new chairman in 1972 saw the adoption of a corporate livery – basically leaf green or poppy red with white relief and a standard style of fleetname accompanied by a new double-N logo. Out went the Tilling shades and all the hues used by the ex-BET fleets. In came NBC's corporate style. Repainting started in the autumn of 1972; by 1976 most of the old liveries had vanished. It was controversial, and the application was not particularly imaginative. There was for a short time a blue variant, used by Sunderland District, Midland General and East Yorkshire, but that was soon stopped – except on the small Jones of Aberbeeg fleet. Coaches were all-over white.

North of the border, the state-owned Scottish Bus Group operated 4,700 vehicles through seven subsidiaries. Here there were Bristols – mainly Lodekkas – but the SBG companies had maintained an independent buying policy and during the 1960s bought Leylands, AECs in declining numbers, and Daimler Fleetlines. Most SBG buses were bodied in Falkirk by Alexander. This had been an associate of the SMT group's Alexander bus-operating subsidiary but it had remained independent when the SMT group was nationalised in 1949. Each of SBG's subsidiaries had its own distinctive livery. One of these was in the throes of change from 1970, as Highland Omnibuses abandoned its traditional maroon and cream in favour of a distinctive poppy red and peacock blue, to which was later added grey relief.

SBG companies were among the first to order rear-engined Bristol VRTs, including some relatively rare long-wheelbase examples. These all had ECW bodies. The VRTs proved troublesome in service and lasted less than two years before all migrated south. After attempts to sell them through classified advertising columns in Commercial Motor and Coaching Journal had failed, the majority went to NBC companies in exchange for Lodekkas.

Other types to disappear in the early 1970s did so by dint of their age. Western SMT had been the last SBG subsidiary to buy new Guy Arab double-deckers, in 1956. These had lowbridge bodies by Alexander and lasted until 1971. Alexander (Northern) managed to eke a long life from its buses. In 1970 it still had some 50 Leyland Tigers in stock, all at least 20 years old. Most had gone by the end of 1971.

On Scotland's west coast, shipping, bus and road haulage services had long been provided by David MacBrayne. This operation had been part state-owned but changes at the end of the 1960s led to its absorption by the Scottish Transport Group which controlled SBG. Consequently at the start of the 1970s MacBrayne's bus operations were being integrated with those of SBG. This primarily involved Highland Omnibuses, but Alexander (Midland) took over MacBrayne's extensive holiday coach tour business, while Western SMT found itself responsible for MacBrayne operations in Kintyre.

This meant the dispersal of MacBrayne's fleet of Bedfords and AECs. All of the latter went to Highland, as did most of the former. Western SMT got four Bedfords, while Alexander (Midland) inherited the Bedford touring coach fleet. MacBrayne's distinctive red, green and cream livery vanished within a couple of years.

The four PTEs set up by the 1968 Transport Act had between them absorbed 20 municipal fleets. The biggest was SELNEC – South East Lancashire North East Cheshire – which had 2,500 buses taken over from the municipalities of Ashton, Bolton, Bury, Leigh, Manchester, Oldham, Ramsbottom, Rochdale, Salford, SHMD (the Stalybridge, Hyde, Mossley and Dukinfield joint board) and Stockport. Next in size came the 2,000-strong West Midlands fleet, which took over from Birmingham, Walsall, West Bromwich and Wolverhampton. Merseyside, with 1,400 buses, acquired the fleets of Birkenhead, Liverpool and Wallasey. Smallest of the PTEs was Tyneside, with 440 buses taken over from Newcastle and South Shields. The PTEs came into being between October 1969 and January 1970.

Two – Tyneside and West Midlands – effectively adopted the liveries of their biggest constituents, yellow and blue respectively. Merseyside initially recognised local loyalties by retaining green for its Liverpool fleet and going for a blue and cream livery for buses on the Wirral peninsula, picking up on the colours which had been used by Birkenhead and Wallasey. Only SELNEC broke the mould, and adopted a bold new orange and white livery which owed nothing at all to any of its constituent fleets.

West Midlands was the only PTE to operate trolleybuses, taken over from Walsall Corporation. There were 46 in the fleet, including 22 Sunbeam F4As which had been the first two-axle 30ft-long double-deck buses to run in Britain, having been first introduced under special dispensation in 1954, in advance of a general relaxation on length limits. No trolleybuses received PTE livery; the system closed in October 1970.

In each of the four PTE fleets the liveries of the constituent operators were to be seen well into the 1970s, as repainting took place at a measured pace. Indeed a handful of buses in pre-1970 municipal colours were still in service after 1974, when local government reorganisation saw a redrawing of PTE boundaries.

The creation of the four PTEs left 67 municipalities running buses in Britain. The biggest was Glasgow Corporation (1,200), while the largest to survive in England was Leeds City Transport (700). The smallest was Colwyn Bay Borough Council with just three vehicles. There were only two really big independent bus operators. In the North West, Lancashire United Transport ran 375 buses serving the area between Manchester and Liverpool, often operating jointly with other operators. In the Midlands Barton Transport had some 320 vehicles covering parts of Nottinghamshire and Derbyshire. Most of the remaining independents were small family-run businesses. There were significant pockets of essentially urban independent bus operation in Doncaster, Durham, Paisley and on the Ayrshire coast. Elsewhere most independents served small towns or rural areas. One notable isolated exception was Mayne of Manchester – observers wondered whether it could survive the integrationist policies of the newly-formed SELNEC PTE.

There were other changes among the municipals, aside from those which had been absorbed by the new PTEs. Two municipal fleets sold out to NBC in 1970. Luton operated lowbridge Titans, alongside Dennis Lolines, Albion Lowlanders and Bristol REs. It was absorbed into the United Counties business. Similarly Exeter, running mainly Leyland Titans and Guy Arabs, was absorbed by Devon General. Luton had operated 71 buses; there had been 65 in the Exeter fleet.

In Yorkshire there had been Joint Omnibus Committees in Huddersfield, Sheffield, Halifax and Todmorden. These were operations which were under municipal control but were jointly owned by the local authority and the railways – originally the LMS and/or LNER, and latterly British Railways. The formation of NBC in 1969 saw this relationship change, with NBC taking over what had been BR's involvement in the JOCs. A new NBC subsidiary, Amalgamated Passenger Transport, represented NBC's interests. The municipalities at Huddersfield and Sheffield bought out NBC's share in September 1969 and January 1970 respectively, leaving APT involved in Halifax and Todmorden.

In March 1971 the Halifax JOC took over some of the local services operated by NBC's Hebble company, along with nine buses. This was followed in September by the amalgamation of the Todmorden and Halifax JOCs to form a new Calderdale JOC, which adopted Halifax's orange, green and cream livery in place of Todmorden's dark green. This arrangement continued until the creation of the West Yorkshire PTE in 1974.

In Keighley and in York there were joint operations which were managed by West Yorkshire Road Car (a former THC business) but which were part-owned by the local authority. The Keighley-West Yorkshire business became a wholly-owned NBC subsidiary and finally vanished in 1974. Its buses were painted in NBC poppy red, but with non-standard gold fleetnames. The York-West Yorkshire business survived into the 1980s.

Despite having lost its country bus operations to NBC, London Transport at the start of the 1970s remained Britain's biggest bus company. Its 6,500-strong fleet was in a state of change. Traditional double-deck types still dominated London's bus services, with RT-class AEC Regent IIIs and Routemasters providing the bulk of services right across the capital. The last of the Routemasters – 72-seat 30ft-long RMLs – had entered service as recently as 1968. A few lowbridge RLH-class Regent IIIs were still running in east London on a route with height restrictions which precluded the use of standard RTs or RMs. But their days were numbered. All other types in regular LT service were set to run for the greater part of the 1970s.

As the 1970s got under way, the PTEs came to grips with their remit to provide an integrated transport service. Each used a different approach to tackling the existence of services being provided by other – generally NBC – operators within the PTE operating area.

The first to make an announcement was SELNEC. NBC's Stockport-based North Western subsidiary (not to be confused with the post-1985 Merseyside-based company of the same name) had much of its operations within the PTE boundary. The solution was a takeover and in 1972 SELNEC acquired the bulk of North Western's bus operations, along with 272 buses and five depots. Most of what was left of North Western was divided between Trent and Crosville. Crosville took over 124 assorted North Western buses, while Trent got 53 single-deckers.

In the West Midlands, the PTE took over a large part of the operations of NBC's Midland Red company, along with 413 buses, in 1973.

Above **For a period in the early 1970s ex-municipal buses could be seen in PTE ownership displaying their new owner's names on their original owner's livery. The point is illustrated by an ex-Wolverhampton Guy Arab IV with fully-fronted Burlingham body of a style more generally associated with Ribble Titans. New in 1958, it survived until 1974.** Iain MacGregor

Right **Rotherham Corporation's bus fleet was taken over by the South Yorkshire PTE in 1974. Most of its double-deckers were Daimlers. This 1965 CVG6LX/30 had a Roe body.** D J Little

Elsewhere the PTEs came to operating agreements with local NBC subsidiaries. This saw NBC buses in Tyneside being painted yellow, while those operated in Merseyside by Crosville and Ribble started to carry the PTE logo alongside the company fleetname.

Two additional PTEs came into being on 1 April 1974. The West Yorkshire PTE took over the municipal operations in Leeds, Bradford, Huddersfield and Halifax, along with the Calderdale JOC. Initially it planned to give each area its own livery using cream as a base which was to be relieved by green in Leeds, blue in Bradford, orange in Halifax and red in Huddersfield – the colours used by the municipal buses in each town. However after a few trial vehicles had been repainted this was abandoned and instead a cream and green scheme was used – remarkably similar to that in Merseyside – with local fleetnames Metro Leeds, Metro Bradford, Metro Kirklees (in Huddersfield) and Metro Calderdale (in Halifax and Todmorden).

In South Yorkshire there was no such equivocation and the PTE quickly adopted a cream and brown livery which wasn't the most inspired but avoided using any of the colours of the constituent municipal fleets – which had been cream and blue in Sheffield, blue and cream in Rotherham and red in Doncaster. The insipid brown was soon changed to a slightly darker shade, but it could hardly be described as a significant improvement.

Innovation in the early 1970s included a first tentative interest in minibuses to provide high-quality dial-a-ride services. High wage costs and inflexibility in trade union agreements militated against small bus operation, but early experiments in dial-a-ride were conducted in Harrogate, Abingdon, Witney, Maidstone, Eastbourne, Harlow, Sale and London. They generally targeted relatively affluent areas where there would be telephones in most homes. In a typical operation would-be passengers phoned a control centre and buses were diverted from their routes to pick people up at or near their homes. Most dial-a-ride services were run by Ford Transits.

There were a few types of bus which disappeared from service in the early 1970s. Fodens are one example. The last buyer of Foden double-deckers had been Warrington Corporation in 1956. In 1970 Warrington actually had eight Fodens in operation; the last were withdrawn in 1972. Sentinel buses – never that common anyway – also vanished, with the last being withdrawn by a small Shropshire operator in 1974.

One of the prime factors in the changes affecting independents' fleets (and others too) was the government's new bus grant, introduced in 1968. This gave an operator a grant equal to 25 per cent of the purchase price of a new bus, provided it met certain criteria, including suitability for one-man-operation. In 1971 the grant was increased to 50 per cent, and many small operators were quick to seize the opportunity of buying what were in effect half-price buses. The bonanza didn't end there. Very quickly operators and manufacturers realised that with little modification coaches could qualify for grant. A slightly wider entrance with power doors saw the introduction by coach bodybuilders of what were generally known as Express models. The only stipulation was that a percentage of the coach's mileage had to be on stage carriage services – the terminology then in use to describe a local bus service.

This is why by the middle of the decade new AECs, Bedfords and Leylands with Duple and Plaxton coach bodies were rapidly replacing older types on service, particularly in rural areas. The biggest operator to take advantage of this was Barton Transport, which in little more than five years changed its fleet from a mixture of newish single-deckers and assorted second-hand double-deckers to one made up entirely of bus-grant coaches. It made life more comfortable for the passengers – but infinitely less interesting for the enthusiast. The bus grant spawned not just modified coach bodies from the two big builders, but the striking new Expressway from Willowbrook. This was in many ways a more honest approach to a dual-purpose vehicle and it actually sold fairly well to small fleets in the first half of the decade, especially on lightweight Bedford and Ford chassis.

It wasn't just old buses which were vanishing. Trolleybuses were disappearing too. At the start of 1970 there were just three systems, in Walsall, Teesside and Bradford. The Walsall system was closed in October 1970, followed by Teesside in April 1971 and by Bradford in March 1972. The last trolleybuses in Wales – run by Cardiff Corporation – actually operated in January 1970, but the system had effectively closed down in December 1969 and was only reactivated for a final farewell.

There were also a few operators which disappeared in the early part of the decade. In 1970 Venture Transport of Consett, which ran 80 vehicles, sold out to Northern General, while Gosport & Fareham was bought by NBC and retained as a separate subsidiary. Venture was to survive as a separate entity until 1975. King Alfred of Winchester sold out to Hants & Dorset in 1973, its Renowns and Tiger Cubs injecting some variety into the NBC company's fleet. Various other, generally smaller, businesses would be bought by NBC subsidiaries as the 1970s progressed; these are covered in the regional sections which follow.

No new half-cab buses were built for service in Britain after 1969; new bus grant made sure of that. Leyland launched an improved Atlantean in 1972, the AN68 (indicating AtlanteaN, 680 engine). The 680 engine had been offered in the CRL6 Fleetline from 1970. The Bristol VRT was available only with Gardner's 6LXB engine until 1974 when the Series 3 model was offered with the Leyland 500 as an alternative.

Single-deck buses had been gaining in popularity from the early 1960s because legislation prohibited the operation of double-deckers without conductors. The urban single-deck models from AEC, Daimler and Leyland were not unqualified successes and this, coupled to the legalisation of one-man-operation of double-deckers from 1966, saw a rapid reversion to double-deck operation in most towns and cities.

The Leyland National, launched in 1972, had originally been developed in the light of falling interest in double-deckers. With the National, Leyland was geared up to build a bus which the market really didn't want, or at least didn't want in the large numbers which Leyland had anticipated. Ultimately the National killed off all competing Leyland group rear-engined single-deck chassis, as well as Seddon's Pennine RU, which appeared in 1969 and lasted until 1974. RUs were sold to a number of independents and a few of the smaller municipalities, but found only one big fleet user – Crosville, which took 100. The Leyland National was a joint project between Leyland and NBC and that did guarantee some continuing business for the model. It also sold in substantial numbers to London Transport.

And that's how the bus industry stood at the start of the 1970s. British Leyland was the only manufacturer of heavy-duty bus chassis in any volume. The purchase of new buses was being encouraged by capital grants. And the bulk of local bus services were provided by public sector operators – NBC, SBG, the PTEs, London Transport and local councils. The chapters which follow look at the middle of the decade, and at who was running what in each region.

Facing page top **The Keighley-West Yorkshire company was jointly owned by NBC and Keighley Corporation at the start of the 1970s, an arrangement which continued until 1974. A Bristol FS6B in the fleet carries NBC's poppy red livery, but retains a traditional style of fleetname rather than using NBC's corporate white lettering.** Stewart J Brown

Left **Britain's last trolleybus fleet was that run by Bradford Corporation. Trolleybus operation ceased in March 1972. A 1946 Karrier W with 1958 East Lancs body is seen in Bradford in 1970.** Iain MacGregor

This page **Not that many Leyland-bodied buses made it in to the 1970s with their original owners. This PD2/10 Titan, one of a pair delivered to King Alfred Motor Services in 1952, has Leyland's Farington-style bodywork. It had been withdrawn by the time Hants & Dorset took over the King Alfred business in 1973.** David Brown

Scotland

159
ABRONHILL
Stirling (A 80)
Kirkintilloch (A
Edinburgh (M8)
Midlan
UMS 94J

GLASGOW has long been Scotland's biggest city, served by the country's biggest public transport operator. From 1973 this was the Greater Glasgow PTE, set up to take over the bus services and underground railway which had previously been under the control of Glasgow Corporation Transport.

The PTE fleet was highly standardised. It had inherited some 700 Alexander-bodied Atlanteans from the Corporation, and this remained the standard type throughout the 1970s. In 1973 Atlanteans accounted for just over half the fleet. The first deliveries to the PTE replaced older types of front-engined buses – late 1950s Leyland Titan PD2s and Daimler CVG6s with rear-entrance bodies, or early 1960s PD3s and AEC Regent Vs with forward-entrance bodies. Most of these buses were Alexander-bodied, although a small number of PD2s and PD3s had Alexander-style bodies constructed by the Corporation in its Coplawhill works on the south side of the city.

Front-engined buses in Glasgow, as elsewhere, were on their way out. The last CVG6s and Regent Vs were withdrawn in 1975, with the Titans following soon after. Glasgow Corporation had in fact switched to Atlanteans as early as 1962, ranking it alongside Liverpool as one of the first major urban operators to abandon front-engined buses, and by 1975 withdrawal of the oldest PDR1s was well under way. Their replacements were Alexander-bodied AN68s which, to most Glasgow bus users, must have looked little different from the buses they were replacing.

Non-standard types included a solitary Alexander-bodied Fleetline, which was sold in 1975 to Graham's Bus Service in nearby Paisley, and 16 Leyland Panthers with Alexander W-type bodies, introduced between 1964 and 1969. In

Facing page **Most Alexander (Midland) Fleetlines had Alexander bodies, but one batch of 12 delivered in 1970 was bodied by ECW. The Fleetline was the company's standard double-decker from 1967 to 1980. A Central SMT Lodekka follows in the background.** Stewart J Brown

Top right **The oldest buses taken over by the Greater Glasgow PTE were 1958 Alexander-bodied Titans. This smart example in Corporation livery carries the PTE logo.** Stewart J Brown

Centre right **In 1972 Glasgow Corporation switched from PDR1 to AN68 Atlanteans, and Alexander's J-type body was replaced by the AL-type with equal-depth windows on both decks. This is one of the first of the AN68s.** Stewart J Brown

Right **Glasgow's Panthers wore a reversed version of the standard fleet livery, with green lower panels and yellow for the upper part of the body, which was Alexander's W-type. New in 1969, this bus survived until 1977.** Stewart J Brown

Glasgow as in most other places the Panthers had not been a great success. They were usually to be found on a route in the eastern suburbs which passed beneath a low railway bridge.

Variety was being introduced to the fleet with the delivery of 40 of MCW's new Scania-powered Metropolitan integrals. The first entered service towards the end of 1974; all were in use by the summer of 1975. The PTE also tried the other model which was challenging Leyland's supremacy in the bus market, the Scottish-built Ailsa. It took 18, all bodied by Alexander, in 1975. However these were but minor diversions and for the rest of the 1970s the Atlantean reigned supreme. When the PTE took over in 1973 the highest Atlantean fleet number was LA695. At the end of 1979 the series had reached LA1333, and was still climbing.

Glasgow's buses immediately prior to the PTE takeover had been green and yellow, applied in a simple style to facilitate spray painting. The PTE retained these colours, but using different shades and brightened up with extensive use of white relief. Both liveries could still be seen in 1975 with the PTE's 'GG' logo.

The PTE's services operated to the pattern established by the Corporation, with few excursions beyond the city boundary. Tight licensing controls still existed to regulate routes, timetables and fares, and in Glasgow a restriction was applied to other operators' services running in to the city. This basically meant that on inward journeys their buses could not pick passengers up within the city boundary, and on outward journeys they were not allowed to set passengers down until they had crossed back over the boundary.

This affected all of the SBG subsidiaries running into Glasgow. It also meant that with less on-off traffic at intermediate stops SBG buses were generally much faster than those of the PTE.

Above left **The Greater Glasgow PTE bought its first Ailsas in 1975. There were 18 with Alexander 79-seat bodies, the highest seating capacity in the fleet. Reflective fleet number plates were introduced by the PTE soon after its formation.** Stewart J Brown

Left **The last Tiger Cubs for Alexander (Midland) had 41-seat Alexander Y-type coach bodies. A 1963 example loads in Falkirk bus station.** Stewart J Brown

Top right **Leyland Titans with lowbridge bodywork could be seen in most parts of Scotland. The last deliveries, in 1961, were PD3As and included vehicles for Alexander (Midland) as seen here in Glasgow. They had 67-seat Alexander bodies. From 1962 the Scottish Bus Group would be buying the lowheight Albion Lowlander.** Stewart J Brown

Right **Central SMT's orders in the 1950s and 1960s were split between Leyland and Bristol. All the Bristols were Lodekkas, culminating in FLF6G models. This 1965 bus replaced a two-year-old Albion Lowlander. A 1968 Central Leopard follows.** Stewart J Brown

Alexander (Midland), based in Falkirk, had a strong presence to the north of the city. It ran to two massive postwar housing estates, at Drumchapel and Garthamlock, and to towns to the north including Milngavie, Kirkintilloch and Kilsyth in each of which it had depots. Local services in Glasgow and in other major towns such as Stirling, Grangemouth, Falkirk and Perth, were predominantly double-deck operated using LD and FLF Lodekkas, Leyland Titan PD3s, Albion Lowlanders and Daimler Fleetlines with the precise mix varying from place to place. The Lodekkas included 15 ex-Eastern National FLFs, exchanged for VRTs in 1971 in advance of a more widespread SBG-NBC vehicle exchange in 1973.

Long-distance services were generally run by Leyland Leopards with Alexander Y-type bodies, while shorter distance routes outside the main urban centres were covered by AEC Reliances and Leyland Tiger Cubs, also bodied by Alexander. A peculiarly Scottish type could also be found on Alexander (Midland) services – the Albion Viking. This odd beast had a Leyland 400 engine mounted vertically in the rear overhang and driving the rear axle through an Albion constant-mesh gearbox. With the long linkage from the driving compartment, gearchanges were distinctly leisurely. The Vikings had Alexander Y-type bodies and had succeeded the Leyland Tiger Cub in SBG's ordering programmes. After the Viking, Alexander (Midland) had then moved on to the Bristol LH, building up a fleet of 41 with Perkins engines.

Dissatisfaction with rear-engined double-deckers saw the balance of the Central SMT fleet change in the 1970s from predominantly double-deck to predominantly single-deck. The company's standard bus was the PSU3/3 Leopard with manual gearbox and 53-seat Alexander body. This bus, seen in Motherwell, had been new to Alexander (Midland) in 1972 and was purchased by Central in 1975. Note that single-deckers used a different style of fleetname from double-deckers. Stewart J Brown

Below **Central SMT experimented with small buses on rail feeder services in East Kilbride, initially running four Bedford VASs, an unlikely type for a fleet otherwise made up of heavy-duty models. Two were ex-MacBrayne buses, the other two were new Duple-bodied coaches. They ran into housing estates where narrow roads precluded the use of buses wider than 7ft 6in.** Stewart J Brown

In Cumbernauld New Town Alexander (Midland) still ran a few vehicles acquired from Carmichael of Glenboig in 1966. These were four short-wheelbase L1-type Leopards (all of the others in the fleet were 11m-long PSU3s). They had BET-style Willowbrook bodies, a design not that common north of the border. Other ex-Carmichael buses which had survived into the early 1970s included five ex-Glasgow Corporation Leyland Worldmasters and a Glasgow-style forward-entrance highbridge PD3 which for a time was the only highbridge bus in the Alexander (Midland) fleet.

In 1974 Alexander (Midland) took over the operations of Aberfeldy Motor Coaches with two Willowbrook-bodied Bedford YRQs. These were used by Alexander (Midland) on rural routes in Crieff. New buses being bought for rural operation in the mid-1970s were Alexander-bodied Fords.

Central SMT, based in Motherwell, ran services from Glasgow south-east through Lanarkshire to East Kilbride, Biggar, Peebles and Lanark. The company also had a depot in Dunbartonshire, running services westwards along the north bank of the Clyde to Helensburgh and Balloch. Substantial local networks were run in Dumbarton, Hamilton, Motherwell and East Kilbride.

The Central fleet had traditionally been a double-decked one. Leyland Titan PD2s and Bristol Lodekkas were bought in large numbers in the 1950s and 1960s, and were still in operation in the 1970s, although the last of the PD2s were withdrawn during 1975. Lodekkas, which had been bought up to 1967, were to survive for most of the decade. As with Alexander (Midland), Central SMT operated FLFs which had come north from NBC in exchange for unwanted VRTs. Central introduced Fleetlines – with ECW rather than Alexander bodies – in 1971. However they were regarded little more highly than the VRTs which had preceded them and in 1975 were being transferred to other SBG companies.

Central SMT at the end of 1975 thus found itself in the unusual position for a 600-vehicle and predominantly urban fleet of having no rear-engined double-deckers. Instead it was buying 11m Leyland Leopards with Alexander Y-type bus bodies. It had first tried the type in 1964, when 53-seat Leopards were used to replace 53-seat lowbridge Titans. But after its experiences with the VRT and then the Fleetline, the Leopard became the fleet standard, and by 1975 there were almost 300 in operation, all with manual gearboxes. This figure would continue to rise as the decade progressed.

Central SMT did experiment with small buses on rail feeder services in East Kilbride, initially running four Bedford VASs, an unlikely type for a fleet otherwise made up of heavy-duty models. Two were ex-MacBrayne buses, the other two were new Duple-bodied coaches. They ran into housing estates where narrow roads precluded the use of buses wider than 7ft 6in.

To the south and west of Glasgow the major SBG subsidiary was Western SMT. It was also the biggest, with a fleet which was 1,000 strong. Western ran local services in Paisley, Greenock, Kilmarnock, Ayr and Dumfries and a substantial network of inter-town services which took its buses as far south-west as Stranraer and across the English border to Carlisle.

Here double-deckers predominated, with the mix much the same as in other SBG companies – Lodekkas, Titans, Lowlanders and Fleetlines. Western had been the biggest buyer of Lowlanders, but some had been moved quite early in their lives to the Alexander (Fife) and Highland Omnibuses fleets. Western (and Central) had split double-deck body orders between Alexander and Northern Counties in the late 1950s and early 1960s, which gave Western a small number of Northern Counties-bodied Fleetlines, a rare combination for SBG. These included six 33ft-long examples which were used on busy Paisley local services.

On long-distance routes Western often used double-deckers (most of its Titans were fitted with platform doors), but these were slowly being replaced by the standard SBG Leopard/Alexander Y-type. Older single-deck types were unusual Alexander-bodied Bristol MWs, a combination unique to the Western fleet and the only MWs to have been bodied by a builder other than ECW. Western avoided light-weight single-deckers. The last of the MWs had been bought in 1962 and the type lasted in Western service until 1978.

In 1975 the company operated on one island, Bute, where Leyland Leopards had ousted earlier generations of Titan PD1s and Bristol MWs. From 1979 it would also be serving Islay, which

Top right **Western SMT was the biggest user of Albion Lowlanders. These had bodywork by Alexander, as seen here in Ayr, and Northern Counties. This was a 1963 bus.** Stewart J Brown

Centre right **Western SMT also ran a sizeable fleet of Leyland Titans and over 150, all PD3s, were still in use in 1975. This PD3 with 67-seat Northern Counties body is seen leaving Anderston bus station in Glasgow, which had opened in 1971. The code above the fleet number was a short-lived year identifier with A indicating the 1950s (B was used for the 1960s) and 9 showing 1959.** Paul Caudell

Right **Northern Counties remained a regular supplier to Western SMT until 1971, and was to win one final order at the end of the decade. A 1967 Fleetline, one of six bodied by the Wigan manufacturer, operates a local service in Paisley.** Stewart J Brown

Most of Western SMT's Fleetlines had Alexander's attractive lowheight bodywork. Similar vehicles were operated in quantity by Alexander (Fife) and Alexander (Midland). This bus was new in 1970. It is crossing the River Cart, near Renfrew. Western SMT was running 178 Fleetlines in the mid-1970s, Scotland's biggest fleet of the type. Stewart J Brown

had once been MacBrayne country but had latterly been served by Maroner Coaches of Lochwinnoch. Other MacBrayne operations taken over by Western included the Glasgow to Campbeltown service and connecting operations to Lochgoilhead and to Oban. The Lochgoilhead service was run by an ex-MacBrayne Bedford, while the others used standard Leyland Leopards. Leopards used on coach duties were painted black and white, rather than red and cream. This livery was also applied to a fleet of impressive 12m-long Bristol REMH motorway coaches running from Glasgow to London. These had Alexander M-type bodies with reclining seats, a toilet, double-glazing and Webasto oil-fired heating, fully a decade before these started to become widespread on coaches.

One other SBG subsidiary ran regular services into Glasgow, Scottish Omnibuses. Trading as Eastern Scottish, the company ran services to the east and also had a network of local suburban services in the east end around Parkhead. These had come with the business of Lowland Motorways in 1958.

Scottish Omnibuses was based in Edinburgh, and its territory extended east from Glasgow through Coatbridge, Airdrie, and Bathgate, and then continued south to the English border at Berwick-on-Tweed. Much of its operating area south of Edinburgh was rural, and this was reflected in its fleet composition, with single-deckers outnumbering double-deckers by a small margin. The company had adopted Eastern Scottish as its trading name in 1964 – for most of its previous existence it had been known simply as SMT, the initials of the original company, Scottish Motor Traction.

Its older double-deckers were mainly Lodekkas; Scottish Omnibuses had bought only one batch of Leyland Titans in the 1950s, choosing not to dual-source double-deckers. The Titans were used on Glasgow area services and had attractive lowbridge bodies by Park Royal. The last were withdrawn in 1975. Similarly the single-deck fleet had been standardised on one type – AECs, with some 250 Reliances in operation in 1975. But also there were Bristol single-deckers, with most of a batch of 20 ECW-bodied MW6G models still being in service in 1975, although earlier batches of LSs had gone. To serve rural routes Eastern Scottish had bought 40 Bedford VAMs in 1967-68, and added 10m YRQs and 11m YRTs in the 1970s. Most of these had Alexander bodies, although 20 of the VAMs were bodied by Willowbrook. And although intended for rural operation they could often be seen on busy urban runs or even on the Edinburgh to Glasgow express. The switch from VAM to YRQ came after a brief flirtation with the Bristol LH.

Modern double-deckers were Lodekkas – the company's VRTs had been banished south in 1973 – and Fleetlines with ECW bodies.

A new type in the Eastern Scottish fleet in the mid-1970s was the Seddon Pennine VII. SBG had a fondness for the economy of Gardner engines, and the Pennine VII was the equivalent of a Gardner-powered Leopard – a straight-

Above right **The oldest buses in Eastern Scottish service in 1975 were Bristol Lodekkas dating from 1956-57. These were 60-seat LD6G models – all SBG Lodekkas were Gardner-engined. The destination is displayed on a bill on the front nearside window, a fairly common practice at Eastern Scottish in the 1960s and 1970s.** Stewart J Brown

Right **In 1973 Eastern Scottish disposed of its 45 Bristol VRTs, replacing them with E- and F-registered Lodekkas from a number of NBC subsidiaries. Eight came from Brighton Hove & District.** Stewart J Brown

forward design with a horizontal mid-mounted engine, developed specifically to meet SBG's requirements. There were 31 with Alexander bodies in operation in 1975 and this number would grow to over 300 by the end of the decade, including 64 Plaxton-bodied coaches. Western SMT also built up a fleet of Pennine VIIs but, unlike Eastern Scottish, continued to buy Leopards too.

In 1962 Scottish Omnibuses had taken over the business of Baxter's of Airdrie, running local services in Airdrie and Coatbridge. The name had briefly been dropped and then quickly revived, along with Baxter's unusual but attractive blue and grey livery. In 1975 Baxter's livery was still in use – although it would be phased out by the end of the decade – and was carried by a variety of Eastern Scottish types including ECW-bodied Fleetlines, FLF Lodekkas and Y-type Leopards. The Baxter fleet had been a modern one and a few ex-Baxter Reliances and PD2 Titans survived until the mid-1970s. The Titans had lowbridge Massey bodies, including some with forward entrances.

Returning to Glasgow, two independents ran local services which crossed the city boundary, even if they didn't reach the centre. Govan, a few miles to the west of the city centre, had been a bustling industrial suburb, but was in steep decline in the 1970s. It was also the site of an Underground station. Two of the Paisley area independents ran services to Govan, Graham's and Paton Brothers. In theory passengers wishing to travel to the city centre could continue their journey by subterranean transport.

Graham's still operated a few Guy Arabs, for much of the postwar period a type characteristic of the fleet. The last of these was a unique Arab V with Strachans body which had been an exhibit at the 1962 Commercial Motor Show. After that Graham's had switched to rear-engined types, buying one Atlantean and one Fleetline in 1963, both with Alexander bodies. A further Atlantean followed in 1971, but by 1975 the Fleetline fleet stood at 15, including two second-hand examples. The company's main route ran across Paisley from Hawkhead to Linwood. A service was also operated to Bridge of Weir, having been taken over from Pattison of Paisley in 1973. The fleet had been 100 per cent

Top left **Typical of the modern buses operated by Graham's, a 1970 Alexander-bodied Fleetline approaches Paisley Cross.** Stewart J Brown

Centre left **Paton had switched from buying old double-deckers to new single-deckers at the start of the 1970s, aided by the availability of the government's new bus grant. After buying Bedfords and Fords, it switched to Leyland Leopards in 1973. This Willowbrook-bodied example, seen at Govan Cross, was new in 1974.** Stewart J Brown

Left **The newest bus in the Cunningham's fleet in 1975 was this Atlantean with Roe bodywork, which was relatively rare in Scotland. The body is basically of the style then being built by Roe for the West Yorkshire PTE. The location is Paisley.** Stewart J Brown

double-deck until the start of the 1970s. New single-deckers included a Seddon Pennine RU and two R-series Fords. Later in the decade they would be joined by new Leopards.

Paton Brothers were based in Renfrew, on the south bank of the Clyde, in a depot adjacent to the Renfrew Ferry landing stage. The company's key route ran south to central Paisley, a busy service operated jointly with Cunningham's Bus Services and facing competition from Western SMT and, occasionally, with McGill's of Barrhead. The level of competition was of course controlled by the road service licensing system still in force.

Paton's buying policy in the 1960s had been based largely around the availability of second-hand Leyland Titans, although there were a few ex-Trent Tiger Cubs and ex-Glasgow Worldmasters. But the introduction of the government's new bus grant changed all that and from 1970 Paton began buying new Bedfords and Fords. There were nine in the fleet in 1975, along with four Leyland Leopards. Most of the new saloons had Willowbrook bodies, although later in the decade Paton would be buying Duple-bodied Leopards. A handful of Titans remained including examples from Blackpool, Plymouth and an unusual PD2A with Strachans body which had been new to A1 of Ardrossan. These were seldom to be found on front-line duties.

Paton's joint operator on the Paisley to Renfrew Ferry service, Cunningham's, was another which used the availability of the new bus grant to change from buying second-hand double-deckers to purchasing new buses. Cunningham's had in fact bought their first ever new 'decker, an Alexander-bodied Atlantean, in 1967, but with the aid of new bus grant then added five more Atlanteans to the fleet in the first half of the 1970s. These had bodies by Alexander, Northern Counties and Roe. Second-hand buses were still being bought and in the mid-1970s were primarily ex-Ribble PD3s with full-front Burlingham bodies, of which there were half-a-dozen in regular service. These replaced older second-hand Titans from Edinburgh Corporation, Trent and Western SMT. Both Cunningham's and Paton ran just over 20 vehicles, while Graham's ran just over 30.

Above right **McGill's ran a smart fleet. In 1975 its oldest bus was a 1958 Daimler CVG6/30 with Willowbrook body, which had originally been a Daimler demonstrator. It joined the McGill's fleet in 1961.**
Stewart J Brown

Right **Between 1963 and 1973 McGill's bought only Fleetlines, taking 14, all but one of which had Alexander bodywork. A 1965 bus is followed by a 1966 example, rebuilt with a later style of front panel.**
Stewart J Brown

The fourth of the Paisley area independents was McGill's Bus Service of Barrhead, running from there to Paisley. The company had been buying new buses from just after the end of World War 2; the only second-hand bus in the fleet in 1975 was a 1958 Daimler CVG6/30 with Willowbrook body which had been a Daimler demonstrator. The only other half-cab was a 1959 Massey-bodied PD2. The remainder of the fleet was made up of Fleetlines. The first, bought in 1963, had Northern Counties bodywork, the other 13 were Alexander-bodied, the newest dating from 1973 and destined to be the company's last new double-decker. In 1976 McGill's switched to Leyland Nationals.

The existence of five operators in central Paisley – Western SMT, Cunningham's, Paton, Graham's and McGill's, all running relatively frequent services, made it a colourful place. There was one other main focus of independent bus operation in Western's territory, the Ayrshire coast from Largs in the north to Ayr in the south.

Largs was served by Clyde Coast Services of Saltcoats with a route between the two towns. Double-deckers were operated until the early 1970s – latterly ex-Trent PD2s. Willowbrook-bodied Fords were the standard vehicles in the mid-1970s, although Plaxton-bodied coaches were also used on service as well as three ex-Hutchison of Overtown Willowbrook-bodied AEC Reliance buses. Clyde Coast was the smallest of the three Ayrshire co-operatives and had two partners.

In Saltcoats the main operator was A1 Service, a 14-member co-operative running 80 double-deck buses. A1 ran inland to Kilmarnock and provided local services in Irvine. A1 seized the opportunities presented by new bus grant to order no fewer than 40 new double-deckers in the early 1970s. Most were Alexander-bodied Fleetlines and Atlanteans, but from 1976 new deliveries included locally-built Ailsas. Alexander was again the favoured body supplier, although two Ailsas delivered in 1977 had striking Van Hool-McArdle bodies of a style being supplied to the South Yorkshire PTE.

Top left **Two 1967 AEC Reliances with Willowbrook bodies were operated by Clyde Coast. New to Hutchison of Overtown, they had joined the Clyde Coast fleet in 1972.** Stewart J Brown

Centre left **A 1956 Daimler CVG6 in the A1 fleet leads a convoy on a school service. The Daimler has a Northern Counties body. Behind are a couple of Alexander-bodied Fleetlines.** Stewart J Brown

Left **Roe bodywork to Leeds City Transport style – down to the tinted glass in the windows – was fitted to this 1973 Atlantean operated by A1 and seen in Kilmarnock. It was a PDR2 and the two-door body had 78 seats — and like most A1 buses it was crew-operated.** Stewart J Brown

Top **No Panthers or Panther Cubs were sold new to Scottish operators, and few second-hand examples found their way north. AA had two ex-SELNEC Panther Cubs with two-door Park Royal bodies. They had been new to Manchester City Transport in 1965 and were just six years old when bought by AA. The DT fleet number indicates Dodds, Troon, one of the members of the AA co-operative.** Stewart J Brown

Above **Most Willowbrook Expressway bodies were built on lightweight Bedford and Ford chassis. This AA example was unusual in being on an AEC Reliance. It was one of a pair purchased in 1972 and is seen in Irvine.** Stewart J Brown

Right **Another of the small operators in the south-west of Scotland was Carruthers of New Abbey. The fleet included this Willowbrook-bodied Ford which had been new to Newton of Dingwall. It has a good load as it awaits its departure time at the Whitesands bus terminal in Dumfries.** Stewart J Brown

A1 had in fact been buying new buses long before the advent of the government's new bus grant. Those still running in 1975 included AEC Regent Vs and Renowns, Leyland Titan PD2As and a number of Fleetlines and Atlanteans. At the start of the decade there had still been a sizeable number of second-hand types in operation, including the remnants of a large fleet of ex-London RTs and RTLs and a few ex-Edinburgh PD2s and Guy Arabs – but while selective second-hand buying remained part of the company's purchasing policy, new buses were now dominating the fleet.

The last of the Ayrshire co-operatives was AA Motor Services with two partners – Dodds of Troon and Young of Ayr. Young's portion of the fleet was made up entirely of Leylands, ranging from a Northern Counties-bodied PD3 to a 1973 National, the first in Scotland. In between these extremes were Leopards and Atlanteans, all bodied by Northern Counties. The two oldest Atlanteans – there were six in all – had Nottingham-style bodies. More Nationals joined the AA fleet as the decade progressed.

The Dodds portion of the fleet had only two Leylands, both ex-Manchester Panther Cubs which were used on a Troon local service. The remainder of the fleet was made up of a diminishing number of Guy Arabs – down to one Roe-bodied Mark IV of 1955 vintage by the middle of the decade – and a growing number of Daimler Fleetlines, most of which had Alexander bodies. There were AECs too, in the shape of Reliance buses and a venerable ex-demonstration Regent III with Saunders-Roe body. Unusual types to find in a Scottish fleet were an ECW-bodied Bristol KSW, ex Notts & Derby, and a Dennis Loline, ex-Aldershot & District. Both ran briefly for Dodds in the early 1970s. Other single-deckers were two Seddon Pennine RUs and the only Daimler Roadliner supplied new to a Scottish operator. It had a Plaxton bus body. New in 1965, it only lasted in AA service for seven years, but that didn't stop Dodds from buying a former PMT example in 1975, so the much-maligned Roadliner obviously wasn't all bad in AA's eyes.

In 1975 AA's services extended north from Ayr, where the company had its own bus station, through Irvine and Saltcoats to Ardrossan. Dodds also operated a modern coach fleet made

Above left **The three-figure telephone number is a delightful period touch on one of Garelochhead Coach Services' six AEC Regent Vs. The two oldest buses had Alexander bodies, as seen on this one getting set to leave its home town for the run down to Helensburgh.** Stewart J Brown

Left **Two Daimler Fleetlines delivered to Garelochhead Coach Services in 1973 had Alexander bodies with the fleet name displayed in a series of illuminated panels above the lower deck windows. These were to be the company's last new double-deckers.** Stewart J Brown

up mainly of AEC Reliances and Bedfords, the majority of which were bought new.

There was a small pocket of independent bus operation in Dumfriesshire. Gibson of Moffat normally used R-series Fords or an unusual ex-Barton Leyland Tiger with full-front lowbridge Northern Counties body, which could be seen on the company's Dumfries service. Carruthers of New Abbey also served Dumfries, running both Fords and Bedfords. The fleet of Blue Band of Lockerbie included a Bedford YRT with 60-seat Plaxton Derwent body, giving it a reasonable claim to be the Scottish single-decker with most seats. The high capacity was achieved by the use of three-plus-two seating. In Western's recently-acquired territory on the Kintyre peninsula West Coast Motor Services operated 20 buses and coaches running local services in and from its base in Campbeltown. The fleet was all single-decked and included AEC Reliances, Bedfords, and a solitary front-engined Seddon Pennine.

Between Kintyre and the Ayrshire mainland the island of Arran had since 1973 been served solely by Arran Coaches, an amalgam of two previous operators. Arran Coaches took advantage of the new bus grant to buy new Y-series Bedfords with Plaxton bodies, both bus and coach.

In Central SMT country there were a number of small and medium-sized independents. In Dunbartonshire there were two local bus operators, whose services effectively extended into rural areas beyond that served by Central. Barrie of Balloch, trading as Loch Lomond Bus Service, ran to Balmaha using Fords. From Helensburgh, Garelochhead Coach Services operated to the town of that name, and to Coulport. It also ran a Helensburgh town service and was heavily involved in services provided under contract to the naval base at Faslane, which had created a rapid expansion of the company's business in the late 1960s. New double-deckers were a feature of GCS, which bought six Regent Vs between 1958 and 1968. These were still in operation. The two oldest ones had rear-entrance Alexander bodies, while the remaining four had Northern Counties forward-entrance bodies. The first of these, a 1964 bus, had a body with a full-width front – unusual in Scotland and rare on Regent Vs outside East Kent. The last, a G-registered

Above right **The services operated by Hutchison of Overtown were covered by AEC Reliances – and one Leyland National. The Reliances had bus bodies by Duple, Willowbrook and, as on this bus, Plaxton. It was one of four identical 55-seaters delivered in 1972.** Stewart J Brown

Centre right **Despite the trucks in the background, this was in fact Lanark's bus station. The Stokes bus is a 1961 Tiger Cub with Willowbrook body, ex-Trent.** Stewart J Brown

Right **Irvine of Salsburgh operated a service between Airdrie and Shotts. This Plaxton-bodied AEC Reliance is typical of the vehicles used.** Stewart J Brown

Top **Edinburgh City Transport bought 10 Seddon Pennine midibuses in 1973. These front-engined buses had neat 25-seat Pennine bodies and were used to evaluate routes which could not justify the use of conventional single-deckers.** Michael Fowler

Above **Perhaps the most famous of Edinburgh's buses were the 300 Titans with lightweight Metro-Cammell Orion bodies which were bought for tramway replacement in the mid-1950s. Almost 90 survived to be taken over by Lothian Region. The last were withdrawn in 1976. These buses weighed less than 6¾ tons.** Malcolm King

Facing page top **Lothian Region Transport inherited 75 forward-entrance PD3s from Edinburgh City Transport. All had 70-seat Alexander bodies. A 1964 bus is seen in Princes Street.** Michael Fowler

Facing page bottom **From 1966 the Leyland Atlantean was Edinburgh's standard bus and by 1975 there were 475 in service, with more to come. All had Alexander bodies, generally with panoramic windows, as seen on this 1967 PDR1. Edinburgh had pioneered the use of big windows on double-deck buses.** Stewart J Brown

example of 1968, was not only the last AEC double-decker for a Scottish operator but was also Scotland's last new half-cab bus.

Subsequent new double-deckers were three Fleetlines and an Atlantean, delivered in the 1971-73 period, but the company's bus fleet was expanded primarily with new Fords. The mid-1970s saw Duple-bodied Leopard buses being bought new. Small numbers of second-hand vehicles continued to be added to the fleet including an ex-Bristol Omnibus MW coach of 1966, an unusual choice for a Scottish independent. The company's front-line coaches were named after Scottish lochs.

In Central's Lanarkshire heartland there was one major independent operator and a few smaller ones. Hutchison of Overtown ran 40 vehicles, with its bus services being concentrated on Motherwell and Wishaw. Its fleet was made up of AEC Reliances with bus bodies by Willowbrook and Plaxton (as well as Plaxton-bodied Reliance coaches) – all apart from one vehicle, a solitary Leyland National bought new in 1973. It remained unique in the Hutchison fleet which subsequently standardised on Duple-bodied Reliances for its bus operations until the cessation of production at AEC.

Smaller companies in Lanarkshire included Irvine of Law, operating between Wishaw and Carluke, and Stokes of Carstairs serving Lanark. Irvine had operated double-deckers until 1974 – the last was an ex-Darlington Daimler – but from 1975 the service was normally being run by an ever-changing fleet of second-hand coaches. The front-line vehicles in the Stokes bus fleet were two former Sheffield Transport AEC Swifts with Park Royal bodies. A Lanark town service was operated by Wilson of Carnwath, generally using a second-hand Albion Nimbus. Further north, Irvine of Salsburgh, trading as Golden Eagle Coaches, operated AEC Reliance buses between Shotts and Airdrie.

Edinburgh is Scotland's second centre of population and here city services were provided by Lothian Region Transport. LRT had taken over the former Edinburgh City Transport operations as a consequence of the reorganisation of local government in Scotland in May 1975. For the good burghers of Scotland's capital there was no outward change in their bus services. The livery remained unchanged, and the operation remained concentrated on services within the city boundary. Out-of-town services were provided mainly by Eastern Scottish, although Alexander (Midland) had routes to Stirling and beyond, while Alexander (Fife) operated services to the north over the Forth Bridge.

Edinburgh City Transport had been a loyal Leyland customer – a policy which LRT continued – and in 1975 its bus fleet was made up almost exclusively of Titans and Atlanteans, with almost 400 of the latter accounting for just over half the fleet. The only exceptions were 10 Seddon Pennine midis, bought in 1973 to test the scope for running small buses on selected

FURS
FURS
Marcus
FURS
MARCUS
OGILVIE
Portobello Craigentinny
Seafield Princes St
Murrayfield Corstorphine
12
BROOMHOUSE
ASC671B
26

ROYAL
BRITISH
HOTEL
West End George St
Bridges Liberton
Gracemount Southhous
20
BARNTON
Trust your insurance to the man from the PRUDENTIAL
EXACT FARE PLEASE
JSC 882E
SPECIAL
BREW

lightly-loaded routes – an idea ahead of its time. Other single-deck buses were a few Tiger Cubs (survivors from 100 supplied around 1960) and the famous Leopard 101 which had started life as a three-door pay-as-you-board bus but by 1975 had been converted to conventional single-door layout.

All of the Atlanteans had Alexander bodies, most with panoramic windows. The older Titans were some 80 Metro-Cammell-bodied PD2s, the remnants of large batches bought in the mid 1950s to replace the city's trams. The newer Titans had Alexander bodies and most were forward-entrance PD3s, although there was one batch of 50 rear-entrance Alexander-bodied PD2s. An unusual feature of Edinburgh's Titans was the use of the original BMMO-inspired new-look front, which Edinburgh continued to specify after 1961 when the St Helens-style bonnet was Leyland's standard. Post-1961 Edinburgh Titans had BMMO-style grilles manufactured in glass fibre in ECT's workshops. The 25 PD3s delivered to ECT in 1966 were the last new Titans for a Scottish operator.

LRT also operated a fleet of 45 Duple-bodied Bedford coaches, ranging in size from little VAS1s to 11m VALs and YRTs. These wore a smart black and white livery and provided tours of the city and its environs.

Although there were no regular independent services into Edinburgh, there were signs of a former private operator, Stark's of Dunbar. Stark's had long been associated with Scottish Omnibuses and while it was still an independent company had in fact operated vehicles with SMT fleetnames on services to Edinburgh. Following its takeover by Scottish Omnibuses in 1964 all of the company's buses started carrying Stark's fleetnames, and this was perpetuated until the late 1970s, typically on Alexander-bodied AEC Reliances in an attractive shade of apple green and cream, rather than the sombre dark green used for the main Eastern Scottish fleet. Stark's three newest buses, Alexander-bodied Tiger Cubs, lasted until 1975. To the east of Edinburgh Wiles Motor Services operated locally in Port Seton using Albion Nimbuses.

North of Edinburgh lies the Kingdom of Fife, and here in 1975 services were provided exclusively by SBG subsidiary Alexander (Fife). It had town service networks in Kirkcaldy and

Top left **Single-deckers played a comparatively small part in Edinburgh's local bus operations. Lothian took over 35 Tiger Cubs with Weymann bodies, which had been new in 1960.** Malcolm King

Left **Ostensibly still independent in the mid-1970s, Stark's of Dunbar had in fact been taken over by Scottish Omnibuses in 1964. Among the more interesting buses operated by Stark's were two 1959 AEC Reliances with Burlingham bodies which had been new to Baxter's of Airdrie.** Stewart J Brown

Right **The first big influx of Ailsas for an SBG company went to Alexander (Fife) which got 40 in 1975. Like all early Ailsas, they had Alexander bodies. This one is in Dunfermline.** Stewart J Brown

Below **Alexander (Fife) had a double-deck fleet which was powered mainly by Gardner. The older buses with Gardner engines were Bristol Lodekkas. A 1964 FS6G lays over in Kirkcaldy bus station.** Stewart J Brown

Dunfermline, the region's two main centres of population, and an extensive interurban network within Fife. Services also ran north to Dundee and Perth, and south to Glasgow and Edinburgh.

The fleet was divided equally between double-deck and single-deck types. The big news in 1975 was the entry into service of SBG's first Ailsas. The front-engined Ailsa had been developed by Volvo distributor Ailsa Trucks to address the widespread dissatisfaction which SBG's engineers felt with existing rear-engined models. This had been most visibly demonstrated in the great VRT/FLF exchange of 1973, but Daimler's Fleetline was not too highly regarded either. The Ailsa was seen as being the answer to a conservative Scottish bus engineer's prayer.

It had one obvious drawback for SBG. It was 14ft 6in high. All other new 'deckers purchased by SBG companies in the preceding 25 years had, without exception, been lowbridge or lowheight types, which were 13ft 6in high. But this was clearly seen as worth putting up with if it brought improved operating reliability. By the end of the 1970s Ailsas would be running for five SBG companies – Alexander (Fife), Alexander (Midland), Central SMT, Eastern Scottish and Western SMT.

Other double-deck types operated by Alexander (Fife) were Bristol Lodekkas, Albion Lowlanders and Daimler Fleetlines. There were 39 Lowlanders – seven bought new in 1962 and the remainder decanted from the Central and Western fleets when just a few years old. And there were 73 Fleetlines. Most had standard SBG-style lowheight Alexander bodies but there were 14 with ECW bodywork and five bodied by Northern Counties.

The Alexander (Fife) single-deck fleet was varied. There were typical SBG Reliances and Tiger Cubs with a variety of styles of Alexander body, culminating in the ubiquitous Y-type. There were also 48 Albion Vikings and 62 Leopards. But more unusual were a dozen Bristol RELL6Gs with ECW bus bodies, the first low-frame rear-engined buses for an SBG company. These dated from 1968 and were the only Scottish examples of a combination commonly found in England and Wales. Alexander (Fife) had also operated 20 of another combination commonly found south of the border, the ECW-bodied LS bus. It had 20, new in 1955 and taken out of service between 1973 and 1975. Ford R-series buses were introduced to the fleet in 1975.

Top left **Rear-engined double-deckers were introduced to the Alexander (Fife) operation in 1968, with the delivery of 20 Alexander-bodied Daimler Fleetlines. By 1975 the company had 73 Fleetlines, some of which were bodied by ECW and Northern Counties.** Stewart J Brown

Centre left **Typical of Alexander-bodied dual-purpose vehicles supplied to a number of SBG operators in the late 1950s is this Alexander (Fife) Leyland Tiger Cub in Dundee bus station. It was new in 1959. The short centre bay housed an emergency door on the offside of the body. Vehicles of this general design were built from 1958 to 1961.** Stewart J Brown

Left **The introduction of one-man-operated double-deckers by Dundee Corporation brought with it an almost military-style two-tone green livery, worn by two generations of Fleetlines seen here carrying the Tayside crest in place of the city coat of arms. Nearest the camera is a 1969 bus; alongside it a 1972 long-wheelbase example. Both have Alexander bodies.** Stewart J Brown

Above **Most of the half-cab buses in operation in Tayside in the mid-1970s were CVG6s, such as this 1957 example with Weymann bodywork. It was withdrawn in 1976, as new Ailsas ousted old Daimlers.** Stewart J Brown

Fife is bounded by the Forth to the south and the Tay to the north. Bridges over both estuaries had been opened in the 1960s and played a part in the extension of the Alexander (Fife) route network to serve areas which had previously not been easily accessible. One of these was Dundee.

Control of Dundee Corporation Transport passed to Tayside Regional Council in 1975 and where the change of ownership was imperceptible in Edinburgh, a rather different approach was adopted in Dundee. The Corporation's

Below **The last new half-cab buses bought by Dundee Corporation were seven Alexander-bodied Daimler CVG6s in 1960. This, the last one, illustrates the effect of Tayside's bright new livery. These were the only buses in the fleet with Manchester-style fronts.** Stewart J Brown

Below **Dundee was sufficiently impressed with its double-deck Fleetlines to buy 25 single-deckers with Alexander W-type bodies in 1970. They required substantial strengthening around the rear end and a number were withdrawn on expiry of their initial seven year Certificates of Fitness.** Stewart J Brown

Top **Among the odd buses operated by McLennan was this Tiger Cub with Northern Counties body. It had been new to Lancashire United.** Stewart J Brown

Above **Greyhound of Arbroath operated local services which ran as far as Dundee. Most of its buses were second-hand. Great Yarmouth had been the original owner of this 1964 AEC Reliance which had Pennine bodywork with an unusually short rear overhang.** Stewart J Brown

livery was green. Drab green. Some buses had a minimum of white relief. A new livery adopted in 1970 for one-man buses had dispensed with even that and introduced a dull two-tone green using shades best described as drab and drabber. Tayside gave the operation a much-needed new image using two-tone blue and white.

As with Scotland's other municipal fleets, services were concentrated within the city and double-deckers were used on most routes. These were mainly Daimlers – some 90 CVG6s bought between 1955 and 1960 and just over 100 Fleetlines. Most of the CVG6s had bodies by Metro-Cammell; all of the Fleetlines had Alexander bodies with post-1973 buses being dual-door 33-footers. Newly arrived in 1975 were the first Leylands to be added to the fleet since 1931. These were 15 ex-Edinburgh PD2s with Metro-Cammell Orion bodies. Tayside did not perpetuate Dundee's vehicle policy. It bought no more Fleetlines and in the latter part of the 1970s standardised on the Ailsa after a brief and unhappy flirtation with the Bristol VRT.

Dundee's last AEC double-deckers, seven 1953 Regent IIIs, were withdrawn in 1974-75, but AECs remained in the single-deck fleet. There were 20 AEC Reliances with Alexander Y-type bus bodies and 10 Alexander-bodied Swifts bought new in 1968. There were also four second-hand Swifts which had been new to Hutchison of Overtown in 1968 and were bought by Dundee in 1971-72 to help extend one-man operation. Dundee was also Scotland's biggest user of single-deck Fleetlines, taking 25 Alexander-bodied buses in 1970. They were not the city's best buy and by 1975 were being extensively rebuilt with reduced seating capacity because the chassis were flexing to such an extent that the bodies were breaking up.

Three SBG companies ran regular services into Dundee and these were the three Alexander companies. Alexander (Fife) came in across the Tay Bridge, while Alexander (Midland) had services from Perth and, indeed, from Glasgow. The major SBG operator in Dundee and to the area northwards was Alexander (Northern).

Two independents ran infrequent services to the city. McLennan of Spittalfield, in Perthshire, operated rural services which embraced an area bounded roughly by Dundee, Blairgowrie and Perth. It had a mixed fleet with both new and second-hand buses. The former ranged from bus-grant specification Willowbrook-bodied Fords, to a 1951 Leyland Tiger with McLennan-built body which could fairly lay claim to be the last half-cab bus in regular use in Scotland. But the bulk of the 40-strong fleet was second-hand and included Bedford SBs, Leyland Tiger Cubs and ex-Aberdeen Daimler CVD6 double-deckers with Alexander bodywork. The last-named had 1951 chassis with 1960 bodies.

The other independent serving Dundee was Greyhound of Arbroath. This fleet also included Alexander-bodied Daimler double-deckers in the shape of ex-Glasgow CVG6s, as well as an assortment of new and used single-deckers. The new vehicles were mainly Fords with bus-grant coach bodies by Duple.

Alexander (Northern) had its headquarters in Aberdeen and served eastern Scotland from Dundee north to Elgin. It had depots in most of the major towns in this predominantly farming area. Vehicles tended to have long operational

Right **Alexander (Northern) operated a varied single-deck fleet, although AECs were in the majority until the arrival of new Fords from 1971. A 1957 Reliance with Alexander body is seen in Stonehaven. It gave 20 years service.** Malcolm King

Below **The first buses delivered to Alexander (Northern) in its new yellow livery were 18 Alexander-bodied AEC Reliances in 1962. These had BET-style bodies; from 1963 the handsome Y-type would be the new standard.** Malcolm King

Below right **To speed replacement of early postwar Titans the Alexander (Northern) fleet received an injection of mid-1950s PD2s from Western SMT in 1970-71. This 1956 bus was 14 years old when it moved north – already time-expired by the standards of many big fleets. It would be almost 20 years old by the time it left the Alexander (Northern) fleet. The body was by Northern Counties.** Stewart J Brown

lives with Alexander (Northern) and in 1975 the oldest buses in the fleet were 20-year-old AEC Reliances and Monocoaches with Alexander bus bodies. There were a few Albion Aberdonians, too, slightly younger, and on their way out as the fleet was being rapidly updated with lightweight Fords.

SBG at the start of the 1970s had been looking for a low-cost replacement for its ageing Tiger Cubs and Reliances – something less robust (and expensive) than a Leyland Leopard which would be suitable for rural routes. Eastern Scottish opted for Bedfords, but the three Alexander companies (and Highland Omnibuses) chose the R-series Ford. The first for Alexander (Northern) arrived in 1971. By 1975 there were over 100 in the fleet and by the end of the decade this figure would be not far short of 200, making the company Britain's biggest operator of R-series Fords. Most had Alexander bodies, but some were bodied by Duple.

Alexander (Northern) also had standard SBG Leopards, and the country's biggest fleet of Albion Vikings, with 94 including six which had been new to Eastern Scottish. Its smallest vehicles were two stretched Ford Dorchester 7-seaters used on a limousine service linking Dundee with Edinburgh airport.

The double-deck fleet was made up of lowbridge Leyland Titans PD3s delivered new and PD2s acquired from Western SMT. There were also two 1963 Albion Lowlanders, the company's newest 'deckers. From 1976 second-hand Fleetlines would join the fleet from Central SMT and Alexander (Midland), and by the end of the 1970s the company would be buying small batches of new Fleetlines with ECW bodies.

In Aberdeen itself, local services were provided by Grampian Regional Transport, successor to Aberdeen Corporation. Here the change of ownership was marked by a slight modification to the fleet livery, with the addition of orange relief and a reduction in the amount of green – but still providing a clear visual link between new and old operators. With 236 vehicles Grampian was the smallest of the public sector bus companies in Scotland and here, as in

Top left **Typifying the front-engined types which Grampian took over from Aberdeen Corporation, this is a 1963 Daimler CVG6 with Alexander body.**
Murdoch Currie

Left **Unusual buses in the Grampian fleet were three ex-Leeds AEC Reliances with two-door Roe bodies. New in 1964, they had been purchased from Leeds City Transport by Aberdeen Corporation in 1971. The last time Aberdeen had bought second-hand buses had been in 1936. One is seen at Castle Street, for many years the hub of the city's bus services.**
Malcolm King

other Scottish cities, most services were run by double-deckers.

The old order was represented by Daimler CVG6s and Regent Vs bought between 1955 and 1965. The C-registered CVG6s were Scotland's last front-engined Daimlers and were among the last rear-entrance buses to enter service north of the border. (The only other C-registered rear-entrance bus in Scotland was an A1 Service Titan; from 1966 all front-engined buses for Scottish fleets were of forward-entrance layout.) Aberdeen Corporation had tried rebuilding some of its CVG6s with forward-entrances for use as one-man buses. Eight were so treated and operated with but limited success. Modern double-deckers were a mixture of Fleetlines and Atlanteans, all bodied by Alexander. There were 78 in all of which slightly more than half were Fleetlines, the newest being 1973 buses. From 1974 all new double-deckers were Atlanteans.

Single-deckers featured in the fleet and comprised Leyland Tiger Cubs, AEC Swifts and AEC Reliances with Alexander bodies. There were also three ex-Leeds City Transport Reliances with Roe bodies, new in 1964 and purchased in 1971, and a trio of 1973 Leyland Nationals, the only examples of the type in use with a major Scottish operator in 1975. A prototype Alexander integral midibus, based on Ford A-series truck units, was on extended loan. Three were purchased in 1976.

Inverness bills itself as the capital of the Highlands. It is certainly the last major town in the north and was the headquarters of what was generally viewed as SBG's most impoverished subsidiary, Highland Omnibuses. Highland covered a massive, but sparsely-populated, area which stretched north to Wick and Thurso, south to Fort William and Oban, and west to Skye. Its fleet had virtually doubled in size at the start of the 1970s with the acquisition of much of MacBrayne's operations, along with the Oban operations of Alexander (Midland).

Traditionally Highland had bought small numbers of new buses each year and augmented its fleet with cast-offs from richer southern SBG subsidiaries. Many of these buses were time-expired before they started their journey north.

Top right **Highland's dark red livery was soon to be but a memory, with few buses remaining in it by 1975. This is a Ford R192 with Willowbrook bus body, one of 12 delivered in 1969. They were to run until the early 1980s.** Paul Caudell

Centre right **Highland took over most of the MacBrayne's bus operations and the vehicles which ran them, such as this 1961 Duple (Midland)-bodied AEC Reliance in Fort William.** Murdoch Currie

Right **Bedford SB buses were an unusual find in a state-owned bus fleet. This 1970 SB5 with Willowbrook body had been ordered by MacBrayne but was delivered to Highland. It was the company's last new Bedford.** Stewart J Brown

But the discovery of the Ford R-series changed all that, and in the mid-1970s Highland's fleet boasted 100 R-series bought new, most of which had bodies by Willowbrook and Alexander. AEC Reliances had featured in the fleet since the mid-1950s and still did so 20 years on, although by this time most were either ex-Eastern Scottish examples or vehicles acquired with the various parts of the MacBrayne operation. Earlier Monocoaches and Reliances which were in use at the start of the 1970s had been replaced by the influx of Fords.

Also acquired from MacBrayne were Bedford VASs and SBs; the fleet's other Bedfords were mid-1960s VAMs with bodies by Alexander and Willowbrook. These had been bought new and included one with a Y-type body with 24 coach seats in the front section and a large mail compartment at the rear. This was normally used on the remote Durness to Thurso service. There were Albion Vikings too. Five were coaches which had been new to Central SMT in 1966 but were transferred to Highland when just 12 months old; the others – eight in all – had come from Eastern Scottish and Alexander (Midland).

Highland's double-deck fleet contained no new buses. The standard, since 1965, had been the Albion Lowlander of which there were 50. Most had come from Central and Western, but one oddity was an East Lancs-bodied example which had started life with Luton Corporation. Short-lived double-deckers included two AEC Bridgemasters and a Renown from Eastern Scottish (part of the Baxter's legacy), and six Edinburgh Corporation PD3s which arrived in 1974 and left in 1976 – vehicles often stayed but briefly with Highland. Modernity was on the horizon, and from 1977 first second-hand and later brand new Fleetlines joined the Highland

Top left **The oddest of many unusual buses operated by Highland in the 1970s was this 1958 Leyland Titan PD3 with unique Holmes glass fibre bonnet. It had been new to Edinburgh Corporation in 1958 and had been bought by Highland, along with five more conventional BMMO-fronted PD3s, in 1974. All had forward-entrance Alexander bodies and ran in Inverness until 1976.** Malcolm King

Left **Willowbrook-bodied Fords changed Highland's fleet make-up in the early 1970s, as new buses replaced old vehicles transferred from other SBG companies.** Stewart J Brown

Right **Sutherland Transport ran to some of the most isolated settlements on the British mainland with Durness, the destination of this 1965 VAS, being a case in point. The body was built in Glasgow by SMT, who were the city's Bedford dealers.** Stewart J Brown

fleet. Double-deck operation was confined primarily to Inverness town services and to operations around Thurso, including services to the atomic energy plant at Dounreay.

There was one old-established independent operator in the far north, the Sutherland Transport & Trading Company of Lairg. Its network of services radiating from the Post Office at Lairg was slowly disappearing, but in 1975 its Bedfords with mail compartments still ran to remote communities in the far north-west. Services only operated once daily, and were timed to connect with the mail train. The biggest independent in Highland's territory was Newton of Dingwall, running Willowbrook-bodied Fords on contract services supporting the region's booming oil platform industry.

One other major operator served Scotland – the Scottish Postal Board with its Postbus fleet. The first was introduced in 1968.

Then the advent of new bus grant made the economics of Postbus operation that much more attractive and by 1977 there were 100 Postbus services in Scotland, serving remote communities throughout the mainland and on many of the islands too. Most of the buses were 11-seat Commer PB2000s, but some services were covered by Morris Marina estate cars, and even by Land-Rovers.

1975: Major bus fleets – Scotland

Operator	*Fleet size*
Greater Glasgow PTE	1,231
Western SMT	1,010
Scottish Omnibuses	889
Alexander (Midland)	808
Lothian Region Transport	755
Central SMT	604
Alexander (Fife)	479
Alexander (Northern)	446
Highland Omnibuses	319
Tayside Regional Council	243
Grampian Regional Transport	236

North West England

THERE are two main centres of activity which dominate the North West, based on Manchester and Liverpool. In 1975 both were the focal points for two Passenger Transport Executives which dated back to 1969, although both had been expanded as a result of local government reorganisation in 1974.

The Greater Manchester PTE, trading as Greater Manchester Transport, had taken over from SELNEC in 1974. This change saw the PTE's operating area extended to include Wigan, with the consequent absorption of Wigan's 127-strong municipal bus fleet. GMT was Britain's biggest bus operator outside London, with some 2,800 vehicles. Double-deckers reigned supreme. There were only 300 single-deckers in GMT service, representing just over 10 per cent of the fleet.

In the five years from the formation of SELNEC much progress had been made in ousting non-standard vehicle types – such as Atkinsons – and in introducing the trend-setting PTE standard bus. There were over 600 standards on the streets of Greater Manchester in 1975; Atlanteans and Fleetlines with outwardly-similar bodies by Park Royal and Northern Counties. But beneath the almost universal orange and white livery, there still lurked remarkable variety, representing the disparate fleets which had been welded together by the PTE. By and large the former municipal vehicles which survived with GMT remained in service in those towns which had originally bought them.

The most striking of the previous generation of buses was the Mancunian, a design developed by Manchester City Transport to introduce double-deck one-man-operation to its services. The square-rigged Mancunian was a remarkable stylistic advance when it first appeared in 1968. Built mainly by Park Royal and Metro-Cammell on Atlantean and Fleetline chassis, there were

Left **Wigan's last Titans had Massey bodies and entered service in 1968. This one is operating from Greater Manchester Transport's Oldham depot in 1977, a relatively rare example in the GMT fleet of a former municipal bus being transferred away from its town of origin. It is seen in central Manchester.** David Brown

Above right **A standard double-decker was developed by SELNEC and continued by Greater Manchester. Most were Atlanteans, with bodies by Northern Counties or, as here, Park Royal. Greater Manchester was running Britain's biggest Atlantean fleet by the end of the 1970s.** Leyland

Right **In the middle of the 1970s a few reminders survived of the days before the PTE, such as this Metro-Cammell-bodied Daimler Fleetline running in Manchester colours. Note the driver's offside mirror, which is in PTE livery, and the multiplicity of types of opening window on the upper deck.** Stewart J Brown

some 500 operating, primarily in Manchester itself. Earlier generations of MCT buses were also still to be seen on the city's streets. There were rather less glamorous mid-1960s Atlanteans and Fleetlines with Metro-Cammell bodies and there were also still sizeable numbers of Daimler CVG6s and exposed-radiator Leyland Titan PD2s, the oldest dating back to 1957 and nearing the ends of their working lives.

Neighbouring Salford City Transport was running large numbers of Daimler CVG6s and Leyland PD2s when SELNEC was formed. By 1975 the PD2s, with forward-entrance Metro-Cammell bodies, were still much in evidence, but only a few of the most modern Daimlers remained in use. The newest of the Titans were 25 E-registered buses which in 1975 were just eight years old. Salford had operated rear-engined buses and these too were still around – five early 1960s Fleetlines and two batches of late 1960s Atlanteans.

Westwards lay Leigh, where the Corporation's legacy to GMT was a fleet of East Lancs-bodied AEC Renowns and a few Leyland Titans, unusual in having side-gangway lowbridge bodies which by the mid 1970s were becoming rare outside Scotland. They were the only lowbridge buses in service with any of the PTEs in 1975. Further west lay Wigan, absorbed by GMT in 1974 and being served by a fleet which had changed little except in its colour, as GMT orange and white was replacing Wigan Corporation's traditional maroon and white. Both liveries could be seen around the town on the Leyland Titans which carried bodies by two local builders, Massey and Northern Counties. All were of forward-entrance layout. There were short PD2s and long PD3s, and each of the three postwar styles of Leyland bonnet were represented – BMMO-style sheet-metal fronts on the

Above left **Manchester City Transport's striking Mancunian was one of the most significant advances in bus styling in the 1960s. A 1968 Fleetline with Park Royal body enters Piccadilly Gardens, the main terminal area in central Manchester.** Stewart J Brown

Left **Wigan's municipal fleet was absorbed by the Greater Manchester PTE in 1974. Most of its buses were Leyland Titans, including four 1967 PD2s with 64-seat Northern Counties bodies. Note the green marker lights alongside the destination display and the fleetname on the upper deck side panels. The conductor leaning on the front wing was a member of a threatened species. There would be few conducting jobs outside London when the 1970s drew to a close.** Royston Morgan

oldest PD3s, St Helens-style glass fibre bonnets on early 1960s PD2As and PD3As and, somewhat bizarrely, old-fashioned exposed radiators on the newest PD2s dating from the 1966-68 period. There were also rear-engined Leylands in the Wigan fleet, with dual-door Atlanteans and Panthers bodied by Northern Counties, and a pair of Massey-bodied Panther Cubs. On order by Wigan in 1974 were six ECW-bodied Bristol LHs; they had entered GMT service, in Wigan, at the start of 1975. A distinguishing feature of Wigan Corporation's buses was a green light beside the front destination screen which allowed would-be nocturnal passengers to differentiate between Corporation and Ribble buses after dark. Needless to say, this idiosyncratic fitment was abandoned by the PTE.

Half-cab buses were fast-disappearing in Bolton – in part because Bolton Corporation had specified full fronts on its last front-engined double-deckers. These had included AEC Regent Vs and Daimler CVG6s, but they had been ousted by new PTE standard buses in the early 1970s so that by 1975 only Leylands remained to represent Bolton's erstwhile municipal bus fleet. These were PD3s (both half-cab and full-front) and Atlanteans, the oldest of which dated from 1963. Bolton had evolved a stylish look for its rear-engined buses, most of which had well-proportioned East Lancs bodies. This had culminated in 1969 with an unusual design incorporating sloping window pillars – or, to be strictly accurate, trapezoidal window frames. The bodies did, of course, retain vertical pillars.

In neighbouring Bury there were a few ex-municipal Titans still in service, but most of the former Bury Corporation buses were Daimler Fleetlines. These included 15 1964 buses with Alexander bodies, at that time a rare southern excursion into a municipal fleet for the Scottish

Top right **Single-deckers played a small part in GMT's operations. They included Panthers with Northern Counties bodies which had come from the Wigan undertaking.** Paul Caudell

Centre right **A unique style of East Lancs body was supplied to Bolton on 15 Atlanteans in 1969. These had sloping window frames and fixed windows. Bolton had been among a small number of operators to pay serious attention to body appearance on rear-engined chassis, breaking way from some of the less-inspired designs which characterised the earliest bodies on Atlanteans and Fleetlines.** Stewart J Brown

Right **Bury Corporation was one of the first buyers of Daimler's SRG-series Fleetline, developed specifically for single-deck operation. It had nine, all with two-door East Lancs bodies. This was a 1969 bus. The panel to the right of the fleet number could be illuminated to advise passengers to pay on entry. It was a common fitment on front-entrance buses in the early days of omo, when many buses of this layout would still have a two-man crew.** Stewart J Brown

Left **Ramsbottom had been the smallest constituent of the SELNEC PTE, with a fleet of just 12 buses, all Leyland Titans. This PD2A dated from 1963 and had bodywork by Northern Counties. It is seen in Bury in 1973, carrying advertising for SELNEC's private hire service.** Paul Caudell

Below **Roe bodies of a distinctive style were fitted to Atlanteans bought by Ashton-under-Lyne, as demonstrated by this 1966 bus heading out of Manchester past Piccadilly railway station in 1976. A PTE standard Fleetline across the road – one of a minority with two-door bodywork – heads towards the city centre.** Stewart J Brown

Above right **Among the most unusual buses in the SHMD fleet were 10 short Fleetlines with Northern Counties bodies. This model had been developed for Walsall, the only other operator to specify it. SHMD had 10. They had Gardner 6LW engines and were 68-seaters. The sliding exit door was a most unusual fitment. This one is in Hyde seen early in the decade, not long after its first repaint into SELNEC livery.** Paul Caudell

Below right **SHMD's buses had been green, as illustrated by a well-loaded Northern Counties-bodied PD2 in Stockport in 1973. It was new in 1959 and survived until the middle of the 1970s.** John Robinson

body builder. In Bury's single-deck fleet there were nine East Lancs-bodied Fleetlines and a pair of Reliances with Alexander Y-type bodies. Ramsbottom Urban District Council had been the smallest of SELNEC's constituents and its buses – assorted Leyland Titans – could be seen running in to Bury. The last Ramsbottom Titan, now in PTE livery, had made the history books by being the last half-cab double-decker for a British operator and one of only four half-cabs with H-suffix registrations (the other three were Guys in Chester). When it was delivered in November 1969 (to the PTE, which had just taken over the Ramsbottom operation) it was thought to be the last front-engined double-decker for a British bus fleet – but who could have known that just four years later the Ailsa would be unveiled. GMT's two smallest buses – a Duple-bodied Bedford J2 and a Weymann-bodied Albion Nimbus – were based at Ramsbottom.

Rochdale Corporation was unusual among Lancashire municipal fleets in that it had standardised on AECs in the mid-1950s, and some 25 Regent Vs and a dozen Reliances were still in GMT service in 1975. Rochdale's more modern buses were Fleetlines and AEC Swifts. The 10 newest Swifts, with bodies built in nearby Oldham by Seddon, had been ordered by Rochdale in 1969, but were not actually built and delivered to the PTE until 1971-72. They were the PTE's last AEC buses – although it did buy Reliance coaches later in the 1970s.

In Oldham the oldest ex-Corporation buses were Roe-bodied Titans, including nine handsome forward-entrance exposed-radiator PD3s. However the bulk of town services were covered by Atlanteans, of which there were just over 70 either acquired from or ordered by Oldham Corporation. Similarly the oldest buses in Ashton-under-Lyne were Roe-bodied Titans, in this case PD2s. Here, too, more modern buses were Atlanteans. The Stalybridge, Hyde, Mossley and Dukinfield joint board had adopted a distinctive vehicle policy in which the common strands were Gardner engines and Northern Counties bodies. Thus there were CVG6s, Fleetlines and Bristol REs running in what was now known as Tameside, all bodied in Wigan and powered by Gardner. And to prove that any rule can be broken, there was also a 1962 Leyland Titan. Most interesting of the Fleetlines were 10 Walsall-style short examples with 68-seat bodies – by Northern Counties of course. These odd buses were of two-door layout with a single jack-knife door ahead of the front wheel, and a one-piece sliding door to the rear of it.

The last, and most conservative, of SELNEC's original constituents was Stockport Corporation, which had a fleet made up mainly of Leyland Titans. By 1975 there were still over 100 in daily operation, the newest being a dozen G-registered PD3s. Most had East Lancs bodies, but a solitary Longwell Green-bodied bus was still in use.

SELNEC had in 1972 acquired a large part of the North Western Road Car Co from NBC. North Western had been a BET subsidiary with a modern fleet, and signs of this in GMT's operations were Alexander-bodied Fleetlines and Bristol RELLs, and a small number of Park Royal-bodied AEC Renowns. There were also Bristol RESLs with Marshall bodies. On order at the time of the take-over were 25 standard NBC-style ECW-bodied Bristol VRTs. These were delivered to SELNEC in 1973 and in the PTE's attractive livery they illustrated just how unimaginative NBC's new corporate identity was. The ex-North Western buses in the GMT fleet served Manchester, Stockport and Altrincham in the main, with a small allocation based at an outpost in Glossop.

SELNEC's main interest in vehicles was the development of its standard double-decker, and these were replacing time-expired ex-municipal buses throughout its operating area. But it had looked at other types too.

In 1972 SELNEC took delivery of four midibuses, neat little Seddon Pennine IV:236 models with 25-seat Seddon bodies. They were evaluated on lightly-used services and by 1975 there were 43, many of which were running on a new Manchester Centreline service, linking the city's two main rail terminals with the main shopping and business areas. It had also tried out new designs of full-size single-decker, and after experimental batches of Metro-Scanias and Leyland Nationals plumped for the latter taking over 100 by the end of 1975. It also bought two Mercedes-Benz O.305s which were bodied by Northern Counties. These had two doors and were among the last buses of this layout to join the fleet. The future standard for operation in Manchester – as in most other British cities – would be single-door.

Although settled on the Fleetline and Atlantean chassis for double-deck operation,

Top left **Ex-Stockport Titans would be the last half-cab buses in regular service in Greater Manchester, with some surviving into the early 1980s. That was still a long way off when this 1968 bus was photographed in the summer of 1973. It is in Stockport livery, but with SELNEC Southern division name and SELNEC fleet number.** John Robinson

Left **This 1958 Tiger Cub in the SELNEC fleet has Crossley bodywork to Park Royal designs. It was new to Stockport Corporation and is seen in the town in 1973. Tiger Cubs were not that common in big urban fleets.** John Robinson

Right **The acquisition of North Western in 1972 was the first major expansion by the SELNEC PTE and it introduced a range of new types to the fleet, such as this 1964 Park Royal-bodied AEC Renown. The over-painting of the North Western fleetname is visible.** Stewart J Brown

Below **The front-engined Seddon Pennine midibus was developed for SELNEC, and SELNEC/GMT became the biggest user of the type, with a 43-strong fleet. Most were used to run an inter-station service in Manchester, linking Victoria and Piccadilly rail stations with the main city centre area. Seddon built the bodies. Two await business at Piccadilly station in 1977.** Stewart J Brown

Below right **Two Mercedes-Benz O.305s were built for SELNEC. They entered service in 1973 and survived until the end of the decade, spending most of their lives in Oldham. Northern Counties bodywork was fitted. This one is crew-operated. The conductor's Bell Punch ticket machine is sitting behind the nearside windscreen.** Stewart J Brown

GMT remained open to other alternatives and took 10 MCW Metropolitans in 1974. These operated on the Trans-Lancs Express. Later in the decade it would become involved with the Foden-NC, among other types.

There were three independent bus operators serving Greater Manchester and breaking up the sea of orange and white buses. They were rather different in scale. Mayne ran nine AEC Regents on a route from central Manchester to Droylsden and also had a coach fleet. In the latter part of the decade the Regents would be replaced by Daimler Fleetlines and Bristol VRTs. The Godfrey Abbott Group in a joint venture with GMT ran a dial-a-ride service in Sale using 10 Bedford CF minibuses with Deansgate bodies. This had been started in 1974.

The other independent, Lancashire United Transport, was Britain's biggest, with a fleet of 360 buses and coaches on a network of services embracing most of the towns between Manchester and Liverpool. Its independence was under threat. A co-ordination agreement with the PTE in 1971 had been followed in 1972 by a further agreement. This saw a change in the constitution of LUT with the PTE gaining the option to buy the company on or after 1 January 1976 – an option which it duly exercised on that date.

However in 1975 LUT was to all intents and purposes still an independent, operating from three depots at Atherton, Swinton and Hindley. LUT's double-deck fleet was an odd mixture of conservative Guy Arabs and modern Fleetlines. The company had bought its first Fleetlines in 1962, but it continued buying Guy Arabs until 1967 and the 26 delivered that year marked Guy's last major British bus order. In 1975 there were some 125 Arabs still in service, making LUT easily the country's biggest Guy user. These were running alongside just over 50 Fleetlines. All of the Fleetlines and the majority of the Arabs had Northern Counties bodies.

The single-deck fleet was of note in that although it was made up of common enough chassis, these were often fitted with unusual bodies. There were Leopards, Bristol REs, Seddon Pennine RUs and a few Reliances. Bodies on the REs were by Plaxton and Alexander (to a unique design for LUT) and most were of two-door layout. The Seddon Pennines also had two-door Plaxton bus bodies, not a common choice on the RU, while the solitary batch of 20 Bristol LHs had two-door Northern Counties bodies. Two-door bodies on the high-framed LH were very rare.

The western extremity of LUT's route network was Liverpool, headquarters of the Merseyside PTE which in 1974 had been expanded to take in St Helens and Southport. The PTE had started life in 1969 with two liveries, dark green and cream in Liverpool – a continuation of Liverpool Corporation's colours and blue and primrose in Birkenhead and Wallasey, picking up the colours used by the two former municipal operators in these towns. In

Firth Carpets Limited
GILROY
The greatest name in King Size
MAYNE
MAYNE
213 DROYLSDEN SUNNYSIDE RD.
PLEASE PAY CONDUCTOR
DAIMLER
LRJ 213P

BOLTON A
59
WIGAN
LANCASHIRE UNITED
187
RTC 352C

Above left **Mayne switched from AEC Regent Vs to Daimler Fleetlines in 1976 with the delivery of five Roe-bodied CRG6LXBs. These were Mayne's first new buses since 1965. The arrival of Bristol VRTs in 1978 with ECW dual-purpose bodies would see the end of this maroon and blue livery, with the company's red and cream coach colours being applied to buses too.** Stewart J Brown

Below left **Lancashire United was the last British operator to run a big fleet of Guys. Around 125 were in service in the mid-1970s, most with forward-entrance Northern Counties bodies. A 1965 Arab V pulls away from the platform in Bolton bus station on the service to Wigan.** John Robinson

Above **Leyland Atlanteans were the most numerous type in the Merseyside PTE fleet. Four Alexander-bodied buses in Liverpool create the illusion that body types were standardised. Alexander became the major supplier to the PTE, but there were substantial numbers of Atlanteans with bodies by other builders, most notably Metro-Cammell and East Lancs. The leading vehicle is one of 340 Atlanteans with Alexander bodies delivered between 1972 and 1976.** Stewart J Brown

the autumn of 1974 there was a rethink, and a new lighter Verona green and cream (officially described as jonquil, a word which no doubt tripped off every Liverpudlian's tongue) was applied fleet-wide. But in 1975 all three liveries could still be seen – as well as red and cream on buses inherited from St Helens and Southport. This livery was retained in Southport for the town's open-top fleet.

This didn't mean that central Liverpool was a mass of colour. There were few transfers between operating districts and where these did happen – noticeably with ex-Birkenhead buses moving to Liverpool – vehicles were repainted in green. The services in St Helens and Southport were generally self-contained, although St Helens buses did venture into the Greater Manchester PTE area at Atherton and also ran to Liverpool and Warrington.

With a fleet of over 1,600 vehicles, Merseyside ranked fourth in size amongst British bus companies after London Transport, GMT and the West Midlands PTE. Most of its buses were Leylands, and most of these were Atlanteans. But where Greater Manchester (and SELNEC before it) had developed a standard body, Merseyside adopted a more individual line and bought bodies to different designs from Alexander, East Lancs and, on Fleetlines, Metro-Cammell.

There were around 1,000 Atlanteans which included 400 newish Alexander-bodied examples, as well as earlier Liverpool-style vehicles. After buying a solitary trial PDR1 in 1959 (which was still in use in 1975), Liverpool had placed an order for 200 which were delivered between 1962 and 1964 and had distinctively-styled Metro-Cammell bodies. These remained in service, along with generally similar buses delivered later in the 1960s. Older Liverpool buses had been AEC Regent Vs and Leyland Titan PD2s. Most of those which had been taken over by the PTE had been rendered redundant by the steady inflow of Atlanteans, but a few of each type survived to 1975, by which time they were a creditable 20 years old. Variety was injected into the Liverpool scene with the transfer from the Wirral division of 41 Massey-bodied PD2s which had been new to Birkenhead. These arrived between 1973 and 1975, some coming via St Helens. A few ex-Southport Titans were also running in Liverpool in 1975.

Liverpool was one of a number of cities to embrace single-deck one-man-operation in the 1960s, buying 110 Leyland Panthers with two-door Metro-Cammell bodies in 1968-69. As elsewhere, the Panthers were not a resounding success and almost half the fleet was out of service – sold or withdrawn – by 1975. To facilitate double-deck omo Liverpool was one of the

Top left **Among the buses which Merseyside acquired from Liverpool Corporation were AEC Regent Vs with Metro-Cammell bodies. The bodies were based on the Orion but were unusual in being of four-bay construction rather than five. Non-standard grilles were specified, similar to those fitted to Regent Vs for Glasgow Corporation. This dark green livery was that which had been used by Liverpool Corporation. This bus was new in 1958.** Stewart J Brown

Top right **Liverpool also ran Leyland Titans, including some which were not painted. The Corporation had extensive bodybuilding facilities and assembled or completed many bodies during the 1950s. This batch of Titans had 1957 chassis which had body framing built by Crossley and completed – in 1961 – by Metro-Cammell. As with the AECs, Liverpool had a non-standard bonnet on its Leyland Titans.** Stewart J Brown

Above left **Leyland Panthers were used to introduce omo to Liverpool and were inherited by the Merseyside PTE. They wore two liveries – originally mainly cream, as shown here, or later mainly green, with cream window surrounds. The bodywork was by Metro-Cammell. This livery with dark relief round the windows quite effectively disguised the two different levels of the windows, necessary because of the raised floor level aft of the centre exit door.** Stewart J Brown

Above right **Ten Bristol REs with 44-seat ECW bodies were delivered to the Merseyside PTE in 1971. They were diverted from an order originally intended for NBC's PMT subsidiary and had Leyland engines.** Stewart J Brown

few cities to convert single-door Atlanteans to dual-door, doing this in 1969. Atlanteans delivered between 1969 and 1971 were built with two doors, but from 1972 single-door buses were once again the fleet standard.

There were Bristols running in Liverpool. The single-deckers were REs. There were 24 ex-Liverpool buses which dated from 1969 and had Park Royal bodies, a unique combination, and two small batches with ECW bodies, the first of which had been diverted from a PMT order. The ECW-bodied buses dated from 1971 and 1975. More unusual were two batches of double-deck Bristols – VRTs with East Lancs bodies. There were 60 long-wheelbase two-door examples delivered in 1970, and 50 short-wheelbase single-door buses dating from 1974-75. Unusually for a VRT, the Merseyside buses had a

Right **Early deliveries to Merseyside included East Lancs-bodied Bristol VRTs which had been ordered by Liverpool. These were long-wheelbase 80-seaters. The detachable skirt panel was a Liverpool feature, designed to contain minor accident damage within the lower area of the body.** Stewart J Brown

Below **All of the PTEs tried the MCW Metropolitan. Merseyside had 60, delivered in 1974-75.** Stewart J Brown

Centre right **Merseyside buses appeared in colours other than green, as shown on this Wirral division Atlantean with Alexander body. The logo was coloured to match the appropriate divisional livery. The bus was new in 1973.** John Robinson

Bottom right **Merseyside's Metro-Scanias could be seen in both Wirral and Liverpool liveries. There were 20 in all, new in 1972. Remember Williams & Glyn's bank?** Stewart J Brown

protruding engine compartment. Most bodybuilders enclosed the VRT's engine within the body structure. The VRTs and the ex-Liverpool REs were Gardner-powered in what was a predominantly Leyland-engined fleet.

The other double-deck type in Liverpool was the MCW Metropolitan. Twenty delivered in 1974 were being followed by a further 40 in 1975. The first batch were in the old dark green livery; the second batch in the new Verona green and jonquil.

The Wirral fleet had been modernised in 1973 with the arrival of 50 Metro-Cammell-bodied Daimler Fleetlines, a type not to be found on the other side of the Mersey. These ousted exposed-radiator Leyland Titans, although a number of ex-Birkenhead examples still remained, including the newest, dating from

Left **The first Titans with Leyland's new glass fibre bonnet were five 1961 PD2A/30s for St Helens Corporation. The sculpted front corner was designed to improve the driver's view of the kerb when compared with the previous BMMO-style sheet metal grille and bonnet. This bus has an East Lancs body and is seen in Wigan in March 1974, just before St Helens was absorbed by the Merseyside PTE.** A Moyes

Right **Southport's last new buses were eight Leyland Nationals. They were to be the only Nationals in the Merseyside fleet until 1978. This one is seen in Lord Street, Southport, in May 1974, with Merseyside fleetnames having replaced the municipal crest.** Stewart J Brown

Below right **Among the North West's smartest municipal buses were Southport's fine Leyland Titans. The last, a batch of four, entered service in 1967 and had forward-entrance Metro-Cammell bodies of a style known as the Aurora – a name which did not gain such widespread currency as did Orion, used for the equivalent rear-entrance model. Similar buses, but bodied by Weymann, had been the fleet standard since 1961. Note that it is a one-man bus; all 16 forward-entrance Titans in the Southport fleet had been adapted for omo by 1970.** Stewart J Brown

1967. Other ex-Birkenhead types were Atlanteans with Northern Counties bodies, including a pair of unusual single-deckers delivered to the PTE in 1971. The only other purpose-built single-deck Atlanteans were supplied to Great Yarmouth and Portsmouth. Other Wirral-based single-deckers were eight Metro-Scanias from a batch of 20 delivered in 1972. The other 12 were in Liverpool depots.

When the PTE was formed the Wallasey fleet was made up primarily of elderly Leyland Titans and early Leyland Atlanteans. Wallasey had in December 1958 been the first operator to put a production Atlantean into service and by 1961 had 30. All of the Titans were withdrawn from service in the early 1970s, as were most of the Atlanteans, with just eight remaining in 1975. They had Metro-Cammell bodies. Wallasey also ran small buses, and the PTE inherited four 1962 Albion Nimbuses and a 1967 Bedford J2. The last of these were replaced in 1974 by two unusual Leyland Redline 550FG truck chassis, built in Bathgate, with 22-seat bus bodies by Alexander (Belfast).

St Helens Corporation had the distinction of giving its name to the new glass fibre bonnet assembly adopted as standard on the Leyland Titan in 1960 and, appropriately, there was a substantial number of PD2A Titans with this front-end style in the fleet when the PTE took over. The oldest dated from 1961; the newest from 1967. There were 30 Titans still running in St Helens in 1975 and also a few AEC Regent Vs. St Helens took an early interest in omo and from 1968 all its new buses were AEC Swifts – 75 provided the bulk of the town's services, all but three having dual-door Marshall bodies. The odd three were ex-LUT buses, bodied by Alexander. The town's other single-deckers were 10 new Bristol REs with ECW bodies.

When the PTE area was expanded in 1974 it coincidentally embraced two fleets with similar red and cream liveries, which were retained for a short period. St Helens was one, Southport the other. Like St Helens, Southport had embraced omo in the late 1960s, but specified Leyland's Panther, taking 22 with bodies by Metro-Cammell and Marshall. Then in 1973 it opted for one-man double-deckers, with 10 Alexander-bodied Atlanteans, the town's first new 'deckers since 1967. The earlier double-deck generation comprised traditional, but very smart, exposed-radiator Titans with forward-entrance bodies by Weymann and Metro-Cammell. Southport's last new buses marked a turning point – eight Leyland Nationals. These were in 1975 Merseyside's only Nationals, although that would not hold true for much longer.

Southport Corporation had a long tradition of running open-top services and in 1975 these were covered by three Leyland Tiger PS2s which had originally operated for Ribble before being acquired and de-roofed by Southport, and by three Leyland-bodied PD2s. These made Merseyside the only PTE with a regular (albeit seasonal) open-top bus operation.

Where SELNEC had taken over the major NBC operation in its area, the Merseyside PTE came to operating agreements with its NBC operators, Crosville (dealt with in the chapter on Wales, where much of its operations were based) and Ribble. This saw both operators' buses in the PTE area carrying the PTE's logo as well as the NBC double-N symbol. Crosville, incidentally, also served Manchester.

Ribble was in 1975 one NBC's biggest subsidiaries, running over 1,000 buses and coaches. Its head office was in Preston (the company took its name from the river flowing past the town) and its operating area extended north to Carlisle, where it provided city services, and south as far as Liverpool and Wigan. Its buses could be seen in every Lancashire town, generally providing services to neighbouring towns and villages. In the days before NBC's corporate identity Ribble's livery had been a rich, if rather sombre, maroon. It was now poppy red.

Having its headquarters barely five miles from the town of Leyland had some considerable influence on its vehicle policy. In the mid-1960s its fleet was 100 per cent Leyland; 10 years on it still comprised all Leyland group products, even if some had been built in Bristol or in Glasgow. The Leyland group connection is perhaps stretching things just a little. Among the company's older buses were eight pre-1966 Bristol single-deckers (ie built before Leyland's shareholding in Bristol) which had been transferred to Ribble with United Auto's Carlisle operations in 1969. This was one of the very early fruits of the creation of NBC, with a former BET company taking over an isolated part of an ex-THC operation.

There were more modern Bristols too, with 40 two-door ECW-bodied REs which despite their appearance as standard THC buses were in fact a BET order. There were also 40 Marshall-bodied REs dating from 1970, and a further 40 ECW-bodied REs from 1972. These marked the end of an era. All subsequent single-deck deliveries were Leyland Nationals, and Ribble had 90 in 1975 – or 91 if you include a unique electrically-powered National which towed its batteries in a trailer but which was never used in service. Before leaving Bristols, there were also 23 ECW-bodied VRTs, generally to be found on Carlisle local services.

Genuine Lancashire-built Leylands still made up the bulk of the fleet, with roughly 800 in use. At the start of the decade there had still been open-platform PD2s, however they had all but vanished, leaving Ribble's unusual full-front PD3s as the oldest buses in widespread use. The

first of these had entered service in 1957 and the distinctive body with its sliding entrance door caused quite a stir. These were trend-setting vehicles and Ribble's commitment to the forward-entrance layout was soon followed by other operators including, locally, Preston and Wigan Corporations. The first batches had Burlingham bodies, built in Blackpool (a town well-served by Ribble), while post-1961 deliveries were bodied by MCW to a design which resembled the original only insofar as it had a full-width front. A total of 236 had been built and around 170 survived. The last examples would still be running at the end of the 1970s.

At the same time as buying full-front PD3s, Ribble was an early convert to the Atlantean, buying its first in 1959. These had both full-height and lowbridge bodies by Metro-Cammell and Weymann. On lowbridge Atlanteans there was an offset sunken gangway at the rear of the upper saloon, with conventional two-plus-two seating and a centre gangway at the front. After its first flush of enthusiasm caution set in, but further Atlanteans – this time PDR1/2s with drop-centre rear axles – were delivered in 1966 and 1967 with lowheight bodies by Alexander and Northern Counties respectively. All were still running in 1975.

The Atlanteans had been Alexander's third order from Ribble. The previous two had been for bodies on Albion Lowlander chassis, 16 in all in 1964 and 1965. These were Ribble's last front-engined 'deckers and the SBG-style lowheight bodies had bulbous full-width fronts intended to provide a family resemblance to the PD3s. The company's newest double-deckers in 1975 were 70 standard NBC-specification Atlanteans with 73-seat Park Royal bodies.

Leyland Leopards dominated the single-deck fleet. These had BET-style bodies by Marshall (on the vast majority), Weymann and Willowbrook. Most were 11m PSU3s, but there were a few 10m PSU4s. Ribble also ran a substantial Leopard coach fleet with bodywork by Duple and Plaxton, as well as the only Alexander M-type body to carry National white coach livery. There were over 500 Leopards in all, making Ribble the country's biggest user of

Top left **The combination of Leyland Titan PD3 chassis and fully-fronted Metro-Cammell body was unique to Ribble. Titans of this style were supplied to the company until 1963. This bus was new in 1961, and is seen in Liverpool in 1973, still in traditional Ribble dark red. The Bus Economy Ticket was a Merseyside PTE initiative giving a discount to buyers who pre-purchased 10-journey tickets in shops.** Stewart J Brown

Top right **Ribble bought large numbers of early PDR1 Atlanteans, including some with 71-seat lowbridge Weymann bodies. The last of these were delivered in 1962 and were long-lived, some surviving into the 1980s. One in NBC corporate livery is seen in Blackburn bus station.** Stewart J Brown

Left **A number of ex-BET companies received Park Royal-bodied Atlanteans in the mid-1970s as an alternative to the standard NBC Bristol VRT with ECW body. Ribble got 70 in 1975, one of which is seen in Liverpool with the PTE logo visible alongside the fleetname.** Stewart J Brown

the type. In addition to the ex-United Bristols in Carlisle there were a few other acquired buses in Ribble's fleet. These were PD3s and Atlanteans taken over from Scout Motor Services in Preston when that operation, acquired in 1961, was integrated into the main fleet in 1968, and an Atlantean and a Lowlander which had come from Bamber Bridge Motor Services, taken over by Ribble in 1967. The Lowlander was an ex-demonstrator which had been used to launch Leyland's new lowheight chassis at the 1961 Scottish Motor Show in Glasgow's Kelvin Hall.

The Standerwick coach business, a Ribble subsidiary since 1932, had been merged with North Western's coaching operations in 1973 to form National Travel (North West) with a fleet of 165 coaches including 30 impressive Bristol VRLs with 60-seat ECW bodies which were used primarily on services to London.

In Ribble's headquarters town most local services were provided by Preston Borough Transport. This was another all-Leyland fleet with PD2 and PD3 Titans, Panthers and Atlanteans. The oldest PD2s still running in 1975 even had Leyland bodies. These were built in 1954, the last year of bus body production at Leyland. Preston had followed Ribble's lead in switching to forward entrances, and from 1958 all of its new Titans had Metro-Cammell bodies of this layout. These had exposed radiators or, on the later deliveries, St Helens-style bonnets. There were no Titans in the Preston fleet with BMMO-style new-look fronts.

Unusual rebuilds in the 1960s saw eight Leyland-bodied PD2s being lengthened from 27ft 6in to 30ft and converted from rear to forward entrance. These had new PD3 chassis frames and were re-registered on re-entering service. The last was an F-registered bus in 1967. All were still in service in 1975.

Top right **When Leyland brought out what was in effect a lowheight PD3, Ribble added some to its fleet. The new model was the Lowlander, developed for the Scottish Bus Group and built by Albion in Glasgow. Ribble ran 16 with Alexander bodies. The full-width front was unique to Ribble; whether it was an improvement on the standard half-cab style is open to question.** Stewart J Brown

Centre right **Among the few non-standard buses in Ribble's fleet was this Burlingham-bodied PD3 acquired from Scout Motor Services in Preston. The body was a half-cab version of that which Burlingham had supplied to Ribble, but it has been fitted with a Ribble-style front panel in place of the conventional vertically-slatted Leyland grille. It is seen in Liverpool.** Malcolm King collection

Right **The Standerwick coach fleet was made up primarily of Leylands. A 1964 Leopard with 49-seat Plaxton Panorama body pauses at Newcastle-under-Lyme in 1973. Standerwick was absorbed by National Travel (North West) and overall white replaced this and other distinctive coach liveries.** John Robinson

After buying five PD3As in 1965 no new buses entered the Preston fleet until 1968 – and they marked a radical change in policy, introducing single-deckers to an all double-deck fleet. The new buses were five Panthers with two-door Liverpool-style Metro-Cammell bodies. By 1972 Preston had bought 36 new Panthers, with later deliveries being bodied by Marshall (in 1969-70) and Pennine (in 1971-72). Three unused third-hand Panthers were purchased at the end of 1971. These had distinctive Marshall Camair bodies – rare outside the North East of England – and had been new to Stratford Blue in 1970. Before they were put into service, the Stratford Blue business was integrated with that of Midland Red. They were repainted red but still did not go in to service. With a third coat of paint and no revenue-earning mileage on the clock, the five Panthers finally entered service in Preston.

Another short spell passed with no new buses being added to the operation when in 1974 a return was made to double-deckers, with the purchase of the fleet's first Atlanteans. These were long-wheelbase AN68/2Rs with two-door Alexander bodies. More AN68s were added during the latter part of the 1970s, with bodies by Alexander and East Lancs. The only other 1970s fleet additions – in 1976 – were three Bristol LHs with Duple bodies for use on new services which were unsuitable for big bus operation.

Also serving Preston, with routes running south to Leyland and Chorley, was Fishwick, an old-established company whose bus interests predated those of Ribble, dating back to 1910. Ribble had been formed in 1919. Fishwick's depot was just a stone's throw from some of Leyland's manufacturing sites – so there were no surprises in the favoured supplier of chassis to this fleet. Titan double-deckers were on their way out – just one 1958 PD2 remained – but there was some variety among the fleet's 13 Atlanteans. The oldest examples had lowbridge Weymann bodies, including three with unusual A-suffix registrations; Lancashire was one of very few authorities to use the A registration suffix. The newest Atlanteans had East Lancs bodies. There was one Alexander-bodied

Top left **Preston Borough Transport's oldest buses were Leyland Titans. A 1958 Metro-Cammell-bodied PD3 pulls out of the town's impressive bus station, which had opened in October 1969. Preston used route letters rather than numbers.** Stewart J Brown

Centre left **Leyland Panthers were added to the Preston fleet between 1969 and 1972. The last 14 had Pennine bodywork of a style generally similar to that fitted to the Seddon Pennine RU.** Stewart J Brown

Left **Three Panthers with Marshall Camair bodies were acquired third-hand by Preston in 1971. New in 1970, they had been built for Stratford Blue and had then passed to Midland Red. Neither company had used them.** Stewart J Brown

Atlantean, a 1962 bus which had run briefly for Glasgow Corporation before being bought by Leyland for use as a demonstrator. It was acquired by Fishwick in 1965. And there was a unique Atlantean with bodywork by Fowler of Leyland. Built in 1972 it was Fowler's only double-deck body and was of unusual angular appearance.

Fishwick was in fact the only user of Fowler bus bodies and had another nine. Five were on single-deck Fleetlines (which had Leyland 680 engines), three were on Leopards and the ninth was on a 1969 Tiger Cub, the last of Leyland's once-popular lightweight model to enter service. Other single-deckers included a 1957 Leyland-MCW Olympian integral, the last example in service in Britain of what had always been a relatively uncommon type, plus a couple of Massey-bodied Tiger Cubs and an ex-demonstration Panther. Two new buses delivered in 1975 represented the shape of things to come in the Fishwick fleet: Leyland Nationals.

To the west of Preston – still very much in Ribble territory – there were two municipal fleets. The bigger was Blackpool, with 134 buses and 99 trams. Blackpool had a long history of running stylish full-fronted buses, typified in the postwar years by a batch of 100 PD2s with centre-entrance Burlingham bodies delivered in 1949-50. These had gone by the 1970s, and by the middle of the decade the double-deck fleet was made up entirely of PD3s

Top right **Leyland demonstrators often found their way into the Fishwick fleet when their demonstrating days were over. One such bus was this 1968 Park Royal-bodied Panther, seen in Chorley bus station. It originally had a centre exit, which was removed by Fishwick.** A Moyes

Centre right **Fishwick operated three short PSU4 Leopards with 44-seat Fowler bodies, which entered service in 1970. Flanked by Nationals, one is seen loading at the company's small bus station, adjacent to its garage in Leyland. Fowler was a Fishwick associate.** Stewart J Brown

Right **For much of the 1970s Blackpool operated only two types of buses – AEC Swifts and Leyland Titans. The Titans had Metro-Cammell bodies, and most were 30ft-long PD3As.** John Robinson

Above left **Leyland Titans figured strongly in the Lytham St Annes fleet over the years. The last were three PD2As with Massey bodies, which were put into service in 1964. This one is seen at Squires Gate in 1973 on a service operated jointly with Blackpool Corporation.** John Robinson

Above **Fylde modified the Lytham St Annes livery with the addition of mustard relief. In 1975 six Atlanteans were added to the fleet. These were unusual in having Wilowbrook bodies built on Northern Counties frames.** Murdoch Currie

Left **Atlanteans with East Lancs bodies were Blackburn's standard double-deckers from 1968. This is one of 12 AN68s which joined the fleet in 1976, photographed when new.** Paul Caudell

with Metro-Cammell Orion bodies. There were just under 100 delivered between 1962 and 1968, the last three having G-suffix registrations. The oldest PD3s did have full front bodies, but these were a mere shadow of the more exuberant designs of earlier decades.

In 1969 Blackpool switched from rear-entrance double-deckers to dual-door single-deckers, and from Leyland and Metro-Cammell to AEC and Marshall. By 1975 there were 55 Marshall-bodied Swifts in the fleet. These were to be the only 1970s single-deckers, and from 1976 the new Blackpool standard was the East Lancs-bodied long-wheelbase Atlantean.

Blackpool Corporation operated a number of services jointly with neighbouring Fylde Borough Transport. Fylde was a creation of the 1974 local government changes, and took over the operations of Lytham St Annes Corporation. Fylde ran services to Blackpool's cavernous bus station, as well as running locally in both Lytham and St Annes. The smart blue and white livery was retained, but Fylde established its identity by adding a rather unfortunate band of mustard-coloured relief.

The fleet (the smallest of the North West municipalities) included some old vehicles – two 1948 all-Leyland PD2s were entering their 27th year, but were about to be replaced by six new Atlanteans, which would also allow the withdrawal of some similar 1951 PD2s. Their departure left five 1957 Titans with Northern Counties bodies as the fleet's oldest buses, and these too would soon be replaced. Other Titans included an ex-Blackpool bus with fully-fronted Metro-Cammell Orion body, and a trio of handsome Massey-bodied PD2As. Three 1970 Atlanteans with Northern Counties bodies to Nottingham style made up the double-deck fleet.

Fylde's single-deckers comprised three Burlingham-bodied Tiger Cubs, three Northern Counties-bodied Panthers and six Seddon Pennine RUs. The Panthers and the Seddons were of the then fashionable two-door layout for use on omo services. Replacements for the Tiger Cubs were imminent in the form of five ECW-bodied Bristol REs.

East of Preston there were four municipal fleets, all still in areas with a strong Ribble presence. The first, and the biggest with 135 buses, was Blackburn. Blackburn borough had been extended southwards in 1974 to embrace neighbouring Darwen, which had operated its own 30-strong bus fleet. Thus in 1975 there were

Above **Darwen's double-deckers were mainly Leyland Titans and included three 1958 PD2s with 59-seat East Lancs bodies. Unusually for municipal buses these were fitted with platform doors and in consequence had to have an emergency exit on the offside of the lower saloon, visible just behind the driver's cab.** Stewart J Brown

Above right **Darwen's newest buses were seven Leyland-engined Bristol REs with 47-seat East Lancs bodies. These had entered service between 1971 and 1973. One passes the Blackburn Corporation Transport offices in February 1974, six weeks before the two undertakings were merged.** Stewart J Brown

Right **The oldest bus to be transferred from Accrington to Hyndburn in 1974's local government changes was this 1958 Guy Arab IV with East Lancs bodywork. It had been withdrawn by the end of the year, but other newer Arabs would run till the latter part of the 1970s.** Stewart J Brown

three different liveries in the fleet – Blackburn's old green and cream, Darwen's red and cream, and the new enlarged undertaking's green, white and red – a colour combination which acknowledged the traditions of both of its predecessors.

The fleet mix illustrated the rather different buying policies of the two constituents, but not surprisingly it was the old Blackburn policy which determined future buying, standardising on East Lancs-bodied Atlanteans. East Lancs' factory was in Blackburn, so there was obvious logic in the fleet being made up entirely of locally-built bodies. Darwen's fleet had been predominantly East Lancs-bodied, but not exclusively so.

Dealing with the ex-Darwen buses first, the newest were seven East Lancs-bodied REs but the majority were double-deckers – PD2 Titans (East Lancs-bodied again, and most with forward entrances) plus one Crossley-bodied PD2, new in 1955 which was the fleet's oldest bus, and a Crossley-badged Regent V of 1957. There was also an AEC single-decker, a one-time Salford Reliance acquired from SELNEC. Most of these were still in Darwen red in 1975.

The former Blackburn fleet contained 24 PD2A Titans delivered in the early 1960s, and 42 East Lancs-bodied Atlanteans. There were also a dozen Guy Arab IVs with East Lancs bodies, the newest of which had been delivered in 1961, and which were due for early replacement. Blackburn's newest Arabs were unusual in having Johannesburg-style fronts, a short-lived option to the more familiar Birmingham-style grille. The only other Guys in the North West with this bonnet assembly were to be found in Chester. At the start of the 1970s an earlier generation of 1949 Arab IIIs with Crossley bodies survived in small numbers on peak-hour services. The last were withdrawn in 1972. Single-deckers were East Lancs-bodied Tiger Cubs, including some late G-registered specimens, and six Seddon Pennine RUs, also with East Lancs bodies rather than the more common Pennine coachwork.

Blackburn Borough Transport operated a joint service to nearby Accrington, running with Hyndburn Borough Transport, the post-1974 operator of what had been Accrington Corporation's bus services. This was another loyal East Lancs user. For most of the 1950s Accrington had bought Guy Arabs. There were 23 in use in 1970, but by 1975 this figure had

Left **All eight Leyland Tiger Cubs in the Hyndburn fleet had East Lancs bodies. The oldest had been built in 1962; the newest in 1965. A 1962 bus picks up passengers in Accrington bus station.** John Robinson

Below left **The last half-cab single-deck buses in regular use with a major British operator were Burnley & Pendle's Leyland Tiger PS2s. This 1954 bus had an East Lancs body and is seen in the summer of 1974. It was withdrawn from service in 1976. The PS2 used the Leyland O.600 engine which powered the much more common PD2 and PD3 models.** A Moyes

Below **Burnley & Pendle was one of the few Lancashire municipalities to buy new Leyland Nationals. There were 15 in the fleet in 1974, including five which had been delivered to Burnley, Colne & Nelson. All were 10.3m-long 44-seaters. Burnley in the mid-1970s was the only place where half-cab Tigers could be seen in service alongside high-tech Nationals.** Stewart J Brown

Left **After a gap of almost 10 years, new double-deckers were added to the Burnley fleet in 1976. These were Bristol VRTs with East Lancs bodies and were the fleet's first rear-engined 'deckers.** Stewart J Brown

Facing page:

Top **For its coaches Burnley & Pendle had a livery reminiscent of that used by East Midland Motor Services in days long gone. This is one of four Leyland Leopards with Alexander Y-type bodies which joined the fleet in 1976.** Stewart J Brown

Centre left **The entire Rossendale fleet in the mid-1970s had East Lancs bodywork. This is a 1960 Leyland Tiger Cub which had been new to Rawtenstall Corporation. The bus in the background is a former Ramsbottom Titan in the ownership of the SELNEC PTE.** Paul Caudell

Centre right **Rossendale was one of the last regular users of exposed-radiator Titans. It had 12 East Lancs-bodied PD3s which had been new to Rawtenstall in the mid-1960s and which towards the end of their lives were to be found on peak-hour workings or, as seen here in Accrington, on contract services to a local supermarket. The last were still in use in the early 1980s.** Stewart J Brown

dropped to just three. These were 1964 buses and had been the last Guys bought by Accrington. Other older types were 10 Leyland Titans, the newest being 1967 models. The remainder of the double-deck fleet consisted of 15 Atlanteans, a model which would continue to be bought until the end of the 1970s. Single-deckers ranged from early 1960s Tiger Cubs to Bristol REs and Seddon Pennine RUs. The REs and RUs had helped replace Guy 'deckers in the early 1970s. One odd vehicle in the fleet was a 1974 Pennine RU with East Lancs coach body with deep side windows which curved into the roof line. Only three bodies of this style were built, with the other two being supplied to Widnes on Leyland Leopard chassis.

The Burnley, Colne & Nelson Joint Transport Committee had been formed in 1933 to amalgamate the bus operating interests of the three neighbouring towns. This arrangement continued until 1974 when local government reform created a new Pendle district council and thus was created the Burnley & Pendle JTC. The new undertaking continued with the maroon and cream livery of its predecessor, but adopted Burnley & Pendle as its fleetname, in place of the initials BCN. Burnley & Pendle not only ran locally, but also had services to Skipton and to Keighley in West Yorkshire. The West Yorkshire Road Car Co operated a joint service with Burnley & Pendle to Colne.

Conservatism in BCN's buying policy led to Burnley & Pendle being the only major English operator of half-cab single-deckers in the mid-1970s (other than open toppers as found in Southport). These were 14 Leyland Tiger PS2s built between 1953 and 1955. Ten were withdrawn in 1974, but four survived in 1975. They had East Lancs bodies – and had been adapted for one-man-operation in the late 1950s when they were rebuilt from rear-entrance to forward-entrance layout.

The rest of the fleet was made up of more conventional types. Most of the older single-deckers were Tiger Cubs with East Lancs bodies, a type which BCN bought between 1959 and 1967. All of the double-deckers were Leyland Titans with forward-entrance bodies by East Lancs and Northern Counties. The last of these had entered service in 1967.

From 1968 only single-deckers had been purchased. First came a batch of Northern Counties-bodied Panthers, followed by a switch to the Leyland-engined Bristol RE with bodies by East Lancs, Northern Counties and Pennine. Pennine bodywork was also fitted to 20 Seddon RUs in 1972. Leyland Nationals were added to the fleet in 1973 and 1974, an unusual choice for a Lancashire municipality where loyalty to East Lancs generally fuelled some resistance to Leyland's new integral. In fact the 1974 Nationals were accompanied by one final batch of five East Lancs-bodied REs, after which Burnley & Pendle went on to buy East Lancs Leopards for its single-deck requirements.

Double-deckers were set to make a fresh appearance in 1976, with East Lancs-bodied Bristol VRTs being used to oust Leyland Titans. These were the fleet's first rear-engined double-deckers and more followed, with lowheight ECW bodies. Burnley & Pendle never operated a Leyland Atlantean.

The last of the east Lancashire municipal operators was Rossendale, whose services ran to Accrington, Bacup, Burnley and Bury. Its

Top left **Old AEC Regents characterised the Morecambe & Heysham operation. Park Royal bodywork was fitted to this 1949 Regent III, one of a dozen similar buses which were still in use when the undertaking was absorbed by Lancaster in 1974. The last of the closed top examples were withdrawn during 1975, but some of those which had been converted to open-top lasted until 1979. There were younger Regent IIIs in the fleet too, the last having been supplied in 1954.** John Robinson

Centre left **A change of manager had brought a switch to Leylands at Morecambe & Heysham, as illustrated by this 1962 Massey-bodied PD2. There were five such buses – three PD2/37s with BMMO-style fronts, and two PD2A/37s with St Helens fronts. All were of forward-entrance layout. The PD2As were to be Morecambe & Heysham's last double-deckers.** John Robinson

Bottom left **Pennine bodywork is fitted to this Lancaster Leopard, one of six purchased in 1972. The first three were 51-seat PSU3s, the second three were 47-seat PSU4s, one of which is seen here in the summer of 1975 with its new – and short-lived – City of Lancaster fleetname.** David Brown

history was rather different from those around it, in that it had been created as a Joint Transport Committee in 1968 by the merger of the bus operations of Rawtenstall and Haslingden Corporations. At that time Rawtenstall had 45 buses and Haslingden had 16. Both had for some years been under the control of one general manager. In 1974 the JTC ceased and a new Rossendale borough council took over.

At this time the fleet was 100 per cent Leyland and apart from two 21-year-old Leyland-bodied PD2s, all had bodywork by East Lancs. The double-deckers were PD2s and PD3s – Atlanteans would not appear until 1977 – while the single-deckers were Tiger Cubs and Leopards. This high degree of standardisation was broken with the delivery in 1974-75 of nine Bristol REs, albeit still with East Lancs bodies and Leyland engines. The last, P-registered buses, were among the last REs to enter service in England.

North of Preston there were two municipal fleets, in Lancaster and Barrow, while NBC was represented by Ribble and by Cumberland Motor Services. Lancaster City Transport had expanded in 1974 as a result of boundary changes which saw a new Lancaster borough taking over the neighbouring Morecambe & Heysham corporation and its bus fleet. Lancaster's buses pre-1974 were red and off-white; Morecambe & Heysham's were green and cream. The enlarged undertaking adopted blue and white. All three liveries could be seen in 1975. Morecambe & Heysham had generally been a buyer of AECs, while Lancaster's fleet was predominantly Leyland. It was Leyland who would continue as the main chassis supplier.

Morecambe & Heysham had a reputation for

Right **The standard post-1974 livery and fleetname for Lancaster's buses is illustrated on this 1963 East Lancs-bodied PD2. Note the use of the registration number as the fleet number, a practice which had been adopted in 1946.** David Brown

Below **The first new buses for the enlarged Lancaster fleet were 26 Leyland Leopards with Alexander Y-type bodies in 1976-77. These were built to a variety of specifications with 41, 45, 49 or 53 seats. This is a 1977 PSU3 with 49 coach seats.** Stewart J Brown

Below right **Barrow favoured single-deckers for the bulk of its operations in the 1970s. Most were Leopards with a variety of bodies, including Neepsend on five 1967 buses. These 11m-long buses were two-door 51-seaters, designed to carry up to 18 standees.** Stewart J Brown

the longevity of its buses and this was borne out by the existence of 25-year-old Regent IIIs which were still in operation in 1975. There were five Regent Vs, and five Titans (Morecambe & Heysham's only Leylands). These all had Massey bodies. The 1962 Titans had been Morecambe & Heysham's last double-deckers. The newer buses in the fleet were 10 AEC Swifts and six Seddon Pennine RUs.

Lancaster had one old bus, a 1952 Daimler CVG5 with single-deck Northern Counties bodywork, retained primarily for a contract requiring a narrow vehicle. It survived to receive the new blue livery. Leylands made up the rest of the fleet with nine exposed-radiator Titans being the only double-deckers. The single-deckers provided a reasonable history of Leyland model development with Tiger Cubs, Leopards, Panthers and three Leyland Nationals which were destined to be the only ones in the fleet and only lasted from 1973 to 1978 when they were sold to Fishwick, by then a confirmed National user. Bodywork on the older Leyland single-deckers was by East Lancs, while the newest Leopards had Seddon bodies.

During 1975 a start was being made on weeding out the oldest of the ex-Morecambe & Heysham AECs, and to expedite this Lancaster bought second-hand Titans from Burnley & Pendle, Maidstone and Merthyr Tydfil. The Maidstone buses only ran for a short period. The late 1970s saw a major fleet upgrade with the purchase of 26 Leopards with Alexander Y-type bodies. Rear-engined double-deckers were finally introduced to Lancaster's operations in 1978. These were 10 Atlanteans from Greater Manchester Transport which had been new in 1965 to Salford. New Atlanteans would ultimately follow.

On the other side of Morecambe Bay lay Barrow-in-Furness which had a self-contained local bus network provided by Barrow Borough Transport. Most services were run by single-deckers. Oldest were six 1963 Leopards with two-door East Lancs bodies, bought well before the big swing to dual-door buses later in the 1960s. There were later Leopards too, with bodies by East Lancs and Strachans. In 1971 Barrow had gone rear-engined, buying five 36ft-long Fleetlines with East Lancs bodies and these were followed in 1974 by five Leyland Nationals, built in nearby Workington. The rear-engined buses had replaced 1958 PD2 Titans, a few of which survived in 1975. The only other

Left **Warrington adopted a brighter layout for its livery in 1974 with more white and less red, as shown on this 1965 Fleetline with attractive East Lancs bodywork which featured unusually deep windows for a body of this period. Fleetlines were purchased up to 1973. From 1977, when double-deckers were next ordered, Warrington would specify Atlanteans.** Paul Caudell

Centre left **Between 1969 and 1972 Widnes Corporation bought 10 Titans from Wigan Corporation. Most ran for four or five years. New in 1958, this Massey-bodied PD2 had been purchased by Widnes in 1972 and survived with Halton Borough Transport until 1978.** John Robinson

Below left **From 1967 Widnes bought new Leopards to replace double-deckers. This was the start of a move which would see the Halton fleet being entirely single-deck from 1980. Two short-wheelbase PSU4s with East Lancs bodies formed the 1969 intake. They were two-door 60-passenger buses with 42 seats and room for 18 standees.** John Robinson

Below right **Halton's most unusual vehicles were two 11m Leopards with East Lancs coach bodies. They were new in 1975. The only other body of this style was supplied to Hyndburn on a Seddon Pennine RU. The Halton Leopards would be rebodied as buses by East Lancs in the early 1980s.** Stewart J Brown

Facing page left **Chester was a staunch user of Guy Arabs, buying no other types of double-decker between 1953 and 1969. In 1970 it had 47 in service; by 1980 this figure would be reduced to 10. Four delivered in 1962 had 73-seat Massey bodies and Johannesburg-style fronts.** Paul Caudell

Facing page right **During the 1970s all of Chester's new 'deckers were Daimler Fleetlines with Northern Counties bodies. By 1979 there were 25 in operation. Most were of lowheight construction and the early examples were CRG6LX models with five-bay bodies, as seen here at Chester railway station in 1973. Later in the decade Chester would be taking FE30AGRs with much more attractive four-bay bodies developed from the SELNEC standard.** John Robinson

double-deckers were 10 PD2As with Massey bodies, which dated from 1961.

Barrow also operated a fleet of nine Bedford coaches. These carried the livery of Hadwin's of Ulverston, a company bought by Barrow in 1972 and run as a separate subsidiary until it was sold in 1977. The area north of Barrow was largely served by Cumberland Motor Services, whose headquarters were in Whitehaven. Cumberland, with just 161 vehicles, was one of NBC's smaller bus-operating subsidiaries. The fleet mix in 1975 was classic THC/NBC with Lodekkas ranging from LDs to FLFs, and single-deckers comprising MWs, REs, LHs and Nationals. Cumberland ran services in Workington, site of England's oldest covered bus station (opened in 1926) and of the Leyland National factory. This made it the appropriate recipient in 1972 of the first production National (and one of comparatively few with a K registration). The company's coach fleet included a dozen Duple-bodied Fords and a Plaxton-bodied LH.

One small bus business in the Lake District merits a mention: The Mountain Goat. This was the unusual trading name of a minibus operation which used Ford Transits to penetrate areas which could not be served by conventional vehicles. Services started in 1972 and were based on Windermere. By 1975 there were seven Transits in the fleet.

There remained three other municipal bus operators in the North West. Two had been in Lancashire until the county's boundaries were redrawn, which moved them to Cheshire: Warrington and Widnes. The third was Chester City Transport. All three served areas which were covered by NBC's Crosville company, whose headquarters were in Chester and whose operating territory covered a broad swathe of the country from Macclesfield across North Wales to Anglesey and south to Aberystwyth.

Warrington, with 75 buses, was the biggest of the three. Its last Fodens had been withdrawn in 1972 and that left it with a fleet composed of Leylands, Daimlers and Bristols. The Daimlers were all Fleetlines. There were 26, bought between 1963 and 1973. The Leylands were mainly Titans of which there 24 PD2s and a pair of newly-acquired ex-Leicester City Transport PD3s. All of Warrington's double-deckers had East Lancs bodies.

The rest of the fleet was single-decked and after buying four Panther Cubs in 1967 Warrington turned to the Bristol RE, building up a fleet of 25 by 1975. Eight had Pennine bodies, rare on an RE; the rest were East Lancs-bodied. Unusually for a municipal fleet the REs marked a return to Bristol as a chassis supplier. Warrington had operated Bristol K-types until 1966. The REs were to be Warrington's last single-deckers for some time. From 1977 the Atlantean was the town's standard bus.

The Widnes Corporation bus fleet changed to Halton Transport in 1974. Double-deckers were on their way out. There were still 21 – half the fleet – and all were rear-platform PD2s, the newest being D-registered buses from 1966. The Titans included five ex-Wigan Corporation buses purchased in 1972 when they were 14 years old. They had been used to replace 20-year-old Titans bought new by Widnes. But by the end of the 1970s Halton's double-deck fleet would be reduced to just six vehicles.

Widnes had started buying single-deckers in 1967, firstly selecting Leopards and then, from 1971, Bristol REs with Leyland engines. By 1975 there were nine Leopards (including two with East Lancs' unusual coach body, as already encountered at Hyndburn) and 15 REs. There were to be no more Bristols. Widnes had in August 1972 been the first municipal operator of a Leyland National and from 1976 this was the Halton standard. Halton served not only Widnes, but also nearby Runcorn, having extended its services in 1961 when a new road bridge had been opened across the River Mersey.

Chester City Transport had been one of the more conservative of municipal fleets and in 1975 this was illustrated by the 32 Guy Arabs still in all-day use. These include three H-registered 1969 buses, the last Guys to enter passenger service in Britain. Among Chester's older Arabs were a batch with the rare Johannesburg-style bonnet in place of the standard Birmingham new-look front. The demise of Guy's bus-building activities brought a change to Daimler Fleetlines from 1970 and there were 12 in the fleet by 1974 when orders were switched to single-deckers – Leyland Leopards with bodies by Northern Counties (who had been bodying the Fleetlines) and, rather more attractively, Duple. Older single-deckers comprised a trio of boxy Massey-bodied Tiger Cubs and two ex-SELNEC Reliances with Willowbrook bodies which had been new in 1961 to North Western.

1975: Major bus fleets – North West England

Operator	*Fleet size*
Greater Manchester PTE	2,741
Merseyside PTE	1,637
Ribble	1,068
Lancashire United	360
Blackpool*	233
Cumberland	161
Blackburn	135
Burnley & Pendle	125
Preston	97
Lancaster	86
Warrington	75
Barrow-in-Furness	67
Hyndburn	62
Chester	52
Rossendale	51
Halton	43
Fylde	36

* The Blackpool figure includes 99 trams.

North East England

The industrial areas centred on Tyneside and Wearside made the North East of England good bus country. The key commercial centre was Newcastle-upon-Tyne, but there was a dense network of bus services throughout not just Tyne & Wear county (a creation of 1974's local government changes) but also in County Durham and south-east Northumberland.

The Tyne & Wear PTE had come into being in January 1970, initially as the Tyneside PTE, taking over the municipal bus fleets in Newcastle and South Shields. Its sphere of influence was extended south to Sunderland in April 1973 when it took over Sunderland Corporation's bus operations, a year in advance of the formation of the new Tyne & Wear county which would embrace Sunderland. The PTE had retained Newcastle's bright yellow and cream livery, extending it to South Shields and then to Sunderland.

Half-cab buses had disappeared quickly from the PTE's Newcastle fleet. There hadn't been many – 11 Titans and 19 Regent Vs – thanks to Newcastle Corporation's adoption of the Atlantean as its standard bus from 1960. Thus by 1975 the Newcastle-based double-deck fleet was made up entirely of Atlanteans, although that changed as the year progressed with the delivery of three Alexander-bodied Ailsas and 10 MCW Metropolitans. The Ailsas clearly didn't impress and no more were ordered. But further Metropolitan orders ultimately swelled the fleet to 140, making Tyne & Wear the biggest Metropolitan operator outside London.

An unusual feature of two-door Alexander-bodied Atlanteans in Newcastle was the fitment of a nearside staircase. Newcastle had been the only British operator to specify this layout, and it was continued by the PTE. Single-deck buses played an even smaller part in Newcastle's local

Facing page **Northern General was the only provincial operator to buy new Routemasters, taking 50 forward-entrance 30ft-long examples. One off-loads in Jarrow bus station in 1977.** S J Butler

Top right **The Tyneside PTE's original livery was that which had previously been used by Newcastle Corporation. This uncharacteristically scruffy ex-Newcastle Atlantean was new in 1962 and had an Alexander body.** Stewart J Brown

Centre right **Three Ailsas were bought by Tyne & Wear in 1975. They had 79-seat Alexander bodies. The PTE developed a clear and attractive lettering style for its destination screens.** Malcolm Keeley

Right **The Tyne & Wear PTE was the biggest operator of MCW Metropolitans outside London, with 140 in use. One is seen in Newcastle in 1979 with the then-new Tyne & Wear Transport fleetname – and with the driver topping up the water.** Stewart J Brown

bus operations than they did in most other major conurbations. Rear-engined types were 14 Alexander-bodied Panthers, inherited from Newcastle Corporation, plus five similar buses (but with one door instead of two) added in 1972. There were also 18 Nationals bought by the PTE in two batches, in 1972 and 1975. To these were added 10 Leyland Leopards with Willowbrook's big-windowed 002 body in 1973, followed in 1975 by nine with Alexander Y-type bodies which had three-and-two seating to give the unusually high capacity of 62.

Across the Tyne in South Shields there was a very different fleet. The bulk of the buses taken over by the PTE had been rear-entrance double-deckers. These were 15 Guys, built between 1957 and 1959, and 49 Daimler CSG6 and CCG6 with manual gearboxes, delivered between 1959 and 1964. Most front-engined Daimlers of this period had pre-selector or semi-automatic transmissions. South Shields' newest buses had been 12 Fleetlines and 11 Bristol REs.

Top **Unusual buses for a big fleet operator were 10 Leyland Leopards with Willowbrook Expressway bodies, delivered in 1973 to Tyne & Wear. The Expressway was more commonly bought by small independents.** D J Little

Centre left **Roe bodywork was fitted to all but 11 of the 87 buses which Tyneside took over from South Shields Corporation. Most were traditional rear-entrance double-deckers, including 15 Guy Arab IVs. This sparkling example was new in 1958, and was an early repaint in PTE colours. The Guys were quickly withdrawn, but generally similar open-platform Daimlers ran until 1977.** D J Little

Left **Photographed in Tyneside PTE ownership but still in full Sunderland livery, this Roe-bodied Daimler CVG5 is one of five similar 1957 buses which were Sunderland's oldest when the PTE took over. There were only a dozen rear-entrance buses in Sunderland by 1973 and the last were withdrawn by the PTE in 1975.** D J Little

All of the double-deckers had Roe bodies; the REs had ECW bodywork and were among the first supplied to an operator which was not in state ownership. This had followed the purchase of a minority stake in Bristol Commercial Vehicles by Leyland Motors, which gave Bristol access to new markets in Britain and abroad.

By 1975 the South Shields Guys had long gone, but there were still 20 Daimlers in regular service. Modern vehicles in the town included some of the PTE's Nationals, and six Fleetlines with single-deck Marshall bodies which had been ordered by South Shields and were delivered to the PTE in 1971.

In sharp contrast to Newcastle and South Shields, the majority of the services in Sunderland were operated by single-deckers. Sunderland Corporation had pursued a policy of using modern one-man-operated buses, initially with a flat fare and, when that proved unsuccessful, with zonal fares. This policy had started in 1966, which meant that in 1975 there were just over 100 two-door single-deckers covering the bulk of Sunderland's bus routes. Most of these were Leyland Panthers but there were also 10 Bristol REs and 10 AEC Swifts. There had been three Daimler Roadliners too, but these had been withdrawn in 1974 on the expiry of their initial seven-year Certificates of Fitness and then sold for scrap. The interesting thing about Sunderland's single-deckers was the bodywork, built to a highly individual style unique to the fleet and intended to convey an image of modernity. Most of the single-deck fleet had Strachans bodies. A modern image had also been adopted for the Roe bodies on Sunderland's Fleetlines, with peaked domes. Although rather less famous than the body designs developed for rear-engined double-deck chassis by other operators such as Bolton, Glasgow, Liverpool, Manchester and

Top **Sunderland Corporation developed this distinctive design of two-door standee body for the widespread introduction of one-man-operation from 1966. By 1968 there were 90 buses of this type in the town's streets. Most were Panthers, but there were also three Daimler Roadliners, ten AEC Swifts and ten Bristol REs. This is an RE with bodywork by Metro-Cammell; the other types were all bodied by Strachans.** D J Little

Centre right **Sunderland ran distinctively-styled double-deckers too. These were Daimler Fleetlines with Roe bodies incorporating peaked domes, a novelty when they first appeared in 1962. As with so many buses in the North East, this one carries an exhortation to shop at Binns. The 1966 Fleetlines, one of which is seen here in 1976, were Sunderland Corporation's last double-deckers.** D J Little

Right **Sunderland's last order for new buses was delivered to the PTE in 1974 and comprised 18 AEC Swifts with Marshall bodies. It was the PTE's last big intake of single-deck buses.** Stewart J Brown

Nottingham, Sunderland's 39 Fleetlines were attractive vehicles. Built between 1962 and 1964 they were the most modern double-deckers in the PTE's Sunderland fleet. Sunderland's last half-cabs, 1958 Roe-bodied CVG5s, made it into 1975 but were withdrawn during the year.

Apart from its early commitment to one-man operation, Sunderland had another claim to fame. It bequeathed to the PTE the last Atkinson buses to enter service in Britain. These were three mid-engined 30-footers with BET-style Marshall bodies of two-door layout. They had entered service in 1964 and lasted until 1977, the last of a never-common marque in regular service. Sunderland's most modern buses in 1975 were 18 Marshall-bodied Swifts, ordered by the Corporation but delivered in 1974 to the PTE.

Two small operators were taken over by the PTE in the first half of the decade. First, in 1973, had been the associated businesses of Armstrong of Westerhope and Galley's Coaches of Newcastle. Most of the coaches acquired – mainly Bedfords – were withdrawn, but new coaches were added to the fleet which ultimately became Armstrong-Galley, and a major force in coaching in Tyne & Wear. Then at the start of 1975 the PTE acquired Economic Bus Service of Whitburn – in fact a partnership of two operators, Anderson and Wilson – running between South Shields and Sunderland. Their buses, all single-deckers, were mainly 1960s AEC Reliances plus a couple of 1974 Bedfords. The Reliances were immediately sold, but the two Bedfords were retained until 1977. One small operator continued to serve Sunderland – Jolly running in from South Hylton using Willowbrook-bodied Bedfords.

NBC subsidiary Northern General Transport and its associated companies were the other major providers of local services in the PTE area, and served much of County Durham too. Sister NBC operator United also had a presence in Tyne & Wear, but routes in the PTE area

Top left **Economic of Whitburn was taken over by the Tyne & Wear PTE in 1975. This Roe-bodied AEC Reliance, new in 1961, was among the 16 operational vehicles – 12 AECs and four Bedfords – acquired by the PTE. All but the two newest Bedfords were quickly withdrawn.** D J Little

Centre left **A service into Sunderland was run by Jolly of South Hylton using Bedfords. This YRT has a Willowbrook body; later purchases were bodied by Duple.** D J Little

Left **ECW developed an attractive coach body for the Bristol RE, although the combination found no customers outside NBC and only 85 were built. Northern General took 14 in 1972, most of which were soon repainted overall white and then ended their days in poppy red.** D J Little represented a much smaller proportion of United's operations – which extended north to the Scottish border – than they did for NGT.

Northern General in 1975 was in the throes of change. Firstly, as part of a move towards integration of services with the PTE it had in 1974 started to adopt a yellow livery on those buses running on services primarily within the PTE area. This was applied in standard NBC style with a single band of cream relief (the NBC standard was, of course, white). And secondly NGT was in the course of rationalising its own business. At the start of 1975 it absorbed Sunderland District, Tynemouth & District and Venture Transport. This was to be followed at the start of 1976 by Gateshead & District and Tyneside Omnibus. Venture had been a substantial independent company until 1970 with an 80-strong all single-deck fleet, but the others, like NGT itself, had been BET subsidiaries prior to the formation of NBC.

Apart from Venture, whose services in the Consett area were in 1975 being run by 44 Leyland Leopards and AEC Reliances with Alexander Y-type bodies, the fleets were generally similar in composition but carried different liveries. Venture's maroon, yellow and white was making way for NBC poppy red. Under BET ownership dark red had been used for buses operated by Tynemouth; green for Tyneside and Gateshead & District, and dark blue for Sunderland District. All could still be seen in 1975 but the new order was yellow for Tynemouth (replacing NBC poppy red), Tyneside and Gateshead. In Sunderland a non-standard blue was being applied in NBC corporate style, but that was about to give way to yellow or red, too, following the company's absorption by NGT. NGT's buses were poppy red, although the absorption of its various subsidiaries in 1975-76 meant that yellow-liveried buses in the PTE area became part of the NGT fleet. From 1975 new buses being delivered to NGT included some in both yellow and red liveries.

Top right **The last survivors of ten Park Royal-bodied Leyland Titan PD2/12s of 1957 were withdrawn by Northern General in 1973-74. This one carries its NBC corporate fleetname on Northern General's traditional red livery. The bus in the background is a 1961 Alexander-bodied AEC Reliance which was also soon to be withdrawn.** David Brown

Centre right **Sunderland District's last half-cabs were 13 Leyland Titan PD3s with 73-seat Burlingham bodies, purchased in 1958. The last of these were taken out of service in 1974.** D J Little

Right **Tynemouth switched to rear-engined buses in 1960 with the delivery of 14 Atlanteans with bodies by Metro-Cammell, as seen here in Wallsend in 1972, and by Roe. Tynemouth was absorbed by Northern General at the start of 1975.** D J Little

Left **The last buses to be delivered to the Tyneside Omnibus company were five ECW-bodied Daimler Fleetlines, in 1973, part of an order for 56 such buses which were shared between five NBC companies. Tyneside's were among the NBC vehicles serving the PTE area which were later repainted yellow. Tyneside Omnibus was absorbed by Northern General at the start of 1976. Note the promotional advertising for NBC.** D J Little

Below left **Gateshead & District's buses were green too, as shown by a 1968 Alexander-bodied Atlantean, one of 12 transferred from Northern General in 1970 and rebuilt from single-door to dual-door layout at the same time.** D J Little

Below right **From 1974 Northern General began repainting some of its buses yellow, to meet the requirements of the Tyne & Wear PTE. For most of the 1970s the yellow was applied in NBC-style, with just a band of relief, but in cream rather than corporate white. This Alexander-bodied Atlantean had started life in the Tyneside Omnibus fleet.** D J Little

Left **Northern General was the main operator of Marshall's distinctive Camair body, with a fleet of 25 on Leyland Panther chassis, some of which started life with associate companies. The Camair had standee windows in the cove panel on the nearside only. The offside had shallower windows with conventional steel panelling above. One is seen in Jarrow in 1974.** D J Little

Centre right opposite **For a short period NBC decreed that single-deckers should be all-over red or green, with no white relief. This is one of Northern General's 1973 Nationals in Wallsend.** D J Little

Bottom right opposite **A total of 45 Park Royal-bodied Atlanteans were delivered to Northern General group companies in 1974. Sunderland District was the original owner of this vehicle, photographed in Sunderland in 1977.** D J Little

Right **Single-deck Fleetlines figured prominently in the operations of Northern General and its associates. There were ultimately 83 in total, including 17 with Alexander W-type bodies delivered to the Sunderland District fleet in 1971 and later absorbed by Northern General, as seen in this view in Sunderland bus station. They only lasted 10 years.** David Brown

The Northern General group companies had been early users of the Leyland Atlantean, buying their first in 1960. Early examples had boxy BET-specification bodywork by Alexander, Metro-Cammell, Roe and Weymann. Later deliveries had Alexander's attractive Glasgow-style bodywork or, in 1972, ECW bodies which at that time were still comparatively unusual on double-deck chassis other than Bristol's VRT. The 1972 Atlanteans were accompanied by ECW-bodied Fleetlines which joined a couple of earlier batches of Fleetlines with bodies by Weymann and Alexander. However Northern General's Fleetline double-deckers totalled only 31 in 1975, compared with some 220 Atlanteans including 45 new AN68s with Park Royal bodies and 27 with ECW bodies. These were of two-door layout.

The only new half-cab purchases after the arrival of the first Atlanteans were 50 Routemasters, the only examples supplied new to a provincial operator. These were 30ft long and had forward-entrance Park Royal bodies and Leyland engines. They were new in 1964-65 and were followed in 1966 by the original forward-entrance Routemaster, built in 1962 as London Transport's RMF1254 but never used in London bus service. Older half-cabs were exposed-radiator Leyland PD3s, most of which had gone by 1975.

Northern General's other double-deckers were a bit of a mixed bag. There were just five of NBC's standard, the ECW-bodied VRT, and even these had non-standard two-door bodies. More VRTs would come later in the decade. Then there were six AEC Renowns, acquired by Tynemouth from East Yorkshire in 1972 as part of an exchange which saw 20 Tynemouth Fleetlines head south. There's no argument about whose passengers and drivers got the better deal out of that particular manoeuvre.

But the oddest double-deckers were two in-house rebuilds. Northern General, in common with many other operators, was keen to extend the use of one-man-operated double-deckers but was concerned about the running costs and reliability of rear-engined models. Older front-engined buses were cheaper on fuel and generally offered higher standards of availability for service, despite their age. NGT had calculated in 1972 that maintenance costs per mile were in the order of 4.72p for an Atlantean, 3.67p for a Fleetline and just 3.3p for a Routemaster. The answer – or so it seemed –

was to convert front-engined buses to make them suitable for omo. A few fleets had tried – notably Aberdeen with CVG6s and Brighton with Titans – but these had been far from an unqualified success, with the driver having to turn round in a cramped cab to collect fares and issue tickets.

Northern General addressed the problem by rebuilding a Metro-Cammell-bodied PD3 into a normal-control double-decker, with the driver sitting behind the front axle, rather than over it, and thus being directly opposite the entrance. This – the Tynesider – took to the road in 1972. It was followed by the Wearsider, a similar conversion of a Routemaster, intended as a pilot for conversion of the remaining 50. No more were built, but both vehicles were still in limited use in 1975.

Older single-deckers were primarily Leopards and Reliances with BET-style bodies by Marshall, Weymann and Willowbrook. The newest were the inevitable Leyland Nationals, including early K-registered examples which

Top **In 1978 Willowbrook won its only major contracts from NBC, to supply double-deck bodies on Bristol VRT chassis for East Kent and for Northern General, which got 20 to full-height layout.** David Brown

Above left and right **In pursuit of improved reliability in one-man-operated double-deckers Northern General carried out two unusual conversions. The Tynesider was a rebuild of a 1958 Leyland Titan PD3 with rear-entrance Metro-Cammell body, which featured a forward entrance located opposite a set-back driving position. It entered service in 1972 with a new K-suffix registration. The Wearsider was a Routemaster conversion in which the driving position was moved back. Both buses were withdrawn in 1978.** D J Little, Malcolm King

Left **Bristol MWs were bought by United until 1967. Like all MWs in England and Wales they had ECW bodies. This is a late 1950s bus, still in Tilling red in the summer of 1973, but sporting a corporate NBC fleetname.** David Brown

had been delivered in NGT dark red and cream and Sunderland District blue and white. But in between there was considerable variety, as Northern General and its associates had in the period from the late 1960s to the arrival of the National tried a variety of rear-engined models, generally with two-door bodies for busy urban services. These included 36ft-long Fleetlines bodied by Alexander and Willowbrook (plus some acquired from Maidstone & District with Marshall bodies), ECW-bodied Bristol REs and some Leyland Panthers with striking Marshall Camair bodies which featured deeper windows on the nearside than on the offside. The Camair-bodied Panther was a rare beast. The only others were to be found in the Preston Borough Transport fleet. Northern General was, incidentally, the biggest user of single-deck Fleetlines buying 43 new and adding 12 second-hand.

United's headquarters were in Darlington. It had a relatively limited presence in the Tyne & Wear area – that had largely been BET territory in pre-NBC days – and the fact that its fleet numbered over 1,000 vehicles was indicative of the huge operating area which it covered. It had depots as far north as Berwick-upon-Tweed and as far south as Scarborough, two towns the best part of 150 miles apart. Most of the fleet was in poppy red, although the previous Tilling red had not completely disappeared.

United's fleet may have been 1,000 strong, but it was also highly standardised in the THC/NBC mould. All of the double-deckers were Bristols – from early 1960s FS and FSF models, through the inevitable FLFs (almost 150 of them, the fleet's most numerous type), to the new generation of VRTs, which included 20 ex-SBG buses. All of United's surviving Lodekkas in the mid-1970s had Bristol engines; later Gardner-powered FLFs had gone north to Scotland in exchange for the VRTs.

The oldest single-deckers were MW5Gs, followed by more-powerful MW6Gs then by REs and LHs. With a large rural area to serve United was an enthusiastic buyer of the light LH and had 150, with more to come. Its REs illustrated

Top right **United had Bristol REs with a range of ECW body styles from two-door buses to long-distance coaches. This dual-purpose 50-seater was deemed sufficiently luxurious to merit local coach livery when first repainted in NBC corporate style. It is seen in Durham in 1974.** Stewart J Brown

Centre right **With a vast rural area to serve, United became a major customer for Bristol's LH model. By 1979 the company would be running 220 which had been bought new, all with 43-seat ECW bodies, plus a few second-hand examples including two with Marshall bodies. A standard ECW-bodied bus is seen in Sedgefield in 1977.** D J Little

Right **The last new bus for Gillett Bros of Quarrington Hill was this Willowbrook-bodied Bedford YRT, seen in Hartlepool in August 1974, a few months before the company was taken over by United Auto.** D J Little

the development of ECW's bus body and included some early 1964 examples with curved windscreens, two varieties of later flat-screened variants with noticeably different windscreen depths, and the final version with the BET screen. Those used on longer distance routes generally had high-backed seats and were in NBC's local coach livery, half red, half white. The original 1962 RELL bus prototype was also still in United's service. There were no Leyland Nationals in the United fleet in 1975 – but they were coming later in the decade.

The real interest in this standardised fleet was created by the existence of a few buses taken over from recently-acquired independents in County Durham. In 1974 United had taken over Gillett Bros of Quarrington Hill and had retained a number of Gillett's AEC Reliance buses, with bodies by Plaxton and Willowbrook. At the start of 1975 Shaw Bros of Byers Green was purchased and a few ex-Shaw coaches were in use. Vehicles from an earlier acquisition, Wilkinson's of Sedgefield in 1967, were also still in use, despite being non-standard in this predominantly Bristol operation. Survivors in 1975 were four Leopards and two Reliances, all with Plaxton bus bodies. Two of the Leopards were in fact delivered new to United in 1967, but had been ordered by Wilkinson's.

Local bus services in Darlington were largely the preserve of Darlington Transport. Its fleet was varied, the common link being that most buses were Gardner-powered. Darlington was one of a number of small municipalities to see the economic benefits of one-man-operation in the mid-1960s. Its last double-deckers – still running in 1975 – had been 11 Roe-bodied Daimler CCG5s delivered in 1964. This was by any standards a conservative specification – Gardner's 5LW engine rather than the more common six-cylinder unit, and a constant-mesh gearbox. The next new buses were radically different – 12 Daimler Roadliners with Cummins V6 engines and two-door Roe bodies in 1967. Most of these were still running in 1975 which, in view of the Roadliner's reputation, some might consider a greater achievement than the survival of the CCG5s.

Top left **Gillett Bros was the original owner of this AEC Reliance in the predominantly Bristol-based United fleet. New in 1973, it had Willowbrook bodywork.** D J Little

Centre left **The last new double-deckers for Darlington were 11 Roe-bodied Daimler CCG5s in 1964. Some survived into the 1980s.** Malcolm Keeley

Left **After buying Roadliners Darlington tried the single-deck Fleetline, building up a fleet of 36 by 1972. Most had Roe bodies, as seen on this bus.** Stewart J Brown

Darlington stayed with Daimler, buying single-deck Fleetlines until 1972 with bodies by Roe and Marshall. It then switched to the Seddon Pennine RU, taking eight in 1974, which were its newest buses. Seddon was by then on its way out of bus production and Darlington's next order, due for delivery in 1976, was for Leyland Leopards with Duple Dominant bus bodies. All of Darlington's single-deckers were of two-door layout.

The other small municipal fleet firmly in United country was in Hartlepool. Its vehicle policy had developed in a similar manner to that at Darlington, but with a sounder choice of vehicle. Here rear-entrance double-deckers were still in use, with around 20 Roe-bodied exposed-radiator PD2s, the newest of which had entered service in 1965. But in 1964 Hartlepool had started running one-man buses, with eight Leopards fitted with neat two-door bodies by Strachans. Another five followed in 1965 and then in 1966, taking advantage of the availability of ECW bodywork, five ECW-bodied Leopards joined the fleet. All of these relatively unusual vehicles were still giving sterling service 10 years later.

But in 1967 Hartlepool had made what many would agree was a wise choice. It standardised on the Bristol RELL with ECW bodywork. By 1975 there were 57 in the 86-strong fleet. In the interests of standardisation with previous generations of Hartlepool bus they had Leyland engines. Many would run for 20 years, although that was certainly not envisaged in 1975.

The big municipal fleet in the North East was Cleveland Transit. This was the catchy trading name of the rather unweildy-sounding Langbaurgh, Middlesbrough and Stockton Joint Transport Committee which in 1974 had taken over from Teesside Municipal Transport. Teesside was itself a relatively recent amalgam – in 1968 – of the separate municipal operations

Above **The only double-deckers in the Hartlepool fleet in the mid-1970s were Leyland Titan PD2s with Roe bodies. There had been 20, delivered between 1958 and 1965. This 1962 bus was one of a pair with platform doors; the others had open platforms. It is seen near Seaton Carew in 1976.** D J Little

Right **From 1967 the standard bus at Hartlepool was the Bristol RE with dual-door ECW bodywork. New in 1968, this one is seen in 1975 after a repaint in a brighter version of the undertaking's traditional maroon and cream. The original livery had the cream relief restricted to the waistband and window surrounds.** D J Little

Left **Cleveland ran a mixed fleet of PD2 Titans which included exposed-radiator buses which had been new to Stockton Corporation. Metro-Cammell bodywork was fitted to this 1963 bus in Middlesbrough, still in Teesside livery. This was one of Stockton's last batch of Titans. From 1964 it specified Atlanteans for its double-deck requirements.** Stewart J Brown

Below **One of six former TRTB Atlanteans, photographed in Stockton High Street in 1974 when owned by Cleveland although still in Teesside colours. It has Roe bodywork – as did all of the TRTB vehicles taken over by Teesside. The bus behind is a Northern Counties-bodied Fleetline CRL6.** Stewart J Brown

run by Middlesbrough, Stockton and the Teesside Railless Traction Board. Vehicle types which had disappeared in the few years prior to the creation of Cleveland Transit included ex-Middlesbrough Guy Arabs and Dennis Lolines, and ex-TRTB Sunbeam trolleybuses with the end of electric traction in 1971. TMT's livery was an unusual turquoise which was still in evidence in 1975. An apocryphal tale suggests that the turquoise was the result of mixing together the three colours of paint used by TMT's predecessors. Cleveland Transit adopted a bold new green and yellow, with coaches being painted orange and yellow. A boomerang-style logo (actually a stylised 'C') was used with the fleetname Transit. The fact that as recently as 1968 there had been three different municipal operators serving the Stockton and Middlesbrough conurbation made for some variety in the Cleveland Transit fleet in the mid-1970s.

The ex-Middlesbrough buses were all Gardner-engined Daimler Fleetlines with Northern Counties bodies, apart from one survivor from a pair of 1966 Panther Cubs. The oldest of the Fleetlines dated from 1962. The ex-Stockton and TRTB buses on the other hand were all Leylands. Stockton's were exposed-radiator PD2s followed by Park Royal-bodied Atlanteans. There were also four Panther Cubs and 10 Panthers; these too had Park Royal bodies. TRTB's Titans were mainly PD2As, including some E-registered 1967 examples with rear-entrance bodies by Roe, TRTB's sole body supplier in the late 1950s and 1960s. The newest ex-TRTB buses were six F-registered Atlanteans. Single-deckers were four 1965 Leopards.

Cleveland Transit's standard bus was the Northern Counties-bodied Fleetline, effectively marking the continuation of a buying policy which could be traced back through TMT to Middlesbrough Corporation. However Cleveland specified Leyland engines, as had TMT. By 1975 there were almost 100 CRL6s in service. More unusual 'deckers were a dozen Atlanteans which TMT had acquired from Standerwick in 1971. These were 10-year-old buses when they moved east – relatively young

for a second-hand Atlantean – but they were high-mileage former Motorway coaches.

Delays in Fleetline deliveries saw Cleveland order one batch of 15 Bristol VRTs, which were delivered in 1977 and had Gardner engines, as had all subsequent Fleetline deliveries, with but one exception.

In 1974 Cleveland Transit took over Saltburn Motor Services, which ran 22 vehicles, most of which were Bedfords built between 1958 and 1972. A few vehicles were still operating in Saltburn's red and cream livery in 1975, but a number of the Bedfords, including quite early SBs, received Cleveland colours. To start replacement of some of the older Saltburn vehicles Cleveland bought two Bedford YRQs with

Top left **A 1970 Atlantean in Cleveland colours. Northern Counties bodywork is fitted. There were 15 buses in this batch and they had been ordered by Stockton Corporation.** Stewart J Brown

Top right **Coaches in the Cleveland fleet carried this livery – although it may be stretching the term 'coach' to apply it to this Plaxton-bodied Leopard with bus seats. The roof-mounted destination display and the two-piece doors were hallmarks of coach bodies built to bus grant specification, most of which had coach seats too.** D J Little

Above left **Three new Northern Counties-bodied Atlanteans were added to OK's fleet in 1973 as the company took advantage of the support offered by the government's new bus grant. They were long-wheelbase 83-seaters, and OK's first new double-deckers since a Titan in 1958. The location is Marlborough Crescent, Newcastle.** David Brown

Above right **Lockey's ex-East Kent AEC Regent V had an attractively-styled Park Royal body with full-width front. New in 1959, it joined Lockey in 1972 and was to see service into the early 1980s. This view was taken in West Auckland shortly after the vehicle was purchased by Lockey. The use of a sliding door was unusual. Most forward-entrance buses had double jackknife doors.** D J Little

the first examples of Duple's new Dominant bus body at the end of 1974. Two more followed in 1975, but most of the company's single-deck purchases in the latter part of the decade were Leyland Leopards with bodies by Plaxton and Duple. Unusual small buses introduced to the fleet in 1975 were two Ford A-series with Northern Counties bodies, and two Leyland EAs, with Irish-built Asco bodies.

Cleveland's double-deckers carried H or L prefixes to their fleet numbers. Buses with L prefixes were low enough to pass safely under the 13ft 6in bridge at Middlesbrough station. Those with H prefixes weren't.

Despite the acquisition of small companies by United and Cleveland Transit, there were still significant members of services being run by independent operators, particularly in County Durham. The biggest was OK Motor Services, with its headquarters in Bishop Auckland and services running north to Newcastle, as well as locally around Bishop Auckland and nearby towns. OK ran 60 buses and coaches, bought both new and second-hand. The coaches, Bedfords and Leopards with bodies by Duple and Plaxton, were generally built to bus grant specification and so spent part of their time on service. Modern double-deckers were four 83-seat Northern Counties-bodied long-wheelbase Atlanteans, new in 1973-74. Older 'deckers included assorted second-hand Titans, some of which were full-fronted ex-Southdown PD3s, and a few Atlanteans which had come from Ribble and the Tyneside PTE. One Titan, a 1958 PD3 with Roe body, had been owned since new. Two-thirds of OK's fleet was less than four years old, and this influx of new vehicles had seen the withdrawal of older second-hand buses, including the last ex-London Transport RTL-class Leylands.

Lockey of St Helens Auckland worked jointly with OK on the Bishop Auckland to Evenwood service. This could be covered by a choice of three second-hand double-deckers – an ex-Ribble PD3, an ex-East Kent Regent V or an ex-Leicester Daimler CSG6/30 – or by a Willowbrook-bodied Bedford Y-series.

Although Bishop Auckland was served by United, who had a depot in the town, it was a key centre of independent bus operation. Trimdon Motor Services ran to Bishop Auckland, and its buses could also be seen as far

Above left **Most of Trimdon's buses in the 1970s were Leyland Leopards. Five with Plaxton Derwent bus bodies were purchased in 1973. Later deliveries included Plaxton coaches to bus grant specification, and Willowbrook buses.** D J Little

Left **Stanhope Motor Services owned this smart Leyland Tiger PS2 which had been rebodied as a double-decker by Roe in 1958. The front bumper bar was an unusual fitment.** David Brown

Right **The Eden favoured Plaxton-bodied Leopard buses for most of the 1970s, as illustrated by a 1972 PSU3 in Bishop Auckland at the end of the decade. It has a Derwent-style body, a popular choice with independents in the North East.** D J Little

Below **Leaving Bishop Auckland for Willington is a 1965 AEC Reliance operated by Bond Bros. It was one of three similar buses with Plaxton bodies, dating from 1965-66.** D J Little

south as Hartlepool and Stockton. This was another company which had seized the opportunity of the new bus grant to update its fleet. At the start of the 1970s the TMS fleet had been made up mainly of Fords but by 1975 there were just 10, compared with 30 Leyland Leopards. Bodies were by Plaxton and Willowbrook.

Weardale Motor Services ran to Stanhope, where it had a subsidiary, Stanhope Motor Services. The fleet included three double-deckers bought new if you include a 1958 rebody of a Tiger PS2 which had been re-registered at the same time. It had a Roe body and was registered YUP6 – 6 being a Weardale theme. A 1959 PD3 with forward-entrance Alexander body, an odd choice indeed for an independent, was 6BUP, while the last new 'decker was a two-door Leeds-style Roe-bodied

Atlantean, GUP6H. High-capacity single-deckers also featured and included one Leopard and two Volvo B58s with 68-seat Plaxton bodies. The Eden, serving West Auckland and Bishop Auckland, had an 18-strong single-deck fleet. Bedfords and Leopards with Plaxton Derwent bus bodies were the most common type on service. Bond Bros of Willington also ran to Bishop Auckland normally using AEC Reliances with Plaxton bodies. Between Ferryhill and Bowburn, to the north-east of Bishop Auckland, Scarlet Band ran a service using single-deck buses which included a Plaxton-bodied Tiger Cub. Martindale of Ferryhill had a local service in the town and in nearby Chilton. Martindale ran Leopards, including two with Plaxton bodies to bus grant specification.

Among the small operators to be seen in Durham city, served by both United and Northern General, was Diamond of Stanley, a co-operative which had once numbered nine members but was now down to two – J H Hammell running in grey and red, and J S Mowbray in cream and green. Both ran Bedfords. Most of Hammell's had Willowbrook bodies, while Mowbray's had bodies by Willowbrook, Duple and Plaxton. The Diamond fleet numbered 17 buses. Also running into Stanley and to Durham (on Saturdays only) was Fulton's of Sacriston, which in 1974 took over two services from Armstrong of Ebchester. These were still operated by ex-Armstrong

Top left **The distinctive colours of Hammel of Stanley, worn by a Willowbrook-bodied Bedford YRQ – typical of many such vehicles delivered to small operators in the early 1970s.** D J Little

Centre left **The other partner in the Diamond Bus Service operation was Mowbray, using the same trading name, but a totally different livery. This is a 1977 Bedford YLQ with Duple Dominant bus body.** John Jones

Bottom left **Fulton's of Sacriston displayed their name prominently on this 1971 Willowbrook-bodied Leopard, a relatively uncommon 10m PSU4 model which they had taken over from Armstrong of Ebchester in 1974. Most small operators specified the 11m PSU3 version of Leyland's popular single-deck chassis.** D J Little

Top right **Gypsy Queen was the trading name of the Langley Park Motor Co, with a regular service into Durham. Bedfords were favoured, as shown by a Y-series with Plaxton bus body in 1975.** D J Little

Centre right **Hunter of Seaton Delavel bought their first rear-engined double-decker, a Roe-bodied Atlantean, in 1971. It was joined by second-hand Atlanteans later in the decade but was still the most modern 'decker in the fleet when the 1970s drew to a close.** D J Little

Bottom right **Tyne Valley of Acomb bought three Plaxton-bodied Bedford YRQ buses in 1972. One is seen in Acomb on the company's Hexham service.** D J Little buses – a Bedford VAM with Plaxton body and two consecutively-registered buses from AEC and Leyland, a Reliance and Leopard respectively with bus bodies by Plaxton and Willowbrook. Armstrong continued to operate their long-established service from Consett to Medomsley with a Leopard and a Bedford YRT, both of which had Plaxton Derwent bus bodies. Between Durham and Langley Park there was the Gypsy Queen service, run by Plaxton-bodied Bedfords. Elsewhere in the north of the county General Omnibus Services ran in the Chester-le-Street area, generally with Willowbrook-bodied Bedford VAMs.

North of the Tyne in Northumberland, Hunter's operated a long-established route from Seaton Delavel via Whitley Bay to North Shields. Pride of the fleet was an Atlantean bought new in 1971 with two-door Roe bodywork. Bus grant Leopard coaches were also used on the service. Further north a Bedlington town service was run by Raisbeck's of Morpeth with a Bedford YRQ with Duple Dominant bus body. Amble, on the Northumberland coast, had a local service provided by Craiggs using a 1971 Bedford YRQ with Willowbrook bus body.

Inland in Hexham, actually on the south of the Tyne but still in Northumberland, local services were run by Rochester & Marshall with a fleet of Bedfords, including a 1972 SB with Willowbrook bus body – an unusual vehicle for an English independent by that late date. Tyne Valley Coaches of Acomb also served Hexham using Plaxton-bodied Bedford YRQs. An odd dual-purpose vehicle purchased by Tyne Valley in 1974 was a YRQ with Caetano Cascais body – most Caetano bodies were pure luxury coaches rather than being built to bus grant specifications.

1975: Major bus fleets – North East England

Operator	*Fleet size*
United Automobile	1056
Tyne & Wear PTE	613
Northern General*	598
Cleveland Transit	262
Hartlepool	86
Sunderland District*	86
Darlington	68
Tynemouth & District*	66
Gateshead & District*	65
Venture Transport*	58
Tyneside Omnibus Co*	19

* These companies all shared the same management, giving the Northern General group a combined fleet of 892 vehicles.

71
PRINCE OF WALES RD
CIRCULAR
200
JWJ 200D

The provision of bus services in West Yorkshire and South Yorkshire had been changed dramatically in 1974 by the creation of two PTEs to serve the two newly-created metropolitan counties formed as a result of 1974's local government reorganisation.

The bigger of the two was the West Yorkshire PTE with a fleet of almost 1,500 vehicles serving Leeds, Huddersfield, Bradford and Halifax. The smaller was the South Yorkshire PTE running some 950 buses in Sheffield, Rotherham and Doncaster. Both PTE areas were also served by NBC companies, with the bulk of Yorkshire Traction's services being in South Yorkshire and a substantial part of the West Riding and Yorkshire Woollen companies' businesses being in West Yorkshire. The West Yorkshire Road Car Co also had a significant presence in the north of the WYPTE area, particularly round Bradford.

The West Yorkshire PTE took over the municipal bus operations in the four main towns in its area, along with the Calderdale Joint Omnibus Committee. It used four trading names on its buses – Metro Leeds, Metro Bradford, Metro Kirklees (in Huddersfield) and Metro Calderdale (in Halifax and Todmorden). By 1975 there had really not been enough time for the PTE to make much of a mark on vehicle purchasing, although there were 100 new AN68 Atlanteans in service with single-door Roe bodies of a style which effectively became the PTE standard and would later also be supplied on Fleetlines. These were 9.5m-long buses with single-door bodies, marking a departure from the practice of Leeds City Transport, the PTE's biggest constituent, which had standardised on long-wheelbase AN68/2s and Fleetlines with two-door Roe bodies featuring panoramic windows.

Left **As the 1970s wore on, SYPTE eliminated the old Sheffield livery by overpainting the blue relief bands cream. The result was unimpressive, as demonstrated by a ghostly Park Royal-bodied Atlantean of 1966 vintage.** Stewart J Brown

Above right **Among early deliveries to the new West Yorkshire PTE were 40 MCW Metropolitan integrals. These entered service in 1975, and more followed in 1976-77. This one is in Bradford.** Stewart J Brown

Right **The Leeds livery was applied in this style to half-cab buses, with dark green being dominant. This Roe-bodied Leyland PD3 was one of 71 delivered in 1959 for tramway replacement, 20 of which were still in operation when the PTE was formed. All had gone by 1975.** Stewart J Brown

Top **The advent of one-man-operation in Leeds City Transport brought with it a new livery layout, and a distinctive style of 78-seat Roe dual-door bodywork, supplied on long-wheelbase Fleetline (as shown here) and Atlantean chassis. This is a 1972 bus.**
Stewart J Brown

Above **Leeds City Transport had been an enthusiastic user of one-man-operated single-deckers in the late 1960s. Its fleet of omo single-deckers included 50 AEC Swifts delivered in 1969 which had two-door Park Royal bodies. This one is seen in PTE ownership in the late 1970s. The 1970 Fleetline single-deck visible alongside carries a later version of the PTE livery with green for the lower half and cream for the top.**
Stewart J Brown

There were also 40 MCW Metropolitans, allocated to Bradford. The Metropolitan fleet would ultimately number 95. One other new type in 1975 was the Ailsa. The PTE bought one, with Alexander body, for evaluation. It remained unique in the fleet. All of the new buses wore the PTE's new livery – Verona Green and Buttermilk, the latter colour looking remarkably similar to Merseyside's more romantically-named Jonquil. To most people it was cream. An odd feature of West Yorkshire's livery was the use of a band of green across the front of the bus, located above the driver's cab and then swept down behind the cab to terminate abruptly at waist level. It echoed a similar and considerably more successful layout which had been used by Doncaster Corporation – which was not, be it noted, a constituent of the West Yorkshire PTE but rather of the neighbouring South Yorkshire PTE.

The bulk of the vehicles in the West Yorkshire PTE fleet in 1975 retained the liveries of their previous owners – it takes a long time to repaint 1,500 buses. In Leeds there were 240 big Atlanteans and 100 generally similar Fleetlines, all but 30 bodied locally by Roe. Other rear-engined types included older 30ft-long Atlanteans and Fleetlines delivered between 1964 and 1966 prior to the adoption of the 33ft version as the fleet standard. Leeds City Transport had also been among the enthusiasts for standee single-deckers in the late 1960s and as a result the PTE inherited 120 AEC Swifts (the biggest fleet of the type outside London) and 30 single-deck Fleetlines. Most of the single-deckers had Park Royal bodies, although some of the earliest Swifts had been bodied by Roe.

The oldest buses running for the PTE in Leeds were 1959 Daimler CVG6s and exposed-radiator PD3s, all with 70-seat rear-entrance Roe bodies. There were also 15 Regent Vs which were unusual in being late examples with exposed radiators. New in 1960, they looked much older. There were later Regent Vs with new-look fronts, the newest being 1966 deliveries, and around a dozen PD3A Titans. The Leeds CVG6s were unusual in having Gardner's 10.45-litre 6LX engines in place of the more common, but less powerful, 8.4-litre 6LW. The smallest buses in Leeds were six Mercedes-Benz L406D which had been converted from vans to 13-seat buses by Deansgate. They were used on a city centre service running from the railway station and were about to be replaced by a batch of ECW-bodied Bristol LHS buses.

In Huddersfield, the Metro Kirklees fleet was basically that inherited from Huddersfield Corporation. Fleet numbers had been altered, by the addition of 4000, but otherwise there was little visible change apart from the gradual appearance of green and cream to replace the municipal red. All pre-1966 double-deckers were conventional half-cab types, mainly Daimler CVG6s, of which there were 64, running alongside 30 St Helens-fronted Titans, a few Regent Vs and a pair of 1959 Guy Arabs which combined out-dated exposed radiators with the modern convenience of semi-automatic gearboxes.

Huddersfield had bought its first Fleetlines in 1968 and these, with Roe bodies, made up the bulk of the modern fleet. Single-deckers were 16 AEC Reliances, a couple of Swifts, two Fleetlines, two Leopards and 23 Seddon Pennine RUs with Pennine bodies. There were also three RUs which had been part of the Calderdale JOC fleet and which had been transferred to Huddersfield in the interests of fleet standardisation shortly after the formation of the PTE. The Reliances included three with Willowbrook bodies which had been taken over by Huddersfield Corporation in 1969 with the local bus operations of Hanson.

Forward-entrance double-deckers had been the Huddersfield standard from 1960, which meant there were only four open-platform buses in the Metro Kirklees fleet. Fleetlines delivered between 1970 and 1973 had two-door bodies but the 1974 delivery, which in fact arrived after the formation of the PTE, was of single-door layout.

Bradford City Transport had adopted forward entrances on its double-deckers in 1959 which meant that there were no rear-platform buses in the Metro Bradford operation. The oldest buses were 30ft-long Regent Vs with Metro-Cammell bodies – there were around 100 in use in 1975 – which had been delivered in the period 1959 to 1964. Then followed Neepsend-

Above **The Huddersfield fleet was made up mainly of Roe-bodied double-deckers, including this 1963 Titan PD3A/2. It was a 70-seater. The last ex-Huddersfield Titans were withdrawn by the PTE in 1980.** Stewart J Brown

Below left **Bradford was running 115 AEC Regent Vs when the West Yorkshire PTE took over. All had forward-entrance Metro-Cammell bodies and they dated from the 1959-64 period. A 1963 example gets ready to move a load of shoppers.** Stewart J Brown

Below right **There were also Daimlers in the Huddersfield fleet. A 1968 Fleetline leads a 1965 CVG6LX/30 in the town centre shortly after the formation of the PTE, whose fleet numbers are carried on both buses. They have Roe bodies.** Malcolm King

Left **Later Bradford buses included Leyland Titan PD3As delivered in 1967 and 1969. The earlier batch had Neepsend bodies. Some buses received Metro Bradford fleetnames prior to being repainted by the PTE, but not this one in the city centre in 1976.** Stewart J Brown

Centre left **Halifax's distinctive livery disappeared gradually in the latter part of the 1970s as the fleet was repainted in PTE colours. This 1965 Weymann-bodied Titan was typical of Halifax's older double-deckers. It was in fact an ex-Calderdale bus and was still running in its previous owner's colours when photographed in Halifax in the summer of 1977.** Gerald Mead

Bottom left **From 1966 most of Halifax's new buses were Daimler Fleetlines. These included SRG6LX models with bodies by Willowbrook and, on two 1969 buses, Pennine. This is a Pennine-bodied Fleetline with Halifax's distinctive destination box which allowed the display of comprehensive route information.** Stewart J Brown

Bottom right **From 1976 a number of ex-Huddersfield buses were operated in Halifax, and ran with the appropriate Metro Calderdale fleetnames. Most were 1963 Roe-bodied Leyland Titans. The bus behind is a standard PTE Leyland Fleetline, also fitted with Roe bodywork. It was new in 1976.** Malcolm Keeley

bodied Daimler CVG6s and in both 1967 and 1968 a curious three-way split of orders between Atlanteans, Fleetlines and PD3As. The last of the Titans were G-registered buses with Alexander bodies, the Falkirk builder's last half cabs for the UK. After flirting with Marshall-bodied Swifts and Panthers in 1969, Bradford turned to long-wheelbase Fleetlines and Atlanteans with Alexander bodies and the PTE inherited 90 of these.

The most varied fleet was to be found at Metro Calderdale. This united the Halifax Corporation operation with that of the Calderdale JOC. The Calderdale JOC had been created in 1971 and was an amalgamation of the Halifax and Todmorden JOCs. By 1974, when the PTE took over, both the Halifax Corporation and Calderdale JOC fleets were in the same livery – Halifax's orange, green and cream – and both had the same general manager.

The ex-Halifax buses were mainly Leylands – Leopards and Titans – and Daimler Fleetlines. All of the Titans had exposed radiators and forward-entrance bodywork, mostly by Weymann but with one batch by Roe. The oldest Leopards were 1962 L1s with Weymann bodies while the newest were 10 1972-73 PSU4s bodied by Plaxton. The Fleetlines were single-deckers with bodies by Willowbrook and (unusually) Pennine and double-deckers which had lowheight Northern Counties bodies. Operational changes in 1971 had seen both Halifax and Calderdale acquire buses from Hebble Motor Services and one of these survived, a 1965 Alexander-bodied Fleetline.

From Calderdale the PTE acquired Leopards, Titans and Fleetlines generally similar to those taken in from the Halifax fleet. But there were also a few Regent Vs, and Reliances with bodies by Pennine, Plaxton and Willowbrook. Former Hebble buses which reached the PTE by way of the Calderdale JOC included three Regent Vs and a Fleetline. Also from the JOC came assorted Leopards which had originally been owned by Todmorden, with bodies by East Lancs, Willowbrook and Pennine. Metro Calderdale had the PTE's only Leyland National which was a former Leeds City Transport bus, new in 1973. No more would be bought in the 1970s.

Services operated by Metro Calderdale extended high into the Pennines and even across into Greater Manchester and Lancashire, where West Yorkshire PTE buses could regularly be seen in Rochdale and Burnley. The PTE also ran coaches, most of them being Fords taken over in 1974 with the 25-vehicle business of Hansons (whose bus operations had been taken over by Huddersfield Corporation five years earlier). The Hanson name was retained – as Metro Hanson.

Baddeley Brothers of Holmfirth ran services to Cubley, and from Huddersfield to Deepcar. Baddeley ran a dozen vehicles, mostly Ford and Bedford coaches but including a former Halifax Albion Nimbus with neat Weymann bodywork. The Baddeley business was bought by the West Yorkshire PTE in March 1976.

NBC's operations to the north of Leeds were run by the Harrogate-based West Yorkshire Road Car Co. West Yorkshire operated services in the Bradford and Leeds areas, to the coast at Scarborough and north to Skipton. It had been a THC subsidiary and this gave it a fairly predictable fleet mix. The company's double-deckers were of just two types – rear-entrance Bristol-engined FS6B Lodekkas, and front-entrance Gardner-engined VRTs. Single-deckers offered only slightly more variety, with MWs, LHs, REs and some 50 Leyland Nationals.

In York, town services were provided in conjunction with the local council; a similar arrangement had been in place in Keighley but was wound up in 1974. The York-West Yorkshire fleet ran 80 buses and it was to survive until 1986. The vehicles carried NBC poppy red livery but with non-standard fleetnames in gold lettering. Later in the decade this would change to a standard NBC-style fleetname accompanied by the York city crest. An innovation in Harrogate in 1972 had been the Chauffeur Coach service, a dial-a-ride operation run by two Ford Transits with 15-seat Deansgate bodies. This service was still in operation in 1975.

Top left **West Yorkshire Road Car had been an enthusiastic early user of the Bristol VRT, running 54 G- and H-registered buses with the original style of flat-fronted ECW body. The location is Harrogate bus station.** Malcolm Keeley

Top right **Still in Tilling red, a Lodekka of the York-West Yorkshire fleet heads past the city's railway station in the summer of 1973. It is a 1961 FS6B.** Malcolm Keeley

Right **An attractive non-standard livery with white window surrounds was used on West Yorkshire Road Car's two Chauffeur Coach Ford Transits. New in 1972, they had Deansgate bodies and were used on a dial-a-ride service in Harrogate. NBC's minibus fleet at this time barely reached double figures.** Stewart J Brown

There were two significant independents in West Yorkshire Road Car territory. Pennine Motor Services of Gargrave, formed in 1925, operated routes from Skipton to the north and west. The fleet comprised 12 Leyland Leopards bought new between 1969 and 1975. The four oldest had BET-style Willowbrook bodies while the remainder had Plaxton bus grant coach bodies. There was also one second-hand Leopard/Plaxton, the survivor of four vehicles taken over in 1972 with the business of Ezra Laycock of Barnoldswick. Pennine had operated few types other than Leylands throughout its 50 year history.

Pennine's was a smart fleet with a distinctive livery, as was the other major independent in West Yorkshire Road Car country – York Pullman. There were 30 buses and coaches in this fleet. The oldest, a 1954 Roe-bodied AEC Regent III was about to be withdrawn and sold for preservation, which would leave two Regent Vs, a Reliance and two Swifts to represent AEC in the York Pullman bus fleet. All had Roe bodies except the newest Swift which had been bodied by Plaxton. The demise of AEC as a builder of double-deckers led York Pullman to order Daimler Fleetlines. Three with Roe bodies were in operation in 1975. Coaches were Bedford VAMs and Y-series models with Plaxton bodies. Reliance of Sutton-on-the-Forest ran from Brandsby to York with a Seddon Pennine RU.

On the Yorkshire coast, a service from Scarborough inland to Ebberston was run by Hardwick's, part of the Wallace Arnold organisation. From 1971 it had been covered by Park Royal-bodied AEC Swifts acquired from Sheffield, but in the middle of the decade these were ousted by Plaxton-bodied Leyland Leopard coaches which had been fitted with bus seats. In Filey Primrose Valley ran three Willowbrook-bodied Bedford YRTs.

The area to the east of York and Leeds was the preserve of East Yorkshire Motor Services, the Hull-based NBC subsidiary. East Yorkshire had for 12 months used a dark blue version of NBC's corporate livery, continuing the

Top left **For a short time East Yorkshire buses were painted dark blue in NBC corporate style (with the addition on this bus of a white band on the roof). The bus is a 1961 Bridgemaster, seen during a lay-over period in Hull.** Stewart J Brown

Centre left **East Yorkshire's livery for most of the 1970s was poppy red. This 1963 Daimler Fleetline carries a style of Metro-Cammell body which in BET fleets was more usually found on Leyland Atlanteans. It had been new to Tynemouth and was one of 10 similar buses acquired by East Yorkshire in 1972.** Murdoch Currie

Left **Rear-engined Leyland Panthers and Panther Cubs actually outnumbered mid-engined Leopards in the East Yorkshire fleet in the first half of the 1970s. Most of the rear-engined Leylands had Marshall bodies, including this 1968 Panther in NBC's local coach livery.** Murdoch Currie

company's traditional colours, but that was stopped in October 1973 and poppy red adopted instead. East Yorkshire had pursued an individualistic vehicle policy in BET days and all of its front-engined double-deckers were AECs. And not Regents, but Bridgemasters and Renowns. These had Park Royal bodies of unprepossessing appearance and there were just under 70 in use, the newest being 1966 buses. From 1967 East Yorkshire had bought Fleetlines. There were 35 in stock, delivered between 1967 and 1971 with bodies by Park Royal and Alexander, plus 20 acquired from Tynemouth & District in 1972, with Renowns having moved north as part of the deal. Five 1971 Alexander-bodied Atlanteans, diverted from a Western Welsh order, were East Yorkshire's first Leyland 'deckers since the mid 1950s. The newest double-deckers were standard NBC Bristol VRTs and Park Royal-bodied Atlanteans. The first batch of VRTs, new in 1973, were delivered in dark blue and some were still running in that livery. But the 1974 VRTs and the Atlanteans were in poppy red. The abandonment of East Yorkshire blue upset the traditionalists, but no one could dispute that the red was certainly a lot brighter.

No account of East Yorkshire's operations would be complete without a mention of the Beverley Bar, an arch in the town which quite literally played a part in shaping East Yorkshire's buses. Double-deckers could pass through the Bar – but only if the sides were canted inwards from the top deck waistrail, to create a shape which matched the profile of the arch. This was a feature of a percentage of the EYMS double-deck fleet from 1934 until the last delivery of Renowns in 1966. The Bar was bypassed by a new road at the start of the 1970s.

The single-deckers in East Yorkshire's fleet were all Leylands. Most were Leopards, but the company also built up a fleet of 24 Panthers and 16 Panther Cubs. These had Marshall bodies for bus use, but five of the Panthers were coaches, of which three were bodied by Plaxton and two by MCW – the latter creating a combination unique to East Yorkshire. The Leyland National was conspicuous by its absence.

East Yorkshire operated local services in Hull under a co-ordination agreement with Kingston-upon-Hull Corporation's transport department. This originally dated back to 1934 when Hull was in the process of abandoning its trams and replacing them with buses. The 1974 local government changes left Hull as the only municipal bus operator in Yorkshire, with some 230 buses. It was a highly-standardised fleet with just over 200 Atlanteans. The first five, delivered in 1960, had Metro-Cammell bodies. The remainder were bodied by Roe to a variety of styles, including some with unusual single-piece flat-glass windscreens.

Hull's single-deckers comprised 14 Weymann-bodied AEC Reliances and a dozen

Above **From 1960 to 1975 all of Hull's new double-deckers were Leyland Atlanteans, most with bodies by Roe. The first vehicles carried an unusual livery with swoops of white relief; a layout first used in the mid-1930s. Hull was one of a number of urban operators to use fare boxes on omo routes. The no-change policy which went with fareboxes was generally unpopular with passengers, but was designed to speed boarding and to reduce the risk of drivers being assaulted for their takings.** Stewart J Brown

Below **A new livery was adopted by Hull in 1972, using a crisp, modern layout. It is seen on a Roe-bodied AN68 Atlantean. By 1972 all of Hull's services were one-man-operated, a rare achievement for a fleet of this size at such an early date.** Murdoch Currie

Roe-bodied Panthers. All had two-door bodies, as had two batches of Atlanteans delivered in 1970-71. The operation's blue and white livery was in the throes of change, abandoning exuberant 1930s-style swoops of white relief for a modern white-based scheme with blue relief laid out in three bands as used by the SELNEC PTE. One small operator served Hull, Connor & Graham of Easington running from Kilnsea and Withernsea. Three second-hand 'deckers were owned, being two ex-Ribble Atlanteans and a former Yorkshire Woollen Regent V. Coaches were used on service too.

To the south and west of Leeds there were two associated NBC operators, West Riding and Yorkshire Woollen District. Although under common management, they had very different histories and this was reflected in the composition of their fleets. West Riding was the bigger of the two and had until 1967 been an independent – the second biggest in the country after Lancashire United Transport. It had then sold out to the THC and in consequence become part of NBC in 1969.

West Riding was heavily involved with Guy and the Wulfrunian. It had the biggest fleet of the type – 126 – and this brought with it problems. The last of these advanced and comparatively young buses had been withdrawn in 1972, which meant that earlier generations of West Riding buses stayed in service rather longer than they might have. Thus there were around 20 Guy Arab IVs of 1957 still in operation. These had lowbridge Roe bodies, the last substantial fleet of lowbridge buses in NBC service. Other pre-NBC types were Daimler Fleetlines bodied by Roe and Northern Counties, and Roe-bodied lowheight Atlanteans. There were also post-NBC Fleetlines, 12 with Alexander bodies and 25 with Northern Counties bodies. All were lowheight buses.

West Riding had a mixed fleet of rear-engined single-deck buses. Those which predated the THC/NBC influence were half-a-dozen AEC Swifts, 49 Leyland Panthers and five

Top left **One of West Riding's claims to fame was its fleet of Guy Wulfrunians. The Wulfrunian had a front-mounted Gardner engine, sitting between the driver and the platform. The last were withdrawn in 1972, replaced by second-hand buses transferred in from other NBC subsidiaries.** A Moyes

Centre left **The premature withdrawal of West Riding's Wulfrunians meant an extended life for the company's last Guy Arabs. These were 1957 Mark IV models with lowbridge Roe bodies. A Fleetline in NBC poppy red is just visible on the right.** Malcolm King

Left **The introduction of NBC's corporate livery saw West Riding's buses change from green to red, as illustrated by two Fleetlines in Leeds. The green bus has a Northern Counties body and was one of 25 delivered in 1972. The red bus was one of 25 with Roe bodywork, and dated from 1969.** Stewart J Brown

Bristol REs. These had bodies by Marshall, Roe and Plaxton. There had also been 10 Daimler Roadliners, but these had followed the same route as the Wulfrunians – out of the fleet. The THC/NBC influence was represented by ECW-bodied REs, Leyland Nationals and Bristol VRTs, all delivered new. To speed the replacement of the Wulfrunians ex-Bristol Omnibus FLF Lodekkas had been transferred north. These dated from the early 1960s. The most modern front-engined buses in West Riding service were five E-registered Dennis Lolines with Northern Counties bodies which had been new to the Halifax JOC in 1967 and had been moved to West Riding in 1970 as part of the changes taking place in the Halifax area in that year. West Riding had at the same time taken over a number of Hebble buses and a few Leopards and Reliances were still in operation in 1975.

West Riding was based in Wakefield, where it was the main operator, and had depots at Castleford, Featherstone and Selby. Yorkshire Woollen's main operating base was Dewsbury, with a depot at Heckmondwike. Both companies' buses were in poppy red (although West Riding had previously used a green livery) and the two fleets were numbered in a common series. Yorkshire Woollen had been a BET subsidiary.

Its BET inheritance included standard 36ft-long Leopards with bodies by Marshall and Weymann. But these formed a minority in what was a predominantly double-decked fleet. The double-deckers were an interesting mix. Yorkshire Woollen had been one of a small number of BET companies to take an interest in rebodying, and the oldest 'deckers were a combination of 1950 Leyland Tiger PS2 chassis and 1963 forward-entrance Roe bodies. These pseudo-Titans were accompanied by one batch of 1962 PD3s and one batch of 1964 Albion Lowlanders, which were YWD's last front-engined buses. There had been Regent Vs in the fleet, but these were withdrawn in the early 1970s. In 1966 Yorkshire Woollen had finally switched to rear-engined types, and unusually for a BET company bought both Fleetlines and Atlanteans. By 1971 there were 12 Atlanteans and 32 Fleetlines, all with Alexander bodies. The new order was demonstrated in the final Fleetlines, delivered in 1972 with bodies by ECW. Atlanteans, with NBC's standard Park Royal bodies, marked a change of direction in 1975.

Two small operators ran a joint service between Dewsbury and Mirfield. One, Longstaff, used a 1972 Roe-bodied Fleetline CRL6. The other, Joseph Wood, generally used a Plaxton-bodied Leopard coach or an ex-demonstration Atlantean.

Above **The half-cabs in service with Yorkshire Woollen at the start of the 1970s included six 1950 Leyland Tiger PS2s which had been rebuilt in 1963 and fitted with new 63-seat Roe double-deck bodies. Despite the age of the chassis, the last of these buses survived until 1977. This one is seen in Dewsbury.** Paul Caudell

Below left **Roe-bodied Fleetlines were bought by a number of independents in the early 1970s. These included Longstaff of Mirfield for use on the company's service to Dewsbury.**

Below right **The last of the old-style BET Leopards with Marshall bus bodies for Yorkshire Woollen were 14 delivered in 1972, accompanied by the company's first Nationals. One of the Leopards is seen in Leeds later in the decade.** Stewart J Brown

Above left **Yorkshire Traction bought Leyland Atlanteans and Titans in the early 1960s, and both types were still in all-day service in the mid-1970s. This Titan was new in 1962 and had a Northern Counties body. It is pulling out of Doncaster's south bus station in the summer of 1973.** Stewart J Brown

Above right **In 1969 Yorkshire Traction absorbed the Mexborough & Swinton Traction Co, and with it 14 lowbridge Atlanteans, including this 1961 bus. It has a Weyman body.** D J Little

Below left **A tired-looking 1957 Roe-bodied PD2 in Sheffield Transport service in April 1973, 12 months before the formation of the South Yorkshire PTE. It was withdrawn before the PTE took over.** Stewart J Brown

Below right **The SYPTE was slow to stamp its identity on acquired buses. A 1960 Weymann-bodied Regent V still carries full Sheffield Transport livery in September 1976, over two years into the PTE's existence.** Stewart J Brown

Most of YWD's operations were in the West Yorkshire PTE area. The Yorkshire Traction Company – known to its friends as Tracky – was based in Barnsley and had one depot in West Yorkshire, at Huddersfield. But the bulk of its operations were in South Yorkshire.

YTC was a former BET company with a predominantly Leyland fleet. Most of its single-deckers were standard BET-style Leopards, with bodies by Marshall, Weymann and Willowbrook. There was one batch of single-deck Fleetlines with two-door Alexander bodies, new in 1970, and a trio of Marshall-bodied Fleetline single-deckers delivered at the same time. These had followed YTC's first Fleetline 'deckers, with Northern Counties bodies, in 1968, which had re-introduced Gardner engines to a Leyland-powered fleet. More had followed and when the last were delivered in 1971 (with Park Royal bodywork) there were 19 new Fleetlines being operated by YTC plus six absorbed with the Mexborough & Traction business (a sister BET subsidiary) in 1969. Tiger Cubs, a part of the YTC fleet for most of the 1950s and 1960s, had all but disappeared by 1975. There had been almost 150 a decade earlier; fewer than six remained.

Most YTC double-deckers were Leylands. The company had been among those pioneering the Atlantean in 1959 and there were 72 in the fleet in 1975 including 14 which had come from Mexborough & Swinton. Among the newest Atlanteans, dating from 1969, were four with comparatively rare Willowbrook bodies which had been diverted from Devon General. Older 'deckers were mainly PD3A Titans, of which there were 34 built between 1962 and 1965, including two which had been new to County Motors of Lepton, absorbed by YTC in 1969. YTC, like YWD, had indulged in rebodying Leyland Tigers and three survived in 1975. They had 1963 forward-entrance Northern Counties bodies on 1949 PS2 chassis. The continued use of 25-year-old chassis bore fine testimony to Yorkshire frugality.

One small operator serving Barnsley was

Right **Alexander bodywork was supplied to Sheffield Transport on 20 Fleetlines in 1972 and on 22 Atlanteans in 1973. All were single-doorway 74-seaters. This is an Atlantean.** Stewart J Brown

Centre **East Lancs bodies were uncommon on VRTs in the early 1970s, the main buyers of this combination being Merseyside and Sheffield. Another 1976 view shows no sign of the PTE's identity on one of the 18 East Lancs VRTs which it operated.** Stewart J Brown

Bottom **Locally-manufactured bodywork by East Lancs' associate Neepsend was fitted to 40 Atlanteans supplied to Sheffield in the 1964-66 period. One in SYPTE livery is seen in the city centre in 1976. Neepsend built bodies in Sheffield to East Lancs designs between 1963 and 1967.** Stewart J Brown

Larrett Pepper of Thurnscoe, using a Bedford YRQ with Plaxton Derwent bodywork.

YTC's services extended south to Sheffield. The major constituent of the South Yorkshire PTE was Sheffield Transport, which had a fleet of 660 buses. Sheffield's livery had been an unusual cream with three bands of dark blue relief – a bright livery for an urban operation in the 1960s and 1970s, where hard-wearing dark colours were usually preferred. Sheffield had first tried Leyland's new Atlantean in 1959, but had approached the rear-engined concept with caution, buying AEC Regents in 1960, and again in 1963-64. These, and some earlier PD3 Titans, were still running in 1975, and retained Sheffield livery until being withdrawn in 1976. Sheffield also operated Daimler Fleetlines, with small batches in the early 1960s being followed by almost 100 in the early 1970s, but it was Atlanteans which were in the majority. Most had Park Royal bodies and from 1968 were long-wheelbase 79-seat two-door PDR2s. Strange double-deckers were 18 Bristol VRTs with East Lancs bodies, added to the fleet in 1972. Like similar buses running in Merseyside, they had protruding rear engines, rather than the flush rear end which was a feature of the much more common ECW-bodied VRTs.

Sheffield had dabbled in single-deck one-man-operation, but not to the same extent as had Leeds. Its single-deck fleet comprised 34 Park Royal-bodied Swifts and 10 Leyland Leopards with Alexander Y-type bodies. The Leopards had been bought for a Sheffield to Leeds express service. Repainting in Sheffield was to be a long drawn out process and in 1975 most of the fleet was still in cream and blue. As the decade progressed some buses would have the blue painted over, making the buses overall cream – and the high standards of turn out which had once characterised the city's buses would become but a memory as the fleet grew increasingly shabby.

In Rotherham, whose buses worked into Sheffield, there was a predominance of Roe-bodied Daimlers. The oldest were 1962

forward-entrance CVG6s; the newest 1973 Fleetlines. The last CVG6s had entered service in 1966; the first of the Fleetlines in 1967. The only single-deckers were two Willowbrook-bodied Fleetlines and nine Plaxton-bodied Seddon Pennine RUs. Rotherham had had a small number of AECs – Renowns and Regent Vs – but these had gone by 1975 after a very short period in PTE ownership.

Doncaster's legacy to the PTE was rather more varied. It included Leyland Titans and Daimler CVG6s, representing the old order, and 31 Fleetlines representing the new. These all had Roe bodies. Doncaster tried single-deck omo in the mid-1960s, but steered clear of rear-engined models, instead buying the only Leyland Royal Tiger Cubs to be built for service in Britain. It had 20, with two-door Roe bodies. The Royal Tiger Cub was a 33ft-long export model designed to marry the low weight of a Tiger Cub with the power of a Leopard. When Doncaster Corporation did go rear-engined, it opted for Seddon's RU, taking 25 in the early 1970s. It also tried another Seddon model, the Pennine IV:236 midibus, originally developed for SELNEC. It had five. There were coaches too – Fords with bodies by Duple and Caetano.

Where the West Yorkshire PTE quickly evolved a reasonably standardised bus – using Roe bodywork on Atlantean or Fleetline chassis for most of its operations – the South Yorkshire PTE did not. Sheffield Transport's last new buses had been Atlanteans and Fleetlines with three quite different bodies – Alexander, East Lancs and Park Royal. The Park Royal bodies were of two-door design and were on the Fleetline chassis. The PTE's first new buses were four Leyland Nationals, a number which by 1975 had risen to 19, including an ex-Leyland demonstration bus. Its first big batch of new 'deckers were 56 Fleetlines with yet another make of body, ECW. The full-height bodies were of two-door layout and featured flat glass windscreens with thick corner pillars into which a small window had to be added to meet the needs of the certifying officer in Yorkshire, who believed that the thick pillars created a potentially dangerous blind spot. (The only other bodies of this style were supplied to Colchester on Atlanteans.) There were also 12 Roe-bodied Fleetlines which had been ordered by

Above left **The oldest buses which SYPTE took over from Rotherham were four 1962 Daimler CVG6/30s with 70-seat Roe bodies. They were in fact out of service when the PTE was formed, but three of the four were overhauled and repainted and put into use at Doncaster, where one is seen in 1976.**
Stewart J Brown

Below left **Doncaster Transport latterly had a stylish livery, as illustrated by this Roe-bodied PD3 of 1963. It was one of 10 such buses which passed to SYPTE.**
Stewart J Brown

Rotherham Corporation. Four MCW Metropolitans were purchased for evaluation in 1975 and operated in Doncaster, but no more were ordered.

What was ordered, after a month-long trial of a demonstrator, was the Ailsa. The order was for 62, and these entered service in 1976 with striking bodywork built in Ireland by Van Hool-McArdle. They had originally been ordered with Alexander bodies but the order was switched because Alexander could not deliver quickly enough. This was England's biggest Ailsa fleet. A Van Hool McArdle-bodied Atlantean was also added to the fleet and was unusual in having a flush rear end, with the engine compartment integrated into the body. The only other buyer of Van Hool-McArdle double-deck bodies was Scottish independent A1 Service, which took two on Ailsa chassis. Further Fleetlines came too, including a batch with Metro-Cammell bodies to the same style as London Transport's DMS-class. Later in the decade there would be further deliveries of Atlanteans, including some with Voith automatic gearboxes in place of the standard Leyland Pneumocyclic.

In August 1975 the PTE announced that it was taking over the business of Booth & Fisher of Halfway. It was to be but the first of many independents to sell out in the latter part of the decade. Booth & Fisher served Sheffield, Dronfield and Worksop. Its 40-strong fleet was made up of AEC Reliances bought new and

Top **Seddon's Pennine midibus found relatively few buyers outside Manchester. Doncaster had five.** Stewart J Brown

Centre right **In 1974-75 South Yorkshire took delivery of 56 Daimler Fleetlines with dual-door 70-seat bodies by ECW. The only other buyer of this style of body was Colchester, with a single- door version on Leyland Atlanteen chassis.** Tony Wilson

Right **Most Seddon Pennine RUs had Seddon bodywork, but Doncaster had 11 delivered in 1972 which were unusual in having Roe bodies. Under SYPTE ownership they remained in Doncaster, where this bus is seen in 1977.** S J Butler

second-hand. The newest Reliance bus was a 1965 machine with two-door Marshall body; subsequent purchases had coach bodywork to bus grant specification. There were also two 20-year-old Monocoaches and no fewer than 11 Albion Nimbuses, two of which had been bought new while the others had come from a variety of operators. The PTE retained Booth & Fisher's red livery and most of the vehicles.

Two other independents ran regular services into Sheffield. Dearneways had a route from Thurnscoe, in what was Yorkshire Traction's operating area. Leopards with Plaxton coach bodies were Dearneways' normal vehicles. The company's name came from the River Dearne, which flowed near the company's Goldthorpe base. The other was Wigmore of Dinnington, operating thence using new Willowbrook and Plaxton bus-bodied Bedford YRTs. Wigmore's was a rapidly-changing fleet based on new single-deckers which at the start of the decade had included Bedford VALs and a Seddon Pennine IV with Seddon body.

Most of the independent operators in the SYPTE area served Doncaster. There were eight Doncaster independents in 1975, primarily running north-eastwards towards Armthorpe, Thorne and Moorends or south-east to

Top left **Single-deckers played a relatively small part in SYPTE's operation, but 18 Leyland Nationals were added to the fleet in 1974-75. One featured kneeling suspension, a concept which would not come in to widespread use for another 20 years.** Stewart J Brown

Centre left **Ailsas with Van Hool-McArdle bodies – 62 of them – were added to the SYPTE fleet in 1976. With their deep windows they were stylish vehicles – but the only other buyer was A1 of Ardrossan.** Stewart J Brown

Left **Booth & Fisher of Halfway was the first of a number of independents to be taken over by SYPTE. Most of its buses were AECs, including four ex-Maidstone & District vehicles with Weymann bodies. The Booth & Fisher name and livery were retained by the PTE.** Michael Fowler

Right **With the end of the Guy Arab, both Store and Morgan switched to the Daimler Fleetline. Roe bodywork is fitted to this 1971 bus operated by Morgan.** Stewart J Brown

Below left **Not all of the buses operated by the Doncaster independents had Roe bodies. The fleet of Severn of Dunscroft included a pair of Atlanteans with Alexander bodywork. They had been new in 1971.** Stewart J Brown

Below right **Typical of the older buses run by Felix was this Roe-bodied AEC Regent V, seen in Doncaster in 1973. Felix was taken over by the PTE in 1976.** Stewart J Brown

Finningley, Rossington and Misson. Although some fleets had second-hand vehicles, the Doncaster independents had a long tradition of buying new buses and Roe bodywork. In 1975 they ran between them 48 'deckers bought new, 45 of which had Roe bodies. These included 18 Fleetlines and six Atlanteans, as well as CV-series Daimlers, Guy Arabs, AEC Regents and Leyland Titan PD3s. Three Alexander-bodied Atlanteans were the only new double-deckers not to have Roe bodies.

To the north-east a complex series of joint services were run by Felix Motors of Hatfield, T Severn & Sons of Stainforth, Harold Wilson (Premier) of Stainforth and the associated businesses of Samuel Morgan (Blue Line) and R Store (Reliance). Key destinations were Armthorpe, Moorends, Stainforth and Dunscroft. Morgan and Store had been the most conservative of the Doncaster operators and stayed with half-cab double-deckers – Guy Arab Vs – after all the others had stopped buying them. The newest were a pair of F-registered buses delivered in 1967. And while second-hand double-deckers were relatively unusual among the Doncaster independents in the mid-1970s Morgan had two, a pair of ex-Wallace Arnold Leyland Titan PD3As – with Roe bodies. The newest buses in the combined fleet were two Daimler Fleetlines which entered service in 1975 and followed four similar buses delivered in 1971. Morgan and Store operated further out than the other companies, with a service to Goole.

Severn's 15-vehicle fleet was made up of five Leyland Titan PD3s, six Atlanteans and four single-deckers – three Bedford coaches and a Reliance bus. All bar one of the Bedfords were bought new. Two of the Atlanteans had Alexander bodies. Felix Motors ran six Regents and three Fleetlines with Roe bodywork. Harold Wilson's share of the Moorends service was generally covered by a 1959 Guy Arab, a 1965 Fleetline or a 1973 Atlantean. The Leyland had an Alexander body, but the older double-deckers had Roe bodies. An Ailsa to be delivered in 1976 (also bodied by Alexander) would be the only one of its type bought new by an English independent.

Leon Motor Services ran south-east to Finningley (the company's base) and Misson.

Top **The last new half-cab bought by Harold Wilson was a Roe-bodied Arab IV in 1959. It was still in use in the late 1970s, by then running alongside an Ailsa.** Stewart J Brown

Above **Bedford VAL buses were few and far between. For most of the 1970s Leon operated this VAL70 with 56-seat Duple (Midland) body. It had been new to Wigmore of Dinnington in 1968.** D J Little

For this the company had one Daimler CVD650/30 (unusual in being Daimler-engined) and two Fleetlines, plus three Bedford VALs with bus bodies by Willowbrook and its successor in Loughborough, Duple (Midland). Leon also ran Bedford Y-series coaches. Leon's three 'deckers had Roe bodies.

A service to Rossington was run by Blue Ensign Coaches and Rossie Motors, operating in conjunction with the PTE and NBC subsidiary East Midland which, incidentally, also had routes in to Sheffield and Rotherham. Blue Ensign was running two Regent Vs and a Fleetline at the start of 1975, but by the end of the year the Regents had gone, with two new Fleetlines taking their place. Rossie Motors was a Daimler user, with two 30ft CV-series models – another rare Daimler-engined CVD6/30 and a more common Gardner-powered CVG6/30 – and three Fleetlines.

Not strictly a Doncaster independent, United Services ran north to Wakefield via Hemsworth, and from Wakefield to Hemsworth and South Kirkby. United Services was the trading name of

Right **Blue Ensign sold out to the PTE in 1978. Its double-deck fleet consisted of three Fleetlines with Roe bodies. New in 1975, this bus is seen in Doncaster shortly after the PTE take-over – note the PTE fleet number.** Stewart J Brown

Centre right **Roe-bodied Fleetlines were bought by a number of the Doncaster operators in the 1970s – encouraged by the availability of the government's new bus grant. Two were added to the Rossie Motors fleet in 1972.** Stewart J Brown

Bottom right **Rare bodywork by Bond was fitted to a pair of PD2s delivered to the original user of the South Yorkshire name, the Pontefract-based independent operator. They were new in 1955 and were to serve the company for 20 years. Further Titans followed and then, from 1963, Atlanteans.** Paul Caudell

two West Yorkshire-based operators – Cooper Bros of South Kirkby and Bingley of Kinsley. Cooper ran only buses – two Willowbrook-bodied Bedfords and an ex-SELNEC Panther Cub – while Bingley had a substantial coach fleet. Bingley's service vehicles were three Plaxton-bodied Leopards, new in 1969-70.

Also running from Doncaster was South Yorkshire Road Transport, with services to Leeds, one of which ran through Pontefract, the company's home town. South Yorkshire also operated to Selby. The company's trunk routes were generally covered by lowbridge or low-height double-deckers, all bought new. These ranged from five Leyland Titans, through eight Atlanteans, to a trio of Fleetlines, which were to become the company's late 1970s standard. Roe bodywork was fitted to two Titans and two Atlanteans, but post-1971 buses had Northern Counties bodywork, the manufacturer who would continue to supply South Yorkshire's bodies for the rest of the decade. The two oldest Titans, 1955 PD2/20s, had unusual Bond bodies.

1975: Major bus fleets – Yorkshire

Operator	*Fleet size*
West Yorkshire PTE	1,492
South Yorkshire PTE	944
West Yorkshire Road Car	456
Yorkshire Traction	358
West Riding	331
Kingston-upon-Hull	232
East Yorkshire	223
Yorkshire Woollen	161
York-West Yorkshire	80

The Midlands

WITH a fleet of 2,600 vehicles, the West Midlands PTE was Britain's second biggest bus operator, after London Transport. Created in 1969, it had originally taken over the municipal fleets of Birmingham, Walsall, West Bromwich and Wolverhampton. To this it had added a substantial part of the business of NBC subsidiary Midland Red in 1973, acquiring 413 vehicles and almost 1,400 employees. This had been followed in 1974 by the acquisition of Coventry City Transport as a consequence of the PTE's boundaries being redrawn in that year's re-organisation of local government.

Three of the four original constituents of the PTE had used blue liveries. The fourth, Wolverhampton, had been green. The PTE accordingly adopted a layout based on that of Birmingham City Transport, but with a slightly lighter shade of blue. By 1975 the number of buses in the liveries of the four founders of the PTE were down to penny numbers and all had gone by the end of the year. Rapid progress had been made in repainting the ex-Midland Red fleet, but a number survived in red. In Coventry red ex-municipal buses still outnumbered blue ones.

Rather than renumber the buses taken over from its municipal constituents these had generally retained their original fleet numbers but with the addition of a suffix letter for vehicles which had not been inherited from Birmingham. Because three of the municipal fleets came from towns starting with W, the suffix used was the last letter of the town name, rather than the first. Thus there were in 1975 four ex-municipal buses numbered 102–102H, an ex-West Bromwich Fleetline; 102L, an ex-Walsall Fleetline; 102N, an ex-Wolverhampton Arab V; and 102Y, an ex-Coventry Fleetline. There was also plain 102, an ex-Midland Red National.

There had been two bus chassis manufacturers in the West Midlands, Daimler in Coventry and Guy in Wolverhampton – or it could be argued that there were three if you counted BMMO building for its own fleet. As a consequence there were precious few AECs or

Left **The archetypal Midland Red double-decker of the 1960s, the D9, seen in central Birmingham with a PTE-owned ex-Midland Red Fleetline in the background. The D9 was built between 1960 and 1966; this is a 1963 bus.** Malcolm Keeley

Above right **Some of Birmingham's classic buses of the 1950s were still hard at work in the 1970s. This Guy Arab with Metro-Cammell body had been new in 1951 and is seen in West Midlands service 24 years later. It was withdrawn in 1976; the last buses of this general appearance came out of service in 1977.** Malcolm Keeley

Right **Birmingham's more modern buses were mainly Fleetlines. This Metro-Cammell-bodied example was one of 50 supplied in 1963. It is seen in PTE service in 1978.** Royston Morgan

Above **Wolverhampton bought six Swifts and six Roadliners in 1967, all with two-door Strachans bodies. All were withdrawn by the PTE by 1975. A Swift in Wolverhampton colours is seen in Bridgnorth.** Malcolm Keeley

Below left **Six Commer minibuses were used by the PTE on a shoppers service in central Birmingham. They had 19-seat Rootes bodies. After operating for a short time in fleet colours they were painted overall orange, making them more visible in pedestrianised streets.** Stewart J Brown

Below right **From West Bromwich the PTE acquired low-height Fleetlines, which were painted in a different livery with more cream and a shallow blue skirt. MCW bodywork is fitted to this 1967 bus which carries two messages advising passengers to pay the driver.** Malcolm Keeley

Leylands in the PTE fleet which with some 1,800 Daimlers in service was the world's biggest operator of the marque – a distinction about to pass to London Transport.

Birmingham City Transport had undertaken a massive fleet replacement in the early 1950s, buying Crossley DD42s, Daimler CVD6s and CVG6s and Guy Arab IVs with standardised bodies by Metro-Cammell (another local manufacturer) and Crossley. The DD42s and CVD6s had gone, but the CVG6s and Guys survived in reasonable numbers. To the untrained eye they were virtually indistinguishable, with Birmingham's attractive new-look front on both chassis types, as it had been on the departed CVD6s and Crossleys too. Those Daimlers and Guys still in use dated from as early as 1950 and as late as 1954, but the Birmingham body harked back to an earlier era and gave these 7ft 6in-wide buses a tall, thin, and slightly old-fashioned air with a touch of faded gentility amongst the brash Nationals and Fleetlines.

The next generation of Birmingham buses was rear-engined. The vast majority were Daimler Fleetlines with bodies by Metro-Cammell and Park Royal, but there were also early Atlanteans with Metro-Cammell bodies. These included a former Leyland demonstrator which had been operated by Birmingham City Transport from new, as Leyland made an effort to win a share of this important undertaking's business. Its success was limited – BCT ordered just 10 Atlanteans, which were still in PTE service in 1975. The Fleetlines included the first to be bodied as single-deckers – 24 with Marshall bodies, delivered in 1965 as BCT sought to standardise its fleet.

Indeed it was in the small number of ex-BCT single-deckers that the greatest variety was to be found. There were a dozen Ford R192s with Strachan Pacesaver bodies. Dating from 1967 they were the first major fleet order to be placed for Ford service buses. There were also 18 Metro-Cammell-bodied AEC Swifts. There were not that many other AECs in the PTE fleet in 1975 – a few Regent Vs at Walsall, plus a Reliance, some Swifts and two Renowns ex-Wolverhampton. More recent single-deck purchases by the PTE included a solitary Metro-Scania, 60 Leyland Nationals (at the time the biggest fleet outside NBC) and six Commer minibuses based on the Walk-thru van and bought for the Birmingham Centrebus service. These vehicles were unusual in having doors on both sides of the body, with the offside door being for use in pedestrian precincts. In 1974 they had been replaced by some of the ex-BCT

single-deck Fleetlines and could be found standing in for conventional single-deckers on ordinary routes.

In West Bromwich the PTE had inherited primarily Daimlers. The oldest were exposed-radiator CVG6s which were soon withdrawn, leaving 20-year-old tin-fronted examples as the oldest ex-West Bromwich buses in 1975. The newest CV-series Daimlers in the PTE fleet were 1965 C-registered buses which had come from West Bromwich. In 1967 and 1969 West Bromwich had bought Fleetlines, 21 in all including seven with ECW bodies, marking a switch from the undertaking's usual supplier, Metro-Cammell. These were all low-height buses and carried a different version of the PTE's livery with more cream and less blue. Two Roe-bodied Leyland Tiger Cubs, new to West Bromwich in 1963, served as a reminder that even loyal Daimler customers found it difficult to justify buying the heavy Freeline when lighter and more efficient single-deck chassis were on offer from other manufacturers.

The PTE's Walsall inheritance was probably the most idiosyncratic of any PTE's acquisitions. From Walsall had come 222 motorbuses of AEC, Daimler, Dennis, Guy and Leyland manufacture, including three ex-London Transport RTLs, plus three makes of trolleybus. The products of no fewer than 10 bodybuilders were represented in the fleet. A lot of non-standard types, which were often the oldest vehicles anyway, were withdrawn in the early 1970s and trolleybus operation ceased in October 1970. One modern bus to go was the unusual Daimler CRC6/36 which had been a 1968 Commercial Motor Show exhibit. This was a 36ft-long double-decker with a compact Cummins V6 engine mounted at the offside of the rear overhang. This allowed the provision of a rear exit on the 85-seat Northern Counties body. It was sold in 1974. The only other CRC6/36s built were exported to Johannesburg.

Not content with running Britain's longest double-deck bus, Walsall had also pioneered the short Fleetline, which had a short front overhang and the entrance behind the front axle. A number of the early examples were crudely rebuilt to incorporate a single-width entrance door ahead of the front axle, allowing them to be used as one-man buses; later deliveries had a slightly longer front overhang and had two doors from new. The majority were still in use in 1975 and a few would run until the early 1980s. The other mid-1970s Walsall survivors were Daimler CVG6s and AEC Regent Vs with forward-entrance bodies by Metro-Cammell, and a solitary 1959 Atlantean.

Wolverhampton Corporation's buying policy had supported its local chassis maker, Guy. As a result much of the town's bus service network was still crew-operated, with 120 Arabs providing transport for many of the residents. These were all forward-entrance buses, and the oldest – accounting for around one-third of the surviving Arab fleet – had fully-fronted Metro-Cammell bodies, not unlike those built for Ribble on PD3 Titans. Other body suppliers on Wolverhampton's Arabs were Weymann, Park Royal and Strachans. The last-named had supplied 31 bodies in 1967 – its biggest single double-deck order in the 1960s. That all were withdrawn in 1974, rather than being recertified for further service, has to say something about the quality of construction. Seven of an earlier batch of Strachans-bodied Arab Vs survived, having been overhauled before the PTE gave up the programme on the grounds of cost.

Above **In 1973 100 standard-length Fleetlines with 76-seat single-door Park Royal bodies joined the WMPTE fleet. These were typical of the PTE's double-deck intake for most of the decade. Older style Fleetlines can be seen behind.** Malcolm Keeley

Below **Walsall's short Fleetlines as originally conceived were quite attractive buses, but most of the early single-door examples were butchered to accommodate an entrance ahead of the front axle, with the original door (which was behind the front axle) then becoming an exit. This work was done in 1971-72. Northern Counties built the bodies – that on the bus behind featured two doors from new.** Malcolm Keeley

Above left **Coventry standardised on Daimlers. Most of the buses taken over by the PTE were CVG6s and, as seen here, Fleetlines. This one is from the city's 1966 batch of 22 with East Lancs bodies. A bright cream square above the destination box shows where the municipal crest had been. The Monobus name was used by Coventry for one-man-operated services.** Malcolm Keeley

Above right **An ex-Coventry CVG6 in PTE service in 1976. It was one of 25 delivered in 1963, which were to be the last of a long line of front-engined Daimlers for Coventry. Like all of the CVG6s which passed from Coventry to the PTE it had Metro-Cammell bodywork.** Stewart J Brown

Below **Although it claims to be a Monobus, this 1968 ECW-bodied ex-Coventry Fleetline appears to be carrying a conductress. Coventry's Fleetlines were the first to be bodied by ECW. The combination remained relatively rare in England, but became one of the Scottish Bus Group's standards, albeit in lowheight form.** Mike Greenwood

With the demise of the Arab in sight, Wolverhampton had in the late 1960s bought a dozen two-door single-deckers, dividing its order equally between the AEC Swift and Daimler Roadliner. These too had Strachans bodies – on the Roadliner surely a double loser – and the last were withdrawn in 1975.

To round off the PTE's ex-municipal vehicles, the addition of Coventry Corporation's buses in 1974 had brought a fairly predictable mixture of Daimler CVG6s and Fleetlines, as the Corporation supported its local bus maker. There were 22 Atlanteans, delivered in 1964, the ordering of which had caused quite a furore in the city. They had in fact been the fleet's first rear-engined buses and had Willowbrook bodies. They were followed in 1965 by similarly-bodied Fleetlines. All subsequent Coventry double-deckers were Fleetlines, with bodies by East Lancs (and its Neepsend associate), ECW and Park Royal. The ECW bodies, supplied in 1968, were the first examples on Fleetline chassis and the first double-deckers to be supplied by the Lowestoft-based builder to a company outside the THC since nationalisation at the end of the 1940s. The 1968 Fleetlines and subsequent deliveries up to 1971 had started life as two-door buses but were in the process of being rebuilt with one door.

Apart from the Atlanteans, the only other non-Daimler buses taken over from Coventry were six 1967 Bristol REs with ECW bodies. Presumably the Corporation's transport department had little trouble convincing the city council that these would be a better bet than Daimler's troublesome Roadliner. Four of the ex-Coventry REs had been put up for sale by the Corporation in 1973 as being surplus to requirements, but the PTE persuaded the Corporation to keep them and following the absorption of the Coventry operation the four were moved to Wolverhampton.

A high percentage of the Coventry fleet was still in dark red and cream in 1975, but with West Midlands fleetnames. Indeed Coventry had modified its livery in advance of the takeover by the PTE and had adopted a PTE-style layout. It had even repainted a few buses in PTE colours in the early part of 1974, but with Coventry Transport fleetnames

Further variety had been introduced to the PTE at the end of 1973 when it had taken over 413 buses and six depots from Midland Red. The only other PTE to buy a substantial part of an NBC subsidiary had been SELNEC, with its acquisition of part of North Western in 1972. The Midland Red takeover brought some recognisably standard types – 135 Fleetlines, albeit with Alexander bodywork, a manufacturer not previously represented in the PTE fleet, and 33 Nationals. The remainder were new types to the PTE, Leyland Leopards and BMMO-built single-deckers and front-engined D9 double-deckers. There were 90 D9s, the newest dating from 1966. To ease the support of these odd vehicles the PTE arranged a maintenance agreement with Midland Red.

New double-deckers for the PTE in the 1970s

Right **The acquisition of part of Midland Red's operations added 135 Alexander-bodied Fleetlines to the PTE fleet. One is seen in Wolverhampton bus station in 1974.** Malcolm Keeley

Below **Among the more unusual buses to carry WMPTE livery were some of the 79 BMMO D9 double-deckers taken over from Midland Red. These advanced buses had independent front suspension and a short wheelbase to aid manoeuvrability – hence the set-back front axle. BMMO also built the 72-seat bodywork. This bus was new in 1961 and is seen in the company of assorted ex-Midland Red buses still running in their original colours.** Mike Greenwood

Bottom **Only marginally less unusual in PTE colours were the BMMO-built single-deckers, such as this 1968 S22. The S22 was powered by a BMMO 10.5-litre horizontal engine.** Mike Greenwood

were mainly Fleetlines with bodies by Park Royal and MCW. However to speed deliveries at a time when Fleetlines were in short supply the PTE placed two orders for a total of 200 Bristol VRTs with MCW bodies. All were in service in 1975 and made West Midlands the world's biggest VRT operator (on the basis that those run by NBC were shared between its various subsidiaries). These were the only VRTs to be bodied by MCW. A grille in the front panel, to provide cooling air for the VRT's front-mounted radiator, distinguished them from contemporary Fleetline deliveries. Three Alexander-bodied Ailsas were delivered in 1974 and prompted the PTE to order 50 which were delivered in 1976.

Although it had lost its PTE area operations, Midland Red was still NBC's biggest subsidiary with a fleet of almost 1,300 vehicles. The next in size was London Country Bus Services (with just over 1,230) and it's difficult not to draw a parallel with their operating areas. Both companies

Above **Production of buses by BMMO ceased in 1970, the last being H-registered S23s. This is a 1968 S22 with BMMO-built 45-seat bodywork. The S23 differed from the S22 in body details.** Mike Greenwood

Below **Midland Red bought Leyland Leopards in 1962-63 to supplement its own-build BMMO S-series models – the first proprietary single-deck buses to be bought new since the 1920s. Standard BET-style Willowbrook bodywork is fitted to this example, photographed at Heath Hayes in 1975.** Michael Fowler

encircled major urban areas but without providing the main services in the central core.

Midland Red covered a huge area. It had depots as far south as Hereford, Evesham and Banbury, as far west as Shrewsbury, as far north as Stafford and as far east as Leicester. It was the major operator in each of these towns (except Leicester, with its municipal network), and in places such as Kidderminster, Worcester, Redditch, Stratford-upon-Avon, Warwick, Rugby, Tamworth, Lichfield, Cannock and Telford – most of which had a Midland Red garage.

What set Midland Red apart from all other NBC subsidiaries was the fact that it had built its own buses. The company's full title had, until 1974, been the Birmingham & Midland Motor Omnibus Company and the BMMO initials had been applied to a range of innovative buses down the years. Double-deckers formed a minority in the fleet – although even then with 330 in stock they still represented a good number of vehicles. They were of two main types, the rear-entrance BMMO D9 which had been produced up to 1966, and the Alexander-bodied Daimler Fleetline, purchased between 1963 and 1970. No 'deckers were added to the fleet after 1970 other than through the acquisition of small operators.

The single-deck fleet also had home-built BMMO types. The oldest were 1963 S16s; the newest 1970 S23s. Production of buses at BMMO's Carlyle Road works came to an end in 1970. With low production volumes – for engines in particular – it is remarkable that it lasted so long in the face of the availability of keenly-priced chassis from the mainstream bus manufacturers with their much higher outputs.

Midland Red did in fact have a sizeable fleet of Leyland Leopards, both buses and coaches. There were just over 400, making the company one of Britain's biggest Leopard operators. These had bodies by Marshall, Plaxton, Weymann and Willowbrook. With a large rural area to serve, Midland Red became one of the first NBC operators to try lightweight R-series Fords in any quantity. It took 100 in 1970-71, followed by 20 in 1972 and a further 20 in 1974. All had 45-seat Plaxton Derwent bus bodies. There were no Bristols of any description in the fleet. This was largely because the company was buying Leopards or building its own single-deck buses when other operators were buying REs, and also because it had stopped buying double-deckers by the time when it might have found itself being allocated VRTs. It did however have over 100 Leyland Nationals. On order for 1975 delivery were 40 Bristol LHs and 20 Leyland Atlanteans. They never arrived.

In BET days Stratford Blue had been a subsidiary of Midland Red, although there were no outward signs of this. Under NBC control the Stratford Blue fleet had been absorbed by Midland Red in 1971 and the only visible remnants were half-a-dozen Leopards. Stratford Blue's double-deckers had either been sold or transferred to other NBC subsidiaries.

Just as Midland Red was losing its operations in the West Midlands, so it sought to consolidate its position in some of the surrounding counties by buying up small independents. In 1973 it took over Cooper of Oakengates and Green Bus of Rugeley, followed in 1974 by Hoggins of Wrockwardine Wood and Harper of Heath Hayes.

Cooper and Hoggins were small businesses. Cooper's fleet comprised 13 Bedfords including three with Willowbrook bus bodies. Two ex-Cooper YRQs with bus-grant Duple coach bodies were still in use with Midland Red in 1975. Hoggins ran six vehicles, three Bedfords and three Fords. One Ford, an R192 with Plaxton Derwent bus body, survived in Midland Red ownership.

Green Bus was a more substantial operation with 29 buses and coaches. These included 10 Seddons, most of which were promptly sold, as were six Lodekkas which had come from Crosville and Cumberland, and four Bristol LSs. Indeed only two Green Bus vehicles survived two years after the takeover. These were front-engined Seddon Pennine VIs with Plaxton coach bodies. The Green Bus name was revived in the second half of the decade by Warstone Motors of Great Wyrley, running in the Cannock area.

Harper was the biggest of the acquired operators, running 52 vehicles. The buses ranged from ex-London Transport RTLs to modern Daimler Fleetlines, along with an assortment of Leyland Titans purchased new, and a Guy Arab V. There were also Bedford and Leyland Leopard coaches. Not surprisingly there was a quick shake out and many of the older and odder buses were sold. By 1975 Midland Red had retained six ex-Harper Titans, built between

Top **Midland Red bought 140 Fords with 45-seat Plaxton Derwent bus bodies, making it England's biggest user of the Ford R-series bus. They were delivered between 1970 and 1974. By the end of the decade half had been sold, and of the survivors a few had been drastically shortened to create 27-seat midibuses.** Mike Greenwood

Centre right **Green Bus of Rugeley operated 10 Seddons, including three unusual front-engined Pennine IVs with Pennine bodies – most Seddon buses in the early 1970s were rear-engined RUs.** Paul Caudell

Right **Harper Bros of Heath Hayes ran 52 buses, including a few quite elderly types. In the spring of 1974 an ex-St Helens RT-type AEC Regent passes an ex-London RTL.** Malcolm Keeley

1962 and 1968, and six Fleetlines. Most of the 'deckers had Northern Counties bodies but two of the Fleetlines were ECW-bodied, a rare choice for an independent. Two more ECW-bodied Fleetlines which had been ordered by Harper were delivered new to Midland Red. Most of Harper's coaches were also still in use by Midland Red.

Among the independents in the west, Vaggs of Knockin Heath operated some rural services and also had a route between Oswestry and Shrewsbury. This had once justified double-deckers, but by 1975 was generally covered by second-hand Willowbrook-bodied Fords or Bedfords, or by a new Marshall-bodied R1014. Local services in and around Oswestry were provided by Hampson's whose bus fleet included two Bedford SBs, a pair of bus-grant Plaxton-bodied YRQs and two ex-London Transport private-hire RF-class AEC Regal IVs which had been in Hampson's ownership since 1964. A service from Oswestry across the Welsh border to Llanfyllin was run by Parish's of Morda using Bedford coaches or an ex-Lancashire United Reliance bus.

Top **All change at Heath Hayes. The takeover of Harper Bros brought a variety of types into the Midland Red fleet, including this pair of Metro-Cammell-bodied Leyland Titans, new in 1966. They are seen in the summer of 1975, one in Midland Red livery with modified destination display, the other still in its original owner's colours.** Michael Fowler

Centre left **The more modern buses which were taken over by Midland Red from Harper Bros were mainly Fleetlines, including four with Northern Counties bodies. This one was new in 1971. It is seen in Navigation Street in central Birmingham in 1979.** Malcolm Keeley

Left **Sentinel buses were never very common, despite the company being among the first to introduce mid-engined designs for general sale. In the early 1970s a few remained in service with Brown's of Dinnington Wood. They had Beadle-built bodies, integrally constructed to support the Sentinel underframe. The last was withdrawn in 1974.** Paul Caudell

In Shrewsbury a route from Whitchurch was run by Salopia Saloon Coaches with Willowbrook-bodied Bedford YRQs. Similar vehicles (and earlier VAMs) were used on services in the Hereford area by Yeoman of Canon Pyon. In Worcestershire Everton Coaches of Droitwich had expanded its rural operations as Midland Red cut back on uneconomic routes. Willowbrook-bodied Fords were the standard bus here, as in so many other rural operators' fleets. A Worcester to Bromyard service was operated by Morris of Bromyard generally using a Leyland Leopard with Plaxton coach body which on delivery in 1972 was the company's first new full-sized coach.

Small companies still running in the northern part of Midland Red's territory included Greatrex of Stafford with R-series Fords on a service to Great Haywood. Bought new, the oldest of these was a 1966 bus with Strachans body. More recent examples had Willowbrook bodies. Happy Days of Woodseaves also used Willowbrook-bodied Fords on a service to Shebdon. To the west, in the Telford area, Brown's of Dinnington Wood ran local services with a fleet which until 1974 had included Sentinels. The last of these – which was also the last Sentinel in regular passenger service anywhere – was replaced by a rather more mundane Willowbrook-bodied Bedford YRT. The Sentinels had been built locally, in Shrewsbury. Brown's was a member of the Shropshire Omnibus Owners' Association which ran services around Telford New Town.

To the north of Stafford the major operator was PMT, the initials of Potteries Motor Traction, an erstwhile BET subsidiary. PMT was based in Stoke-on-Trent and its red and cream livery was disappearing as NBC's poppy red gained ground. PMT served the Potteries towns with a network of essentially urban services. In earlier decades the fleet was renowned for its variety, but that was rapidly disappearing with

Top right **At the start of the 1970s PMT was still running this AEC Reliance with rather old-fashioned looking Willowbrook bodywork. New in 1955 it was one of three which had been ordered – and registered – by City of Oxford, but was owned from new by PMT. It is pulling out of Hanley bus station.** A Moyes

Centre right **In the early days of NBC's corporate identity, buses in liveries which featured cream relief often appeared with cream fleetnames and logos, in place of the corporate white. A lowbridge Atlantean in the PMT fleet shows the combination of old livery and new logo, at Newcastle-under-Lyme in 1973. The body was by Weymann.** Malcolm Keeley

Right **It is widely known that there were two common variants of ECW body on the Bristol VRT chassis – the lowheight 13ft 8in version, normally specified by NBC, and the full-height 14ft 6in version used by a few NBC companies such as London Country and Northern General. Less well known is the ultra lowheight 13ft 4in variant used by just a few companies, one of which was PMT. The ultra low version of the ECW body can be identified by the absence of the thin white relief band above the front windscreen.** Stewart J Brown

Above **Alexander Y-type bodies were bought by a few BET and ex-BET companies up until the early 1970s. Among the Y-type deliveries in the NBC era were 10 on AEC Reliances for PMT in 1970-71. They were delivered in traditional PMT livery, but on their first repaint received NBC's local coach scheme. The definition of local was clearly flexible. This Reliance is seen 150 miles from its home base – in London.** Stewart J Brown

Below **Berresford's was the biggest independent in the Potteries in the 1970s, with a 30-strong fleet made up of a variety of types. The most numerous in the middle of the decade was the Leyland Titan, of which the oldest were former Stockport Corporation buses dating back to 1949.** John Jones

the arrival in the early 1970s of ECW-bodied Bristol REs and VRTs, and integral Leyland Nationals. Older double-deckers were Leyland Atlanteans, with over 80 early PDR1s in regular use. These dated from the 1959-62 period and were PMT's oldest buses – there were no half-cabs left in the fleet. From Atlanteans with boxy Weymann bodies in 1962, PMT had in 1963 switched to Fleetlines, first taking 16 with Northern Counties bodywork and then 34 with lowheight Alexander bodies. These had been the most modern double-deckers operated by PMT until the arrival of the first VRTs in 1974.

Between 1965 and 1974 PMT had bought only single-deckers. These had included typical BET Reliances and Leopards – as well as untypical Daimler Roadliners. To PMT went the dubious honour of being the world's biggest Roadliner operator, and by a handsome margin. It had bought 64 – 58 buses and six coaches – although by 1975 this figure had been slashed to just 20. These included the newest ten, 1969 buses with dual-door Plaxton bodies. In 1970 PMT had switched to the single-deck Fleetline with two-door Alexander bodywork – out of the frying pan and into the fire, some might suggest. There were 21 single-deck Fleetlines. After that, salvation had arrived in the shape of the trusty Bristol RE.

The biggest independent in the Potteries was Berresford's Motors of Cheddleton, serving the Leek, Hanley and Longton areas. Berresford's ran 30 vehicles ranging from 25-year-old Titans to new Bedford YRTs. The front-line bus fleet included a mixture of double-deckers – two ex-PMT PD3s, a fully-fronted ex-Blackpool PD2, a former Doncaster Regent V and an Atlantean which had started life in 1962 with Silver Star in Wiltshire. Single-deckers ranged from ex-Maidstone & District Reliances to Y-series Bedfords with bodies by Duple and Plaxton.

Also serving Leek was Procter of Hanley. This small fleet was the opposite of that run by Berresford with all but one of the company's 16 buses and coaches having been bought new. For bus work Procter had two Alexander-bodied Fleetlines dating from the mid-1960s, and two 1974 Alexander-bodied Atlanteans. The Atlanteans had panoramic windows. Stonier of Goldenhill ran between Hanley and Bentilee in a joint operation with PMT. The company's bus fleet included ex-Wallace Arnold PD3s and a Massey-bodied PD2 which had been new to Turner of Brown Edge in 1964 and had joined the Stonier fleet in 1972. There were also two single-deckers with BET-style Willowbrook bodies – a 1963 Leopard from Jones of Aberbeeg and a 1967 Reliance which had been new to Hutchison of Overtown. Turner's of Brown Edge operated a service to Hanley using five Northern Counties-bodied Fleetlines, all

bought new. From Newcastle-under-Lyme Poole's Coachways ran to Alsager Bank (the company's base) and Audley using Willowbrook-bodied Leopards, while Princess Bus Service had a route to Silverdale which was operated by an unusual Seddon Pennine IV with Seddon bodywork.

To the east Stevenson of Uttoxeter ran to Burton-on-Trent and from there to Ashbourne. Stevenson operated 40 vehicles – with little attempt at standardisation. There were Leyland Leopards, Atlanteans and Titans; AEC Regents, Reliances and a Renown; Daimler CCG5s; and assorted Fords, Bedfords and a Seddon in the coach fleet. The double-deckers came from a variety of sources including Brighton, Burton-

Top left **Alexander bodywork was not a common choice for small operators, partly because the company preferred to build large production runs to standardised specifications. Procter of Hanley took two Alexander-bodied Fleetlines in the 1960s, and followed that with two Atlanteans in 1974. The bodies on the Atlanteans were broadly similar to those being supplied to the Greater Glasgow PTE.** A Moyes

Top right **Two ex-Wallace Arnold PD3s were operated by Stonier of Goldenhill. New in 1962, this bus had been with WA's Kippax & District fleet. It was bought by Stonier in 1968.** A Moyes

Centre right **Turner's first Fleetline was delivered in 1965 and had Northern Counties bodywork. This combination became Turner's standard, and in 1975 this bus was replaced by a new Fleetline/Northern Counties.** John Jones

Right **In the mid-1970s Poole's Coachways ran Willowbrook-bodied Leopards on routes from Newcastle-under-Lyme. The oldest was this 1969 PSU3.** John Robinson

on-Trent, Devon General, Lancashire United, London Transport, City of Oxford, Portsmouth, Sheffield and Yorkshire Traction. Variety was clearly the spice of Uttoxeter life. A smaller operator running to Burton-on-Trent was Victoria Motorways with a Measham service covered by a Bedford YRT coach or a Willowbrook-bodied Ford bus. Victoria was an associate company of Viking Motors. The giant Midland Red company also ran to Burton, with services from Leicester and Birmingham.

In Burton-on-Trent the reorganisation of local government in 1974 had led to a name change for the local authority bus fleet, which was now run by East Staffordshire District Council. A red, white and green livery had been introduced in 1971 following the appointment of a new general manager who had come from Gelligaer in South Wales and had brought his livery with him. By 1975 this had been applied to the whole fleet, replacing the previous maroon and cream colour scheme.

With just 36 buses East Staffordshire ranked as one of England's smallest municipal fleets. It was the same size as Fylde; in England only Waveney was smaller. The oldest 'deckers in the fleet illustrated municipal conservatism. They were 14 Daimler CCG5s with crash gearboxes and rear-entrance Massey bodies, built between 1964 and 1968. The three 1968 vehicles were the last 5LW-powered buses built for a British operator. After the CCG5s came Fleetlines, initially Willowbrook-bodied single-deckers then double-deckers with bodies by Northern Counties and Willowbrook. The newest of these were 1974 buses.

Added interest was created by a few second-hand buses – two Royal Tigers and two Tiger Cubs from Bournemouth, two Atlanteans from Portsmouth, and two former Wigan Titans from Greater Manchester Transport. The Bournemouth Royal Tigers, veterans from 1954, were East Staffordshire's oldest bus – and had been the first Leylands in the Burton-on-Trent fleet since a 1934 Lioness. The ex-Bournemouth buses had introduced omo to

Top left **The varied Stevenson's fleet contained more Leylands than any other make, including this early Leopard, a 1960 L1, which had been acquired from Sheffield Transport. It had Burlingham bodywork.** Malcolm Keeley

Centre left **Among Stevenson's double-deckers in the early 1970s was this ex-Oxford AEC Regent V with Weymann body. New in 1958, it was one of a number of ex-Oxford buses in the Stevenson fleet.** Paul Caudell

Left **Burton's first rear-engined buses were three Fleetlines with Willowbrook bodies. They were new in 1969 and were the first one-man buses in the fleet.** Stewart J Brown

Burton's services, which were confined to the local Burton area.

By contrast Derby Borough Transport had routes which stretched as far out as Burton, thanks to its takeover in 1973 of the independent Blue Bus Service of Willington. Derby was a confirmed Daimler user and in 1975 was running just two types supplied new – 47 CVG6s and 95 Fleetlines. All had Roe bodies, bar five of the Fleetlines which were single-deckers with bodies by Willowbrook. A two-tone blue livery, initially adopted to distinguish one-man buses, was applied to most of the fleet, although a few vehicles still carried the previous green and cream. Some of the single-deck Fleetlines had orange fronts and were used on a service linking the railway station and the town centre.

Derby's fleet was standardised, but the acquisition of Blue Bus Services had added some variety. The ex-Blue Bus vehicles were still garaged at the former independent's base in Willington. Blue Bus was a Daimler user and its fleet included six Fleetlines. The oldest of these was 7000HP, the original Weymann-bodied Daimler demonstrator. The others were five with Northern Counties bodies and one bodied by Alexander. Older 'deckers were two CVG6s with lowbridge Willowbrook bodies – all Blue Bus vehicles were of lowbridge or lowheight design so that they could pass under a bridge in Willington. Between the CVG6s and the Fleetlines Blue Bus had bought a couple of Dennis Lolines and one of these, with Willowbrook body, was still in service. In fact the bulk of the Blue Bus fleet would not see much service beyond the end of 1975. In January 1976 a fire at the depot destroyed 19 buses and coaches, leaving one CVG6 and the Loline as the sole Blue Bus survivors. One small operator with a regular service to Derby was Felix, running from Ilkeston with a Bedford YRQ.

Derby was the headquarters of NBC's Trent company. This had been a BET subsidiary with a fleet of almost 400 vehicles but at the start of 1972 it took control of Midland General, a

Top right **When East Staffordshire took over in Burton most of the fleet was in a bright new livery based on that used by Gelligaer. It is seen on an ex-Portsmouth Atlantean of which there were two in operation in 1975, followed by a further four in 1976. They had 76-seat Metro-Cammell bodies.** Stewart J Brown

Centre right **Derby standardised on Roe-bodied Daimlers from 1961 to 1976. This 1970 Roe-bodied Daimler Fleetline was one of 15 with dual-doorway bodywork; earlier and later Fleetlines were of single-door layout.** Stewart J Brown

Right **This immaculate Fleetline in the Blue Bus fleet, seen in Burton-on-Trent in 1973, was one of the victims of the 1976 depot fire. It had lowheight bodywork by Northern Counties.** John Jones

Left **Leyland Leopards loomed large in Trent's fleet, including 24 with Willowbrook dual-purpose bodies which dated from 1963. Although adapted for use as a one-man bus – indicated by the covered-up pay-on-entry sign above the nearside headlamp – this one had a two-man crew when photographed in Stockport in 1973.** John Robinson

Centre left **The types of vehicles which received NBC's local coach livery varied tremendously. This 1962 Trent Tiger Cub must have been among the oldest. The BET-style body was built by Alexander.** A Moyes

Bottom left **Alexander-bodied Fleetlines were bought by Trent from 1965. Ultimately there were 80 in the fleet. The number plate was positioned above the windscreen to reduce accident repair costs.** Royston Morgan

former THC company, and this swelled the fleet to almost 600. Soon after it expanded further by adding the Buxton and Matlock operations of North Western, as a result of the sale of the bulk of North Western's business to SELNEC. Midland General retained its own identity, but its blue livery was changing to poppy red. The North Western operations were absorbed into Trent, whose operating territory in 1975 stretched from Nottingham to Buxton. One significant independent in this area was Silver Service of Darley Dale, running a varied fleet which included a new AEC Reliance with Willowbrook Expressway body, as well as assorted second-hand types such as a pair of ex-Doncaster Roe-bodied Reliances. One of the more unusual buses in the fleet was a 1965 Bedford SB5 with Strachans body. Silver Service ran a number of services from Matlock, including one to Bakewell. In 1978 Silver Service expanded by taking over Hulley's of Baslow.

Trent's buses, a few of which survived in pre-NBC red and cream, comprised Leyland Tiger Cubs and Leopards, most of which had BET-style bodies by Marshall, Willowbrook and Metro-Cammell, although some had Alexander's version of the BET standard body which was quite different in appearance, particularly around the windscreens. There were also Alexander Y-types. Trent's oldest double-deckers were a few late 1950s exposed-radiator Titans. The company had been one of a number of BET operators to switch to rear-engined buses quite early on, taking Atlanteans from 1960 and then Fleetlines from 1963. The former had bodies by Roe and Weymann, to the uncompromisingly square design preferred by BET, but the Fleetlines had bodies by Northern Counties and Alexander and, on post-NBC additions to the fleet, ECW. Delivered in 1972 these were to be the last new buses in traditional Trent livery. Subsequent Trent 'deckers were ECW-bodied VRTs in NBC poppy red.

The buses acquired from North Western

Right **Later Trent double-deckers – Fleetlines, Atlanteans and VRTs – had ECW bodies. This 1976 Atlantean had its original ECW body destroyed by a fire and was fitted with a new Willowbrook body in 1977. This was the standard style of Willowbrook body for an Atlantean at this time; but it was the only body of this design supplied to an NBC fleet.** Royston Morgan

Centre right **Built in 1964, this ECW-bodied Bristol RELH coach in the Midland General fleet had been demoted to bus work by the early 1970s. It was a 51-seater.** Royston Morgan

Below left **Midland General had been unusual amongst THC companies in using a blue livery. It is seen in 1974 on a 1968 Bristol Lodekka FLF6G. The cream window-mounting rubbers had been fashionable in the 1960s.** Stewart J Brown

Below right **The Midland General name lived on – until 1977 – but not the livery, which became NBC poppy red. An FS6G Lodekka in Nottingham illustrates the new look.** Stewart J Brown

were all single-deckers. Willowbrook-bodied Reliances and Marshall-bodied Bristol REs survived in Trent service in 1975, along with five ECW-bodied REs which had been ordered by North Western but were delivered new to Trent.

The Midland General fleet was quite different in its make-up. As a THC subsidiary it was dominated by Bristols – MWs, REs and a few LHs made up the single-deck fleet, while the company's double-deckers were the inevitable Lodekkas and VRTs. The Lodekkas included the last to be built – two G-registered buses. A few survived in blue, but poppy red had been applied to most of Midland General's buses. The two fleets were numbered in a common series.

Both Trent and Midland General ran in to Nottingham, served by what was now England's biggest municipal operator, Nottingham City Transport. Ten years earlier Nottingham had

Above **Nottingham developed its own distinctive style of double-deck body with BET windscreens, a hefty front bumper and high seating capacity. This is a Leyland Atlantean with East Lancs body. Generally similar bodies were also built by Northern Counties. A glazed panel by the stairs ensured maximum illumination of the stairwell.**
Royston Morgan

Below **A few 1950s buses were still running for Nottingham City Transport in the mid-1970s, including this 1959 Leyland Titan PD2/40 with 65-seat Metro-Cammell body.**
Royston Morgan

ranked sixth in size (or eighth if Scotland is included) – but all of the bigger English municipals had been absorbed by PTEs. The Nottingham fleet was also one of the most individual, running distinctively-styled double-deckers designed to provide maximum seating capacity within a nominal 9.5m overall length. Nottingham managed to squeeze 77-seats into a two-door East Lancs or Northern Counties body on a standard-length Atlantean or Fleetline chassis. For comparison, a Park Royal- or ECW-bodied Atlantean to NBC specification typically had 73 or 74 seats – and only one door.

The Nottingham fleet was predominantly double-decked. The first Fleetlines had arrived in 1962, followed by the first Atlanteans in 1964. Dual-sourcing had continued and by 1975 there were 140 Fleetlines, against 210 Atlanteans. Most of the older Leylands - PD2 Titans – had gone from the fleet by 1975, but there were still a good number of half-cab AECs. These included a few exposed-radiator Regent Vs with handsome Park Royal bodies and 42 Renowns with unusual full-height forward-entrance bodies by Weymann and Northern Counties. Most buyers of Renowns used the low-frame chassis to obtain a low overall body height, but Nottingham specified it to provide a low floor and easier entry than would have been possible on a comparable Regent V.

There were two low-height Renowns in the fleet. These were East Lancs-bodied buses which had been taken over in 1968 with the operations of neighbouring West Bridgford UDC. Other ex-West Bridgford buses were three Swifts, also with East Lancs bodies. These were the only survivors of 28 AECs, mainly Regents, which had been operated by West Bridgford. Nottingham had six Swifts with Northern Counties bodies which had been bought new in 1969. They were sold during 1975 to Grimsby-Cleethorpes Transport.

Other single-deckers included 16 Leyland Nationals, some of which were used on a free city centre service. Nottingham was among the first cities in Britain to take positive action to try and limit the growth of car use in its city centre, recognising the damaging effects which cars were having. The free city centre bus service was part of this policy, as was the introduction of a fleet of specially-liveried single-deckers for park-and-ride services – the Lilac Leopards – which had Duple Dominant E bodies using the Dominant coach shell but fitted with 53 bus seats.

There were four independent operators with regular services into Nottingham. The smallest was Skill's, running Plaxton-bodied Leopard coaches to East Bridgford, a route which had until 1970 been covered by an altogether more interesting pair of forward-entrance Metro-Cammell-bodied PD3s.

The biggest was Barton Transport, which with 316 buses and coaches was one of only two independents running over 300 vehicles – the

Right **Barton Transport was one of Britain's biggest independents and it entered the 1970s with an interesting fleet. Its double-deckers included rebuilds and rebodies of early postwar Leyland Tigers. The new lowbridge body on this bus was built in 1959 by Northern Counties, but some Tigers were also rebodied by Willowbrook.** Malcolm Keeley

Bottom **The changing face of Barton in the 1970s is captured in this Nottingham view, with a second-hand double-decker on the left representing the old order, and a new coach on the right showing the face of the future. The 'decker was a Park Royal-bodied AEC Renown which had been new to Smith of Barrhead. The coach was a 1972 AEC Reliance with 64-seat Plaxton body. Many more Plaxton bodies would follow, but these were to be Barton's last Reliances.** Royston Morgan

other being Lancashire United Transport. Barton was based at Chilwell, and its routes covered not just Nottingham but also Leicester, Derby, Ilkeston and Long Eaton. The company had a coaching operation in South Shields, established in 1967 when it took over Hall Bros. The government's new bus grant brought dramatic change to the Barton fleet. In the 1950s and 1960s the company had bought an amazing variety of new and used buses, and had been a major proponent of rebuilding old vehicles to extend their lives.

Double-deckers had survived in small numbers at the start of the 1970s, including distinctive forward-entrance lowbridge Duple-bodied PD1s and ex-London RTLs. But in 1973 the company placed a massive order for 145 new bus-grant coaches – 73 Plaxton-bodied Leopards and 72 Duple-bodied Bedfords – and this meant that the last double-deckers came out of service in 1975 by which time the entire fleet was made up of post-1970 coaches. The majority had Plaxton bodies although there were a substantial number with Duple bodies and a handful with bodywork by Willowbrook. AEC Reliances had been bought up to 1972; all later purchases were Leyland Leopards and Bedford YRTs. Approximately half of the vehicles in the fleet were new M-registered Leyland and Bedford coaches with grant-specification bodies, giving Barton's passengers standards of luxury which a decade before would have been unimaginable.

The third of the independents running into Nottingham was the South Notts Bus Co of Gotham, with services to Clifton, on the south-western edge of the city, and to Loughborough. South Notts' routes were run mainly by double-deckers, although the company did have a few Bedford coaches and a YRQ bus too. The 24 'deckers ranged from Leyland-bodied PD2s, through PD3s with lowbridge forward-entrance Northern Counties bodies, to Albion Lowlanders, Leyland Atlanteans and Daimler Fleetlines. There were five Lowlanders, including the last to be built, an E-registered 1967 bus. South Notts was the only independent to buy new Lowlanders. The Atlanteans were comparatively rare lowheight PDR1/3s with drop-centre rear axles and dated from the 1968-71 period, after which South Notts bought Leyland-engined Fleetlines. The company was half-owned by Barton Transport.

Gash of Newark also operated to Nottingham, although most of the company's services were to villages to the south-east of Newark. In 1975 Gash ran 20 buses and 10 Bedford coaches – and its bus fleet contained a few gems. There were nine double-deckers – eight Daimler CVD6s dating from the late 1940s and early 1950s and one relatively young Massey-bodied CVG6 which had a new-look front and was a mere 21 years old. The four oldest CVD6s had been rebodied by Massey in the late 1950s. Of the other four, three had Duple bodies and one a body by Roberts of

Left **South Notts ran frequent services to Nottingham, generally using lowbridge or lowheight double-deckers. The latter included the only Albion Lowlanders bought new by an independent operator. They had Northern Counties bodies. Like most English Lowlanders, they carried Leyland lettering on the grille.** Paul Caudell

Centre left **Gash's last Daimler was a 1954 CVG6 with new-look front – all of the company's other Daimlers had exposed radiators. From 1954 until the delivery of an Atlantean in 1979 it was the most modern 'decker in the fleet. Massey built the bodywork. It is seen here about to take up service after being fuelled at the depot.** Stewart J Brown

Bottom left **Lincolnshire Road Car started buying Bristol LHs in 1968 and by the time this example was delivered at the start of 1973 had 60 in operation. Perkins engines were fitted to those LHs delivered up to 1972; this batch marked a switch to Leyland power.** Stewart J Brown

Wakefield – these were the last Duple-bodied double-deckers in regular service (and the last Roberts-bodied 'decker, too, come to that). Despite their antiquity, all were smartly turned-out. The more modern buses run by Gash were Leopards with bodies by Willowbrook and Plaxton, and a trio of unusual Marshall-bodied Bristol LHSs.

Newark was served by NBC's Lincolnshire Road Car subsidiary, an ex-THC company where corporate leaf green had virtually replaced the previous Tilling green livery. Although the fleet totalled only 330 buses, it covered a broad swathe of Eastern England, from Grantham up to the Humber, and with depots in the key coastal towns of Grimsby, Mablethorpe and bracing Skegness. As in most former THC fleets, there were few types other than Bristols. VRTs were ousting Lodekkas, most of which were low-powered FS5G models delivered between 1960 and 1966. There were four of the rare FL6G type, the rear-entrance 30ft-long model which was supplanted by the forward-entrance FLF-series after a short production run of just 45 chassis. There were just two FLFs. There were 20 VRTs bought new, including three early G-registered 1969 examples, plus 10 ex-SBG buses.

Single-deckers made up the bulk of the fleet, with MW5Gs having been considered adequate for Lincolnshire's relatively untaxing territory in the late 1950s and 1960s. There were over 50, including late D-registered buses. From 1968 Lincolnshire had switched to the LH with 43-seat ECW body and by 1975 had almost 70. Those built up to 1972 had Perkins engines; the newer deliveries were Leyland-powered. There were a few RE buses and in 1975 the company got its first 12 Nationals. More would soon follow.

There were two municipal fleets in the area

Right **Two LD6G Lodekkas of Lincolnshire show the difference between Tilling green, on the left, and NBC's leaf green, on the right. Under NBC rules there was only one band of relief and no black coach-lining. The location is Boston in the summer of 1973.** John Robinson

Below left **From 1969 Grimsby-Cleethorpes specified two doors on its double-deckers, a layout which it had used on single-deckers from the late 1950s. The first two-door 'deckers were eight Roe-bodied Fleetlines, which had Gardner 6LW engines rather than the more powerful 6LX which was specified by most operators and was adopted by Grimsby-Cleethorpes from 1970.** S J Butler

Below right **Most of Grimsby-Cleethorpes' single-deckers in the mid-1970s were AECs. The oldest were Willowbrook-bodied Reliances. This one was new in 1960. Note the glazed cove panels, an unusual feature on what was essentially an urban bus.** S J Butler

served by Lincolnshire Road Car. The bigger of the two, with almost 100 buses, was Grimsby-Cleethorpes, a 1957 amalgamation of the previously separate municipal operations in the two adjoining towns. Two manufacturers' products were operated, AEC and Daimler. Most AECs were single-deckers and most Daimlers were double-deckers. The surviving half-cabs were six CVG6/30s with forward-entrance Roe bodies, dating from 1961-62, and five similarly-bodied Regent Vs from 1963-64. From 1965 all of the fleet's double-deckers had been Fleetlines and there were just over 40, with bodies by Willowbrook on the first nine and Roe on the remainder. Those supplied from 1969 were of two-door layout, relatively uncommon in a fleet of this size.

The AEC single-deckers ranged from 1959 Willowbrook-bodied Reliances to brand new East Lancs-bodied Swifts, among the last to enter service and also among very few of the type to have P-suffix registrations. All of the single-deckers were of two-door design. There were 18 Swifts in all (including six newly acquired from Nottingham) and 18 Reliances. There were also four single-deck Fleetlines built in 1966-67 and among them the first of the SRG-series which had been designed specifically for single-deck bodywork.

In Lincoln most local routes were provided by Lincoln City Transport, which ran buses of Leyland and Bristol manufacture. All of the pre-1970 buses were Leylands and included Tiger Cubs, Panthers, Titans and Atlanteans, all with Roe bodies. There were four Atlanteans, new in 1965, which had been followed in 1967 by more Titans in the shape of four exposed-radiator PD2s. The fleet's oldest buses were also PD2s, which dated from 1961. Panthers were the most numerous type, accounting for 25 vehicles in the 60-strong fleet. The first Bristols were a dozen REs, delivered in 1973-74 and unusual in having Alexander Y-type bus bodies. The only other user of this combination in its bus form was North Western. Five VRTs with ECW bodies

Left **A 1961 Roe-bodied Titan in the Lincoln City Transport fleet, a type which was still running in the latter part of the 1970s, alongside modern rear-engined single-deckers. These were Lincoln's last open-platform buses.** D J Little

Below left **Between 1967 and 1970 Lincoln bought 25 Leyland Panthers with Roe bodies, to extend one-man-operation on the city's services.** Stewart J Brown

Below right **Bristol REs with Alexander Y-type bus bodies were rare. Lincoln had 12, delivered in 1973-74. They had Leyland engines. The absence of polished mouldings below the side windows made the Y-type bodies look somewhat spartan.** Stewart J Brown

in 1975 were the undertaking's first new double-deckers since the 1967 Titans. More followed in 1976. An unusual vehicle for a municipality was a Bedford YRT with Caetano bodywork, purchased in 1975 for use on private hires.

Appleby of Conisholme was an expanding Lincolnshire operator, its most recent acquisition having been the business of Hudson of Horncastle at the end of 1974. Services were generally operated by Plaxton-bodied coaches, although among the 12 vehicles taken over from Hudson had been two Fords with Plaxton Derwent bus bodies. Appleby's routes reached Lincoln, Grimsby and Skegness. Three services were operated from Scunthorpe by Hornsby, all run jointly with Lincolnshire Road Car. Hornsby ran assorted second-hand double-deckers which included Renowns from City of Oxford, a Regent V from Western Welsh, and Atlanteans from Ribble and Maidstone & District. A new Atlantean would join the fleet in 1977. Grayscroft of Mablethorpe ran to Louth, using a Duple-bodied Bedford coach. In the Grantham area local services were provided by Reliance of Great Gonerby with Bedford YRQs with Willowbrook and Plaxton bus bodies, and a Leopard with 64-seat Duple Dominant bus body. Kime of Folkingham ran from Grantham to Billingborough, a route taken over from Lincolnshire Road Car in 1972, as well as running a number of market day services. Kime operated Bedford YRQ coaches. A Grantham to Sproxton service was run by Skinner of Saltby, near Melton Mowbray, with a K-registered YRQ with Duple Viceroy Express body.

The area to the west of Lincolnshire Road Car's territory was served in the main by East Midland Motor Services. East Midland ran 240 buses and from 1972 had also been responsible for the 100-bus Mansfield District Traction Co. East Midland was a former BET company, while Mansfield District had been a THC subsidiary. Both fleets were in NBC leaf green. Mansfield District buses had been Tilling green, but East Midland's had been dark red. The area of Mansfield District operation was pretty much what you would expect from the company's title, covering the rural area between Mansfield and Newark and with services in to Nottingham. East Midland was based in Chesterfield and had services running in an area which embraced Sheffield, Rotherham, Doncaster, Worksop, Retford, Mansfield and Nottingham.

As might be expected, the Mansfield District fleet was made up of the inevitable mix of Bristols – varieties of Lodekka from LD via FS to

Right **When NBC was set up, East Midland's buses were dark red. The company ran Bristol REs with bodies by Marshall and ECW, and the K-registered batch was to be the last – subsequent full-size single-deckers would be Leyland Nationals.** Stewart J Brown

Centre right **East Midland's last half-cabs were 1966 Albion Lowlanders – the only Lowlanders to be bodied by Metro-Cammell. East Midland ran 18, the biggest Lowlander fleet in England. This one is seen in Chesterfield in 1978.** S J Butler

Bottom right **East Midland operated a variety of single-deck types, including standard BET-style 36ft-long Leopards with 53-seat bodies by Weymann, Willowbrook and, as here in Doncaster, Marshall.** Stewart J Brown

FLF, the last of these being 1968 models. There were also MW, REs and LHs. The real vehicle interest lay in the East Midland fleet, with its BET inheritance. Leyland Titans had been operated at the start of the 1970s, but these had gone by the middle of the decade to leave 18 Albion Lowlanders as the only half-cabs in service. This was England's biggest Lowlander fleet. Most had Alexander bodies but the last four, delivered in 1966, had Metro-Cammell bodywork. Like all Lowlanders they were of forward-entrance design. East Midland's other double-deckers were Atlanteans built between 1960 and 1971. The oldest had lowbridge Weymann bodies, but the bulk were Alexander-bodied, including five low-height PDR1/3s delivered in 1971 which were East Midland's last Atlanteans. From 1971 all new double-deckers for both East Midland and Mansfield District fleets were NBC's standard ECW-bodied VRTs.

Older East Midland single-deckers were BET standard types, mainly on Leyland Leopard chassis, although there were a few AEC Reliances. But some odd types – for a BET fleet – had appeared towards the end of the 1960s and were still in service. First were 10 AEC Swifts with Marshall bodies and a dozen ECW-bodied Bristol REs, all delivered in 1967/68. These had been followed in 1969 by 10 Willowbrook-bodied LHs, and then by REs with Marshall bodies. More modern single-deckers were the inevitable Leyland Nationals, delivered from 1972.

Local services in Chesterfield were provided by the Corporation with a varied fleet which included a high proportion of one-man-operated single-deckers. The first of these had been eight Reliances with dual-door Park Royal bodies in 1963, which had been followed two years later by 22 with Neepsend two-door bodies. All 30 Reliances were still in all-day service, along with three Willowbrook-bodied examples which had been new to London Transport in 1960 (as its RW class) and had joined the Chesterfield fleet in 1963.

The advantages of low-framed rear-engined single-deck chassis were seized in 1967 with the delivery of 10 Daimler Roadliners with Neepsend bodies. These were still in service, but were not to last as long as the 20 Panthers which followed them. The Panthers were in two batches of ten with bodies by Neepsend and Northern Counties. Although the Panther was considerably better than the Roadliner it was a model which was still far from universally popular. Chesterfield was one of the operators which made them work and it bought five six-year-old Marshall-bodied examples from the West Yorkshire PTE in 1975. These had been new to Bradford City Transport and had been the only Panthers in the WYPTE fleet.

Chesterfield's oldest buses were Weymann-bodied PD2s and PD2As built between 1958 and 1961. Supplied around the same time were its first rear-engined buses – four 1960 Atlanteans which had been followed in 1962 by four Fleetlines. That these were followed by Daimler CCG6s suggests a certain disenchantment with the new types and it was not until 1971 that Chesterfield started introducing significant numbers of rear-engined 'deckers to its fleet. First came more Atlanteans – 18 in 1971-72, but from 1973 orders were switched to the Daimler Fleetline. Most had two-door Roe bodies. All of these types, including the early rear-engined models, were still in operation.

Top left **From 1963 to 1969 most of Chesterfield's new buses were two-door single-deckers. In 1965 it took delivery of 22 AEC Reliances with bodies by Neepsend. These were 42-seaters, licensed to carry up to 18 standees.** S J Butler

Centre left **The Reliances were followed by Roadliners and Panthers. Those still running in the latter part of the 1970s received a revised livery with more cream and less green, as seen on this Neepsend-bodied Panther.** S J Butler

Left **Chesterfield's modern double-deckers were Atlanteans and Fleetlines. In 1971 10 Atlanteans with Northern Counties bodies joined the fleet; subsequent double-deck deliveries were bodied by Roe.** A Moyes

There was one other big municipal fleet in the Midlands, at Leicester, which was running just over 200 buses. Leicester's was an interesting fleet. Its oldest buses included three 1963 Atlanteans which clearly hadn't been a great success because the bulk of the undertaking's new vehicle intake in the 1960s was made up of Titans. There were just under 90 Titans in service in 1975 – not far short of half the fleet – all 30ft-long PD3As with rear-entrance bodies by three builders, East Lancs, Metro-Cammell and Park Royal. The newest were 20 F-registered buses. Leicester had in fact been the biggest English municipal user of PD3s with a fleet which had peaked at 117 and had only started to decline from the beginning of the decade. With the PD3s had come AEC Renowns with East Lancs bodies, albeit in considerably smaller numbers – just 13 in all.

The switch to one-man-operation saw Leicester divide its orders between double- and single-deckers and at the end of the 1960s it was taking Atlanteans and Bristol REs into stock. The REs had two-door ECW bodies while the Atlanteans had bodies by ECW (delivered in 1968 and among the first of that chassis/body combination) and Park Royal. A complete change of policy came in the 1970s. Leylands were out; Scanias were in. In 1971-72 Leicester bought 35 two-door Metro-Scanias as it spread omo to more routes. This was the biggest fleet of Metro-Scanias in England – Newport in Wales actually had the biggest fleet of all. Then when Leicester needed more double-deckers it took the Metropolitan, with 43 being delivered in 1974-75. Leicester City Transport was an urban operation. Out-of-town services were run in the main by Midland Red.

Small operators in the Leicester area included Gibson of Barlestone running Bedfords with Willowbrook Expressway bodies, and Astill & Jordan of Ratby with a Willowbrook-bodied Ford. Hylton & Dawson of Glenfield ran in to Leicester with Bedford coaches.

To the south of Midland Red's Leicestershire area the NBC operator was United Counties,

Top right **At the start of the 1970s there were over 100 rear-entrance Leyland Titan PD3s in service with Leicester City Transport; by the end of the decade there were around 20. This 1960 PD3/1 has 74-seat East Lancs bodywork. It is seen in the city centre in 1974.** Stewart J Brown

Centre right **After trying a small number of Atlanteans in the early 1960s Leicester stayed with the trusted Titan until 1968, when its final order for 20 Titans was converted to one for Atlanteans. These included ten with ECW bodies with shallow flat windscreens – similar bodies were built on Atlanteans for Ipswich around the same time. The plain front panel originally carried an Atlantean badge.** Malcolm Keeley

Right **The 20 Atlanteans which entered service in 1968-69 were to be Leyland's last significant order from Leicester. In 1971-72 the undertaking's new buses were 35 Metro-Scanias like this one.** Stewart J Brown

Top left **Most of United Counties' double-deckers were Bristols, and at the start of the 1970s the bulk of these were Lodekkas. A few second-hand Lodekkas were acquired from other NBC companies, including a pair of former Brighton Hove & District FSFs which came from Southdown in 1973. They were new in 1961.** Malcolm Keeley

Top right **A rare type to find in Tilling green was the Dennis Loline. United Counties ran eight, taken over with the operations of Luton Corporation in 1970. They were unusual in having Leyland O.600 engines. East Lancs built the bodywork on the two oldest machines, which had entered service in 1960. All of the ex-Luton Lolines were withdrawn in 1973 and only one saw further service as a psv.** Peter Davies

Left **United Counties received its first VRTs, eight in all, in 1969. The bus behind is a Willowbrook-bodied Swift owned by Red Rover of Aylesbury.** Michael Fowler

based in Northampton and serving most of Northamptonshire and Bedfordshire, as well as part of Buckinghamshire. It was the main operator in Luton, Dunstable, Milton Keynes, Bedford, Wellingborough and Kettering. Like all of the other former THC companies there was a predominance of Bristols in its fleet. All 320 of its double-deckers were ECW-bodied Bristols, providing a record of the marque's development from LD, through FS, FSF and FLF to VRT. Most of the Lodekkas were Bristol-engined and a few had started life with other THC operators, having been moved to United Counties in the early 1970s to speed the withdrawal of non-standard buses such as lowbridge Leyland Titans, Dennis Lolines and Albion Lowlanders which had been taken over with Luton Corporation's operations in 1970.

ECW-bodied Bristols dominated the single-deck fleet too with MWs, REs and a few LHs. Thirty of the REs were ex-Luton Corporation buses. These, and another 10 which had been ordered by Luton, could be distinguished from the remainder of the fleet by their two-door bodies. They were still used mainly on Luton local services. There were Leyland Nationals too, arriving in steadily-increasing numbers. But of more interest were 60 Y-series Bedfords with Willowbrook bus bodies, the last of which were in course of delivery in 1975. United Counties was one of very few NBC subsidiaries to try the low-cost Bedford as an alternative to either the LH or the Leyland National. The first Mercedes-Benz buses to be operated by NBC joined the United Counties fleet in 1975. These were six L406D vans with 15-seat conversions by Deansgate and were used on a dial-a-ride service at Woughton in Milton Keynes.

In 1969 United Counties had taken over the Rushden-based operations of Birch Bros, the London independent. Four 1965 Leopards with BET-style Marshall bodies survived as reminders of the Birch business. There were also a few Plaxton-bodied Fords in the fleet which had been taken over from Court Line in 1974 and were used primarily on the ex-Court Line (and before that London Country) service between Dunstable and Hemel Hempstead. One other well-known independent, York of Northampton, had provided a local service in the area – using a Willowbrook-bodied YRQ or an unusual Marshall-bodied Ford R1014 – until it was taken over by United Counties in 1975. No vehicles were involved.

1975: Major bus fleets – The Midlands

Operator	*Fleet size*
West Midlands PTE	2,601
Midland Red	1,272
Trent	617
United Counties	576
Potteries Motor Traction	462
Nottingham	441
Lincolnshire Road Car	330
Barton Transport	316
East Midland	240
Leicester	205
Derby	174
Chesterfield	137
Mansfield District	102
Grimsby-Cleethorpes	98
Northampton	80
Lincoln	60
East Staffordshire	36

Bus services in Northampton were run by the District Council's 80-strong fleet which was made up of just four different types of vehicle. The double-deckers were 46 Daimler CVG6s with 59-seat rear-entrance Roe bodies. The oldest ones dated from 1959 and had Birmingham-style new-look fronts, while more recent examples had the glass fibre Manchester bonnet assembly. The newest, five G-registered buses which entered service in 1968, were the last front-engined Daimlers to enter service in Britain, and the last open-platform buses too. The double-deck livery was in the process of minor revision, with white relief being applied to the window surrounds instead of just being used for a band at upper deck floor level.

Northampton's next purchases had been single-deckers and these comprised 20 Willowbrook-bodied Fleetlines in 1973 and a dozen Leyland Nationals in 1974. The only other buses in the fleet were two Strachans-bodied AEC Swifts which had been new to Wolverhampton Corporation in 1967 and had reached Northampton via the West Midlands PTE in 1972. The single-deckers were all two-door one-man-operated buses.

Top left **This 1968 Northampton Transport Daimler CVG6 was the last open-platform rear-entrance bus to enter service in Britain. It had Roe bodywork and was the end of a long line of Roe-bodied Daimlers for Northampton. This is a 1977 view.** Stewart J Brown

Top right **After buying single-deck Fleetlines in 1973, Northampton bought 12 Leyland Nationals in 1974. One is being driven in to the town's cavernous bus station in 1977 in a spirited fashion.** Stewart J Brown

Above **From 1977 Northampton bought Bristol VRTs, its first double-deckers since the last of the CVG6s. They had Alexander bodywork and there would ultimately be 36 of them. The only other buyers of Alexander-bodied VRTs were Cardiff and Tayside.The VRTs introduced a new livery, with cream relief between decks.** Stewart J Brown

East Anglia

See the CIS for INSURANCE
University
610
EASTERN COUNTIES
LFS 50v
50 CNG
621

One of the distinguishing features of East Anglia is its topography. Most of it is flat. Very flat. And this was recognised in the specifications of buses operated by the major NBC operator in the area, Eastern Counties. It had the country's – possibly the world's – biggest fleet of buses powered by Gardner's economical 94bhp five-cylinder 5LW engine. In 1975 there were around 200 – almost one-third of the fleet – chugging their way around Norfolk and Suffolk and into Cambridgeshire and Essex.

As a former THC subsidiary these 5LW-powered buses were all Bristols – LD and FS series Lodekkas, and MW saloons. The oldest of these dated from 1955; the newest from 1966. Earlier in the decade there had been 4LK-powered Bristol SCs too, but the last of these had come out of service in 1973. There had even been rare 4HLW-powered MWs, which had only just made it into the 1970s, with the last coming out of service in 1971. The fleet was not built entirely around low-powered buses. The switch to 30ft-long Lodekkas in 1963 saw the introduction firstly of six FL6Bs (with Bristol engines) and then, from 1966, FLF6Gs. Five of the FL6Bs had been repowered with Gardner 6LW engines by the middle of the 1970s.

There were also six-cylinder Bristol single-deckers, mostly REs but including a few MWs. For operation in deep rural country there were 57 LHs. These included the first F-registered prototype, which had originally been operated by Bristol Omnibus, and five which had been built for Luton Corporation but were first used by Eastern Counties. All of the early LHs had Perkins engines, built in Peterborough which was one of the major towns served by the company. Later in the decade Leyland-engined LHs would join the fleet.

Before the introduction of the LH, Eastern Counties tried an alternative approach to rural operation buying four Bedford VAMs in 1967. Two were VAM5s, with Bedford engines, and the other two were VAM14s with Leyland 400 units. They were unusual in having ECW bodies – the first on Bedford chassis – and they survived in service until 1976.

The modern fleet comprised Leyland Nationals and Bristol VRTs, the latter including 30 ex-SBG vehicles among which were some 33ft-long 83-seaters from the only batch of ECW-bodied long-wheelbase VRTs built. These had been new in 1968 to Eastern Scottish. Originally Eastern Counties had been allocated

Left **FS-series Bristol Lodekkas with Gardner 5LW engines were added to the Eastern Counties fleet until 1965. A 1963 bus is seen in Norwich city centre. There were 120 FS5Gs in Eastern Counties service in the mid-1970s.** S J Butler collection

Top **A contrast in Bristol saloons in Norwich bus station in 1973. Nearest the camera is a 1957 LS5G, newly repainted in NBC livery. Alongside stands a 1961 MW5G still in Tilling red. Both have ECW bodies.** Stewart J Brown

Right **The ECW body for Bristol's RE chassis went through a number of different front-end arrangements before settling on the double-curvature BET windscreen. This attractive version was delivered to a number of operators in the mid-1960s, including Eastern Counties. This RE is unusual in being a short 10m RESL model – most THC fleets took 11m RELLs – and was one of 14 with 46-seat ECW bodies. Their original Gardner 6HLX engines had been replaced by less powerful 6HLWs in 1969.** Stewart J Brown

46 of SBG's unwanted VRTs, but in the end the other 16 went to Lincolnshire and Eastern National, from which fleets Eastern Counties received Lodekkas in their place.

In 1974 Eastern Counties took over part of the operations of Mascot Coaches of Norwich, with two Duple-bodied Bedford YRQs. These had been used on a service to the University of East Anglia. In the autumn of 1975 a Deansgate-bodied Ford Transit joined the fleet to provide a service in the Holt and Fakenham area. This was run jointly by the company and Norfolk County Council, and was manned by volunteer drivers. A second similar service was to follow in 1976 in the St Ives area, using an Alexander S-type, built in Belfast and using Ford A-series running units. It was operated in conjunction with the county councils of Cambridgeshire and Northamptonshire. More such services would follow.

Eastern Counties was the main bus operator in Norwich, Cambridge and Peterborough, as well as in smaller towns such as King's Lynn and Cromer. In two coastal towns, Great Yarmouth and Lowestoft, there were local municipally-run bus services.

Great Yarmouth, with 64 buses, had an interesting fleet. Double-deckers had last been bought in 1966 – three Roe-bodied Atlanteans. There were in fact 15 Atlanteans in total, ranging from 1960 Metro-Cammell-bodied PDR1s, to a trio of unusual Marshall-bodied single-deckers bought in 1968. There were Daimlers in operation too, four 1963 Fleetlines, five front-engined CV-series models delivered in 1961, and seven rare Freeline single-deckers. All of the Daimlers had Roe bodies. The Freelines were the last to be built, and had Gardner 6HLW engines. They were also the last Freelines in revenue-earning service. After buying the single-deck Atlanteans in 1968, Great Yarmouth turned

Top left **From 1968 to 1973 all of Great Yarmouth's new buses were single-deckers. These included 12 AEC Swifts with two-door ECW bodies which were delivered in 1973.** Royston Morgan

Centre left **New double-deckers reappeared in the Great Yarmouth fleet in 1977, with the arrival of the first of 12 Bristol VRTs with lowheight ECW bodies. At a time when the vast majority of ECW-bodied VRTs were in NBC leaf green or poppy red, the Great Yarmouth buses looked refreshingly different. This one is seen soon after entering service.** Stewart J Brown

Left **Waveney's front-line buses were 10 AEC Swifts with 45-seat bodies built in Lowestoft by ECW. The first had been new in 1969. When Waveney's services were sold to Eastern Counties the two newest Swifts moved up the coast to Great Yarmouth Transport.** Stewart J Brown

to AEC and took delivery of 33 AEC Swifts between 1970 and 1973, and these made up half of the fleet. They were all two-door buses designed for one-man-operation, and had bodies by Willowbrook and ECW. More ECW bodies would follow – 12 on Bristol VRTs in 1977-78.

The ECW bodies supported local industry, as they were built at Lowestoft, just 10 miles down the coast. Lowestoft was served by England's smallest municipal bus fleet, known since 1974 as Waveney District Council Transport. It ran just 20 buses, the newest of which were 10 ECW-bodied Swifts which while generally similar to those in Great Yarmouth had flat glass windscreens rather than the BET-style screens specified by its presumably more prosperous northern neighbour. There were two other single-deckers in the shape of Pennine-bodied Reliances, bought from Great Yarmouth in 1970. Waveney's double-deckers were interesting too. The newest were two 1967 Massey-bodied Titans. There were also two Titans with East Lancs bodies, and two Regent Vs with Massey bodies. But the stars of the fleet were two 1951 Regent IIIs with Massey bodies – which were real veterans in 1975.

Lowestoft Corporation and Eastern Counties did not always see eye to eye. A scheme to co-ordinate services had been adopted in 1974 but did not work to Lowestoft's satisfaction and in 1975 the council applied to the traffic commissioners for licences to run the entire local bus network. This provoked Eastern Counties to submit counter applications. It was a battle which would rumble on, while Waveney District Council weighed up the pros and cons of selling its bus operation to Eastern Counties. In the end Waveney would give up. The operation was sold to Eastern Counties in 1977.

The biggest municipal bus fleet in East Anglia was owned by Ipswich Borough Transport, although this included a fair number of spare buses which were often hired out to other operators; Southend Transport in fact provided a bigger network of services over a bigger area, albeit with a slightly smaller fleet. At the start of the 1970s Ipswich still operated Regent IIIs and Regal IVs, but by 1975 the oldest buses were 1958 Regent Vs. Regent Vs made up half of the fleet, the last having been bought in 1966. All were 65-seat rear-entrance buses, the later examples being bodied by East Lancs, Neepsend and Massey. Subsequent double-deck orders went to the Leyland Atlantean, and by 1975 there were 25 in operation. The first four, dating from 1968, had ECW bodies of a style similar to a batch supplied to Leicester around the same time. They were ECW's first bodies on Atlantean chassis. Subsequent Atlantean deliveries were bodied by Roe. The balance of the fleet consisted of AEC Swifts with bodies by Willowbrook and East Lancs. A low bridge near the station meant that there were always single-deckers in the Ipswich fleet. Eastern Counties had a depot in Ipswich and provided out-of-town services which reached as far west as Colchester.

Colchester, in Eastern National country, had a respectable municipal fleet too. Late 1950s

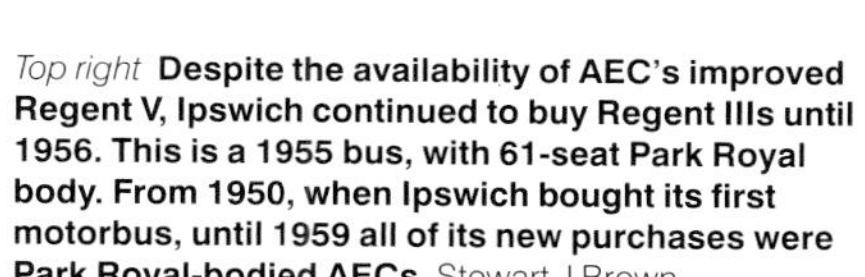

Top right **Despite the availability of AEC's improved Regent V, Ipswich continued to buy Regent IIIs until 1956. This is a 1955 bus, with 61-seat Park Royal body. From 1950, when Ipswich bought its first motorbus, until 1959 all of its new purchases were Park Royal-bodied AECs.** Stewart J Brown

Right **In the 1970s Ipswich bought Leyland Atlanteans with two-door Roe bodies. This is a 1973 example. By 1977 there were 46 in operation.** Stewart J Brown

Regent Vs were on the way out, leaving 16 Leyland Titan PD2s dating from the 1963 to 1966 period as the oldest buses being operated by Colchester. Unusually Colchester had standardised on 7ft 6in wide buses long after the Construction & Use regulations had been amended to allow the use of 8ft wide vehicles. Its 1966 PD2s had been the first 8ft-wide buses in the fleet. All of the front-engined 'deckers had rear-entrance Massey bodies, and it was to Massey that Colchester turned when it placed its first Atlantean orders. Ten PDR1s with square-rigged Massey bodies were delivered in 1967-68. Massey bodies were uncommon on rear-engined double-deckers. The only other sizeable fleet was to be found at Maidstone Borough Transport, which had 20.

Colchester switched to single-deckers in the 1970s, initially running second-hand Reliances

Top **From 1953 to 1968 all of Colchester's new buses had Massey bodies. The last half-cabs were six Leyland Titan PD2A/30s in 1966.** Stewart J Brown

Left **Massey bodywork was rare on rear-engined buses, with the only buyers being the municipal fleets at Colchester and Maidstone, and A1 of Ardrossan. Colchester had 10 Massey bodies on Leyland Atlantean chassis, delivered in 1967-68. They were the undertaking's first rear-engined buses. This one is seen in 1979.** Malcolm Keeley

Above **In 1972-73 15 ECW-bodied Bristol REs were added to the Colchester fleet. Later in the decade they received a more attractive livery with dark red relief for the skirt, waistband and roof.** S J Butler collection

(the last of which was withdrawn in 1976) and then buying 15 Bristol REs with ECW bodies. The Reliances introduced one-man-operation to the fleet. No more Bristols were bought, but the link with ECW was maintained with the arrival in 1975 of eight Atlanteans which were bodied in Lowestoft. These had an unusually-styled front, also used on Fleetline bodies supplied by ECW at around the same time to the South Yorkshire PTE. Colchester would buy more ECW-bodied Atlanteans as the 1980s progressed; the later deliveries would incorporate BET windscreens.

Eastern National served all of Essex, from Harwich across to Braintree and Brentwood, and into Hertfordshire, with a depot in Bishop's Stortford. The company even had a depot in London, at Wood Green. Its headquarters were in Chelmsford. As with most former THC subsidiaries, there were few surprises in the Eastern National fleet. The double-deckers were Bristols. The single-deckers were Bristols too, with Leyland Nationals having featured from 1973. By 1976 there were almost 100. Unusual buses added to the fleet at this time were five Ford R1014s with Duple Dominant bus bodies.

Below **Colchester's later Atlanteans had ECW bodies. Between 1975 and 1980 a total of 36 joined the fleet. A 1977 bus is seen in the High Street when new.** Stewart J Brown

Left **The newest Lodekkas in the Eastern National fleet were FLF6Gs. Some of the 20 delivered in 1968 were used for a short period in the early 1970s as one-man buses. This one is seen on the Southend to Wood Green service in 1977. The last of Eastern National's FLFs were withdrawn in the early 1980s.** David Brown

Centre left **The most interesting double-deckers operated by Eastern National in the early 1970s were the Massey-bodied Guy Arabs which had been taken over from Moore of Kelvedon in 1963. Two 1961 buses had Johannesburg style fronts and lasted until 1974. The last of the Arabs, ordered by Moore but delivered new to Eastern National, came out of service in 1975.** Stewart J Brown

Bottom **A more conventional bus in the Eastern National fleet, this 1961 MW5G is seen in Braintree in 1977, by which time it was among the oldest buses in service – disregarding special types such as the open-top K-series double-deckers. It survived until 1979. Alongside stands a 1964 Lodekka.** S J Butler

These were based at Bishop's Stortford and were bought for use on lightly-used services.

Eastern National had adopted the forward-entrance FLF Lodekka as its standard as early as 1960. Consequently only a handful of rear-entrance types, a few LD5Gs and two FS5Gs, survived to the middle of the decade. The last were withdrawn in 1976. Prior to SBG's overall disenchantment with the Bristol VRT one SBG subsidiary, Alexander (Midland), had decided to dispose of the 15 which it owned after just 18 months in service. These went to Eastern National in 1971, with 15 Eastern National FLFs heading north in exchange. Further SBG VRTs were acquired in 1973. Perhaps the most interesting double-deckers in the fleet were two 1963 Guy Arab IVs with lowbridge Massey bodies. These had been ordered by Moore of Kelvedon, an independent which had been taken over by Eastern National in 1963. Four generally similar buses taken over with the Moore business – including two with Johannesburg-style fronts – lasted until 1974. Unusually, indeed possibly

Right **Southend Corporation ran a smart fleet of traditional Leyland Titan PD3s with rear-entrance Massey bodywork. The last big batch – 12 – was delivered in 1965, to be followed by three more in 1967 which were the undertaking's last half-cabs.** David Brown

Centre right **In 1966 Southend purchased two Leyland Leopards with Marshall bodies. These were basically to the BET standard design but incorporated Southend's generous destination display and were of two-door layout. The peremptory notice below the windscreen typifies attitudes in some parts of the bus industry in the days before passengers became customers and marketing became an issue.** S J Butler

Below left **From time to time second-hand buses appeared in the Southend fleet, such as this Leyland Titan PD3 which had been new to Ribble in 1958. Southend operated a few ex-Ribble Titans for 12 months in 1974-75. All had Burlingham bodies and ended up with China Motor Bus in Hong Kong.** David Brown

Below right **The standard Southend bus in the mid-1970s was the 80-seat long-wheelbase Daimler Fleetline, with 48 being delivered between 1971 and 1976. The registration marks for the last 10 were obtained from the Bolton licensing office by the bodybuilder, Northern Counties, because the Chelmsford licensing office was unable to provide registrations to match the vehicles' fleet numbers.** Tony Wilson

uniquely, for 30ft-long double-deckers they had Gardner 5LW engines. Ten Bristol KSW open-toppers were owned for use on a sea-front service in Southend.

Southend Borough Transport and Eastern National ran co-ordinated services in and around the town. The most numerous type in the Southend fleet was the Daimler Fleetline. By 1976 there were 48 in service, all long-wheelbase CRL6 models with Leyland 680 engines and two-door Northern Counties bodies. The first had arrived in 1971, and they were replacing earlier double-deckers – mainly Leyland Titans and Albion Lowlanders. A few Lowlanders with Alexander bodies remained, along with around 20 exposed-radiator PD3 Titans with bodies by Massey – or on the last

three F-registered 1967 buses – East Lancs. The older PD3s included a couple of side-gangway lowbridge examples dating from 1958 which were the last lowbridge buses in service with an English municipal operator. Single-deckers played a small part in the Southend fleet. At the start of the 1970s they had included five ex-Glasgow Corporation Leyland Worldmasters, but by 1975 there were just six saloons in service, all two-door Leyland Leopards. Two had Marshall bodies while the other four were bodied by Massey.

There was a strong tradition of independent bus operation in East Anglia, particularly in the Colchester area. The biggest of the Colchester area independents was Osborne's of Tollesbury, with a 50-strong fleet of buses and coaches. Osborne's ran services from Tollesbury to Colchester, and also had routes to Witham and Maldon. Most of Osborne's buses were single-deckers. There were modern Willowbrook-bodied Bedfords bought new and a couple of similarly-bodied 1970 Leopards. The Leopards' Glamorgan registrations had been booked by their intended owner, Bebb of Llantwit Fardre, although Osborne's was in fact the first operator of the buses. There were also R-series Ford buses and, as in so many small fleets, new coaches built to bus grant specification.

But the real interest in the Osborne's fleet lay in its double-deckers. The oldest were two AEC Bridgemasters and a 1962 AEC Renown. All had Park Royal bodies, and were ex-AEC demonstrators. The Renown had originally demonstrated to London Transport's country area, where it had been allocated fleet number RX1. The rest of the 'deckers were rear-engined but again of some interest. There were two Roe-bodied long-wheelbase Atlanteans, which had been new to Hall's Coaches of Hounslow and had been built to operate airline contracts at Heathrow. There were also two Bristol VRL prototypes with 80-seat ECW bodies. These were the only VRL buses built for service in Britain and had come from Bristol Omnibus, although one had started life in Scotland with Central SMT. The VRL had a longitudinal engine, located in the offside of the rear overhang, while the more common VRT had the familiar transverse engine. There were also two ex-Western SMT VRTs. Before SBG and NBC agreed to exchange the former's VRTs for the latter's Lodekkas, SBG had advertised the VRTs for sale in the classified advertising columns of Commercial Motor and Coaching Journal, which is how Osborne's came to acquire a pair.

Top left **This was an early AEC Renown, built as a demonstrator in 1962 and bodied by Park Royal. It is seen in Colchester running for Osborne's.** Stewart J Brown

Left **Osborne's livery was not unlike that used by Western SMT and in 1977, four years after joining the Osborne's fleet, this former Western SMT VRT is still in its original owner's livery, complete with fleet number.** Stewart J Brown

Right **New Bedfords featured strongly in Osborne's purchases in the 1970. They included in 1975 a YRT with Willowbrook bus body, seen here at Witham Station.** S J Butler

Below left **Only one example of Marshall's Camair body was built on a Bedford, a 1973 YRT which was bought new by Hedingham & District. It is seen in Colchester bus station soon after entering service. Compared with heavyweight chassis from AEC and Leyland, Bedford's Y-series usually had a short life but this one was still in service with its original owner two decades later.** Stewart J Brown

Below right **Went's ran from Boxted to Colchester using a 1961 Bedford SB1 with Yeates Europa bodywork. It had been new to a Derbyshire coach operator, Frost of Stanley. Loughborough-based Yeates ceased building bodies in 1964.** Stewart J Brown

Bottom **Most of the buses bought by Chambers of Bures in the 1970s were Y-series Bedfords with bodywork by Willowbrook and Plaxton. A 1973 YRT with Willowbrook body stands alongside a 1975 YRT bodied by Plaxton.** Stewart J Brown

Hedingham & District ran from Halstead and Great Bromley to Colchester, operating jointly with Eastern National. The Great Bromley service had been taken over from Vines Luxury Coaches in 1973; Vines had been operating it with a new Bedford YRQ with Willowbrook Expressway body. Hedingham & District also served Sudbury and Braintree. There were 15 vehicles in the fleet, all bought new in the 1970s. One was a Leopard, delivered in 1974; the remainder were Y-series Bedfords with bus bodies by Marshall and Willowbrook or, on two YRQs, coach bodies by Plaxton. One of the Marshall bodies, on a YRT, was of the distinctive Camair style. L-prefix fleet numbers harked back to the days before the formation of Hedingham & District in 1960, when the operations were run by Letch of Sible Hedingham. From Boxted to Colchester a service was provided by Went, using a 1961 Bedford SB1 with Yeates Europa body.

Chambers of Bures, in Suffolk, ran from Colchester to Bury St Edmunds. At the start of the decade there had been double-deckers in the Chambers fleet but the last, a 1957 Guy Arab, had been replaced by a Bedford YRT in 1973 and by 1975 the service was being run by Willowbrook-bodied Bedfords. Chambers ran 10 vehicles, all Bedfords and Fords. At Sudbury, which was served by Chambers, a town service was run by Mulley's Motorways of Ixworth. Mulley's also served Bury St Edmunds. Plaxton-bodied Bedford coaches were generally used. Theobald of Long Melford had services in the Sudbury area, most of which were operated by Y-series Bedfords, including two with bus bodies, by Willowbrook and Duple. Theobald also had a YRQ with the relatively short-lived Duple Viceroy Express body, in production for less than 12 months before being superseded by the new Dominant.

Other Suffolk independents included Norfolk of Nayland, running to Colchester using an ex-Aldershot & District Loline which later in the decade was replaced by a former Bolton Corporation Regent V. Norfolk also operated ex-City of Oxford Reliances. Further east, Beeston's of Hadleigh had a service between Elmsett and Ipswich, generally covered by Bedford coaches, including a YRQ with Caetano Cascais body built to meet bus grant specifica-

Top left **Theobald of Long Melford used Y-series Bedfords, both buses and coaches. The first of the buses was a 1972 YRQ with 52-seat Willowbrook body, seen here in Sudbury.** G R Mills

Centre left **This one-time Bolton Corporation AEC Regent V was purchased by Norfolk's from the Greater Manchester PTE in 1976. New in 1961, it had a 72-seat body by Metro-Cammell.** Malcolm Keeley

Left **The biggest bus in the Squirrel fleet was a 1975 Bedford YRT with 64-seat Plaxton bus body. It is seen in Ipswich when new.** D J Little

tions. Also running into Ipswich was Bickers of Coddenham, with a 1970 Willowbrook-bodied Ford R192 bus, or with Ford/Plaxton coaches, all bought new – although expansion in the latter part of the decade would see second-hand buses dominating the fleet, including unusual Bristol SUs. Partridge of Hadleigh used second-hand AEC Reliance coaches on services to Stowmarket, Bury St Edmunds and Ipswich. Ipswich was also served by Squirrell of Hitcham, using a Bedford VAM70 with Plaxton bus body, which in 1975 was replaced by a high-capacity 64-seat Plaxton-bodied YRT. A service from Woodbridge to Ipswich was provided by JDW Transport using a new Plaxton-bodied Bedford YRT coach. JDW had taken over from the Ipswich Coach Company, which had on occasion used a rather more interesting ex-Ipswich Regal IV in place of the route's regular Plaxton-bodied YRQ coach. The service had originally been run by Eastern Counties.

In Norfolk, Culling of Norwich operated a few rural services, normally using Willowbrook-bodied Bedfords. Simonds of Bottesdale had an extensive network of routes, with services running to Norwich, Ipswich, Stowmarket, Bury St Edmunds and Diss. The bus fleet was made up primarily of Fords and Bedfords with bodies by Willowbrook, Plaxton and Duple. In the north of the county, King's Lynn was served by Rosemary Coaches of Terrington St Clement. The only independent in Norfolk running a new double-decker in the mid-1970s was Pegg of Caston, located between Attleborough and Watton. This was a long-wheelbase Leeds-style Atlantean with Roe bodywork incorporating panoramic windows and two doors. Pegg also had a Willowbrook-bodied Regent V which had been new to Cottrell's of Mitcheldean.

There were three well-known independents in Cambridgeshire. The biggest was Premier Travel of Cambridge running 50 vehicles – all AECs. In 1975 four were ex-City of Oxford Bridgemasters (survivors from a batch of eight) while the remainder were Reliances, most of which had been bought new. Unusually for an independent, Alexander Y-type bodies were favoured and there were 32 in the fleet. All of the other Reliances had Harrington bodies, although until 1973 there had been a number of Burlingham Seagulls. The company operated

Top right **Simonds of Bottesdale was one of many small operators to buy new Ford and Bedford buses in the 1970s. In 1975 the company added this Bedford YRT to its fleet. The Duple body had 66 seats.** Stewart J Brown

Right **Most 36ft-long Willowbrook bodies had BET-style curved windscreens, but some of the early examples, such as this 1962 bus, used this style of front end. This AEC Reliance was a 65-seater and had been new to Somerset operator Hutchings & Cornelius. It was bought by Pegg of Caston in 1964 and ran for the Norfolk operator for the following 15 years.** Stewart J Brown

local services in Cambridge, Huntingdon and Haverhill, and was also heavily involved in express services.

Another operator running in to Cambridge was Burwell & District, with a fleet of 15 vehicles which included two Daimler Fleetlines with Willowbrook bodies, bought new in the early 1960s. Other double-deckers were an ex-demonstration AEC Renown, an ex-South Wales Regent V, and a 1953 London Transport RT which was easily the oldest bus in the fleet. It ran until 1977. Single-deckers were mainly second-hand Reliances, but there was a Willowbrook-bodied Bedford YRQ, bought new in 1971. By the end of the decade Burwell & District would be no more, having sold out to Eastern Counties.

Whippet Coaches of Fenstanton had local services in an area which embraced Cambridge, Huntingdon and St Ives. Two Atlanteans – a 1966 Willowbrook-bodied bus and a 1973 example with Northern Counties body – were about to be joined by a third, with Roe body. However most services were operated by bus grant coaches – Plaxton-bodied Bedford YRTs and Volvo B58s. Volvos on stage carriage services were rare indeed in 1975. Second-hand double-deckers – mainly ex-Trent PD3s – were used on school contracts but did appear on stage services too.

From Bourne in Lincolnshire, Delaine ran services south to Peterborough, as well as to Stamford and to Spalding. Delaine ran 16 vehicles – all immaculately turned-out and all bought new. The oldest was a 1956 Leyland Titan PD2 with Willowbrook body, followed by two PD3s which were the only double-deckers to be bodied by Yeates. Modern 'deckers were two Atlanteans – a 1966 Willowbrook-bodied PDR1/2 and a 1973 Northern Counties-bodied AN68/2. The single-deckers were predominantly Bedford coaches. Services in the Spalding area were also operated by Elsey of Gosberton, using Bedford and Ford coaches.

Finally, back on the edge of Eastern National territory, Biss Brothers ran from Bishop's Stortford to Furneux Pelham, using a 1966 Bedford SB5 with Duple (Midland) body, something of an anachronism in southern England in the era of big operators running Leyland Nationals. The Biss fleet was made up largely of Plaxton-bodied coaches.

Above left **The standard Premier Travel single-decker was the AEC Reliance, and in 1975 most of these had Alexander Y-type bodies, an unusual choice for an independent fleet. This was the last of the type. Subsequent new Reliances had Plaxton bodies.** D J Little

Left **Burwell & District operated both new and second-hand Fleetlines. This 1963 bus with Northern Counties body had been new to Nottingham City Transport. It was bought by Burwell & District in 1976.** D J Little

Above **Whippet occasionally bought new double-deckers. This Roe-bodied Atlantean joined the fleet in 1976. It is seen in Cambridge.** S J Butler

Right **The Delaine had a reputation for the immaculate presentation of its fleet. A 1973 Northern Counties-bodied Atlantean makes the point. It is a long-wheelbase AN68/2. There were five double-deckers in The Delaine's 16-vehicle fleet. Note the unusual mouldings on the body side.** David Brown

1975: Major bus fleets – East Anglia

Operator	*Fleet size*
Eastern Counties	660
Eastern National	614
Ipswich	78
Southend	73
Great Yarmouth	64
Colchester	53
Waveney	20

South East England

Facing page **London Country became the world's biggest Leyland National operator. Up until 1976 a number were delivered in local coach livery to operate Green Line services. While early Green Line Nationals had bus seats, later ones had high-backed coach-type seating. This one is seen at St Albans when brand new in 1974.** Capital Transport

Above left **That classic London bus, the RT, could be seen in service right until the end of the decade. In the mid-1970s a few were still on routes serving central London, as shown by one skirting Trafalgar Square on its way south to Tooting.** Malcolm Keeley

Above right **The Routemaster was the most common type in London service for much of the decade, outlasting newer types which followed it. A 1963 bus passes Wimbledon Station in 1976.** S J Butler collection

Right **London Transport pioneered overall advertising, which became quite fashionable in the 1970s, and most overall adverts were applied to Routemasters. Heating, ventilating and air conditioning equipment was promoted on RM 1196 seen in Becontree in August 1975.** Capital Transport

In the mid-1970s London Transport was still easily Britain's biggest bus operator, a position it had held unchallenged since the formation of the London Passenger Transport Board in 1933. True, it had lost its country area operations and 1,267 buses to NBC in January 1970, with the creation of London Country Bus Services. But that still left a red bus fleet of around 6,500 vehicles. These were shared between no fewer than 67 garages, ranging in size from Holloway, with a scheduled allocation of 194 buses, down to Loughton with just 34.

The most numerous type was still the Routemaster. There had been 2,760 built. Of these 209 had been transferred to London Country and a small number had been taken out of service, which meant that there were still over 2,500 running in the capital's streets. A Routemaster had been the country's first overall advertising bus in 1969, promoting Silexine paint, and during the early 1970s overall adverts were applied to a number of the type (and also to one Red Arrow AEC Merlin). However a rethink on advertising policy saw overall adverts being phased out by London Transport in the middle of the decade.

Routemaster production at Park Royal spanned the years from 1958 to 1968, with the last entering service long after all other major British city operators had switched to rear-engined buses. There was one odd Routemaster in service – FRM1, the only rear-engined example. It, too, was an AEC/Park Royal product but with a transverse AEC AV691 rear engine and an entrance in the front overhang. However in the pursuit of standardisation with the existing fleet, some 60 per cent of standard Routemaster parts were used. It spent the early 1970s running in Croydon as an omo bus, and then moved to Potters Bar. By the end of the decade it would be working on the Round London Sightseeing Tour.

While Routemasters could be seen throughout London Transport's operating territory, the same could not be said for its classic predecessor, the RT-class of AEC Regent IIIs. AEC built 4,825 RTs for London Transport between 1939 and 1954 which meant that by the mid 1970s the youngest survivors were 20 years old. There were still around 600 in the operational fleet, running from 19 garages. Major RT allocations were held at Sidcup and Bexleyheath, in south-east London, and at Barking in east London. Barking was, in 1979, to be the scene of the end of regular RT operation by LT.

Bodywork for the postwar RT class had been built by five manufacturers – Cravens, Metro-Cammell, Park Royal, Saunders and Weymann. Most of those which survived into the 1970s had Park Royal bodies, although there were a few Weymann-bodied buses. Vehicle shortages in the early part of the decade had seen LT actually add RTs to its fleet, buying 34 from London Country and repainting them red before putting them back into service. The RTs carried a slightly different livery from the Routemasters, with grey relief (instead of white) above the lower deck windows, and retaining London Transport fleetnames in gold capital letters, rather than using the white roundel which had been used in place of the fleetname on Routemasters (and most other types) from 1974. Later in the decade history was to repeat itself, with LT buying back most of the surviving Routemasters from London Country; many were non-runners.

After the Routemaster, the most common type in LT service was the Fleetline. There were just over 2,000 in the middle of the decade – ultimately there would be 2,646 – and the first had entered service in 1970. Orders for Fleetlines had first been placed – for a modest 117 – after trials from the mid 1960s between Leyland's Atlantean (the XA class) and Daimler's Fleetline (the XF). At that time Leyland and Daimler had been rival manufacturers, but by the time LT started placing orders for its new generation of double-deck bus, Daimler had been taken over by Leyland. The 1960s trial vehicles, incidentally, had operated until the early 1970s (the XAs mainly with LT and the XFs with London Country) when they were sold to China Motor Bus in Hong Kong.

Above left **The unique rear-engined Routemaster spent the 1970s either on outer suburban services or, towards the end of the decade, the Round London Sightseeing Tour. It passes Marble Arch with an uneconomic load in the late summer of 1979.**
Malcolm Keeley

Left **The Daimler Fleetline was one of a number of unloved types in service in London in the 1970s. The use of a band of white relief at upper deck floor level was limited to Park Royal-bodied buses delivered in 1972-73. Earlier and later deliveries were all-over red, then from 1975 red with white upper deck window surrounds. DMS 163 is seen in March 1974.**
Capital Transport

The saga of the new breed of omo double-decker – briefly referred to as the Londoner, although the tag didn't stick – turned out to be a sad one, in many ways mirroring earlier experience with omo single-deckers as will be explained shortly. Suffice it to say that a combination of lower levels of in-service reliability, inherent in all first-generation rear-engined double-deckers, was exacerbated by LT's inflexibility in its approach to maintenance. The Fleetlines quickly earned a reputation for unreliability – not wholly deserved – and before the 2,646th was delivered, LT had confirmed that the whole class would be withdrawn and sold. This happened in the early 1980s – when eager operators elsewhere would quickly snap them up.

The Fleetlines – LT class DMS and, from 1974, DM for crew-operated buses – had Gardner 6LXB or Leyland 680 engines and dual-door Park Royal or Metro-Cammell bodies with 68 seats on omo buses and 71 seats on those built for crew operation. The difference in seating was accounted for by the fitment of automatic fare collection equipment over the front nearside wheelarch on omo buses. Initially the DMSs were painted unrelieved red. White relief was applied above the lower deck windows from 1971, but was quickly abandoned. From 1975 the livery on new deliveries was considerably improved by the use of white relief for the top deck window surrounds.

To assist partially-sighted travellers, entrance doors were painted yellow on Fleetlines (and other types) from 1973. This was so that they would not be confused with exit doors – although the logic is flawed; if someone had enough sight to locate a door and identify its colour, they could presumably also identify the outline of the body round it.

The first of a new generation of double-decker started arriving in London in 1975: the Metro-Scania. This was a joint venture between Scania of Sweden and Metro-Cammell and LT ordered 164, delivery of which was spread over two years. The type was allocated to Peckham and used on the 36 group of routes to Victoria, and on the 53 and 63. They were 72-seat crew-operated buses and were to prove even less successful than the Fleetlines. Severe body corrosion meant that Metropolitans in London and elsewhere seldom saw further service after the expiry of their initial seven year Certificate of Fitness.

There was one other double-deck type running in LT colours in 1975, the six-strong OM class of BMMO D9 open-toppers. These were owned by an independent, Obsolete Fleet, which had from 1972 been running a 1930 ST-class AEC Regent on a daily vintage bus service in the West End.

Above left **The XA-class Atlanteans ended their period in London Transport service in Croydon. New in 1965, they were exported to Hong Kong in the mid-1970s. The bodywork was by Park Royal.** Stewart J Brown

Above right **Arguably the last in a line of unsuccessful rear-engined types operated by London Transport was the MCW Metropolitan. LT ran 164, delivered between 1975 and 1977. They operated from LT's garages at Peckham and New Cross, and were withdrawn in the early 1980s. The yellow entrance doors were intended to help partially-sighted passengers.** David Brown

Below **The concept of heritage bus services could be said to have started when Obsolete Fleet returned this 1930 ST-class AEC Regent to service in 1972. It carried advertising for its sponsors – Burberrys – in 1974.** Stewart J Brown

Above **London Transport's AEC Swifts and Merlins were of generally similar appearance but of different lengths. This is a Metro-Cammell-bodied Swift in Merton. Designed to carry more standing than seated passengers (34 standees, 33 seated) they were unpopular with passengers. The curved windscreen was also used in the DMS-class Fleetlines.** Capital Transport

Below **Six Metro-Scanias were purchased by London Transport in 1973. They lasted just three years in service. They had been purchased partly to obtain operating experience of the Scania running units which would be used in MCW's Metropolitan model then under development.** Stewart J Brown

Back to London Transport and its single-deck fleet. Single-deckers had come to prominence in the late 1960s, following the publication in 1966 of the Bus Reshaping Plan which envisaged the widespread use of omo standee single-deckers on short routes based on suburban centres. The first major conversion took place in Wood Green and Walthamstow in 1968.

The brave new omo world which LT's planners envisaged was not a resounding success. Standee buses were unpopular, and the new fleet of rear-engined AEC Swifts and Merlins was not the most reliable. LT had ordered 665 11m-long Merlins and 838 10m-long Swifts and these were delivered between 1967 and 1972 (including 138 Swifts which went to the new London Country operation). By 1975 most of the Merlins had been withdrawn, and 350 were stored on an airfield at Radlett as LT sought, largely in vain, to find buyers. Indeed by this time the only Merlins left in regular service were those used on the central London Red Arrow network of limited stop services. These, the MBA class, numbered almost 90 and had 73-passenger Metro-Cammell bodies with just 25 seats.

The Merlins had AEC's big 11.3-litre AH691 engine. The Swifts, which lasted longer but were really not that much more successful, had the smaller 8.2-litre AH505. Engine failures were not uncommon, which meant that at any given time in the middle of the decade a fair number of the type could be found parked up in garages rather than out on the road. Visually similar to the Merlins, the Swifts had bodywork by Marshall, Metro-Cammell and Park Royal and while the majority were of two-door layout, there were 140 single-door buses. The Swifts did not generally penetrate the central area, but could be found in suburban services in most parts of outer London. By the end of the 1970s there would be few Swifts left in operation.

The Leyland National was to be the successor to the ill-fated AECs. In 1973 LT took delivery of six Leyland Nationals and six Metro-Scanias and operated them on the S2 route in Clapton. All 12 carried a new single-deck livery which incorporated a white roof, a feature which, sadly, was not perpetuated. The Metro-Scanias were still in use in 1975 but were to have a short life with LT, being taken out of service in 1976. Most were sold in 1978 to Newport Borough Transport. The S2 service was of interest in that it was in part the successor to the last route in London to be operated by side-gangway lowbridge buses, in the shape of the RLH class of AEC Regent IIIs. The last of these came out of service in April 1971.

The six Nationals clearly acquitted themselves rather better than the Metro-Scanias, and further orders were placed for a total of 101 in 1976-77. All were two-door 36-seaters and, as with the AECs they were replacing, were to be found in the suburbs rather than in the central area. They were delivered in all-over red. Subsequent orders in the later part of the decade eventually took LT's National fleet up to 506 buses. The high-tech integral Nationals were ne face of LT's single-deck fleet. Another was the AEC Regal IV. Before its ill-judged involvement with standee Merlins and Swifts, LT's last big order for single-deckers had been at the start of the 1950s. In the period 1951-53 no fewer than 700 RF-class Regal IVs were delivered, all with Metro-Cammell bodies. Many operated in the Country Area and when London Country was formed the bulk were transferred to the new company, which took 413. But there were still pockets of RF operation in red bus territory, with just under 100 still in the fleet in 1975. Indeed RF operation did not finally cease until 1979, which meant that the last of the Regal IVs had clocked up over 25 years service – the comparison with the later Merlins and Swifts is perhaps too obvious...

The RFs were solid. They weighed $7\frac{3}{4}$ tons, which was more than a double-deck RT and a bit over $1\frac{3}{4}$ tons heavier than the type which was used to replace them on routes where either physical restrictions or low passenger numbers dictated the use of a smaller vehicle than the 10m Swift. The choice was the Bristol LH. This was just 9m long (or 30ft, to use the Imperial terminology appropriate to the time) and, like the RF, was 7ft 6in wide. LT ordered 95 with ECW bodywork for delivery from 1976. These initially wore an attractive livery with white window surrounds, although later in life they were to be repainted all-over red.

The 9m LHs were not LT's first modern Bristols. In 1975 six short-wheelbase LHSs, just 24ft long, were delivered for operation on the C11 in Cricklewood. A further 11 followed in 1976. These were 26-seaters, also bodied by ECW. The LHSs were bought to replace LT's Ford Transit minibuses.

Twenty Transits, with Strachans Pacemaker bodies, were delivered in 1972-73 for trial operation on routes which could not justify full-size buses. The costs of the trial were underwritten by the Greater London Council and routes were selected in Wood Green, Cricklewood, Brixton and Peckham, followed by a dial-a-ride service in Hampstead Garden Suburb. The last named ran from 1974 to 1976 when it was converted to a conventional timetable, but still using the Ford Transits, including a 21st bus which had Dormobile bodywork. All of the minibus routes were judged worthwhile, to the extent that LHSs ousted most of the Transits in 1975-76.

One other vehicle type was operated by LT in the mid 1970s – the British Airways fleet of forward-entrance Routemasters. These had been built in 1966-67 for British European

Top **London Transport's oldest single-deckers in the 1970s were RF-class AEC Regal IVs. These had 39-seat Metro-Cammell bodies, of a design unique to LT. The Leyland National shows how much urban bus design had progressed in two decades.** Royston Morgan

Centre right **On routes where vehicles of 7ft 6in width were deemed desirable London Transport replaced RFs with Bristol LHs. These had 39-seat ECW bodies and when new featured an attractive livery with white window surrounds.** David Brown

Right **London Transport's smallest buses were Ford Transits with 16-seat Strachans Pacemaker bodies. They were used in 1972 to introduce new services where passenger demand was thought unlikely to justify bigger buses. These were the country's first true urban minibus routes.** Capital Transport

Airways. There were 65 in all, and on the service linking the Gloucester Road air terminal with Heathrow they generally pulled two-wheel luggage trailers built by Marshall. Reductions in the service had rendered a number of these coaches redundant, and in 1975 LT bought 13 from BA, numbering them in a new RMA series, and putting them into service in Romford. This was an unusual move.

The buses had no destination displays – there had been no need for them on the airport express – and destination boards had to be displayed in the front nearside window. They were also the only forward entrance buses in the LT fleet – all other types were either rear entrance or had a front entrance opposite the driver. They entered service in BA livery, but most were repainted in LT red before they were withdrawn in 1976 and transferred to the driver training fleet.

Vehicle shortages in 1975 also led to the hiring of ten 1965 Leyland Titan PD3s from Southend Transport. With their exposed radiators and manual gearboxes they seemed more like buses from the RT rather than the RM era and they operated on the 190, running from Croydon to Old Coulsdon. Plans to hire in other types were thwarted by trade union opposition.

Above **A link between Heathrow Airport and the British European Airways' terminal in Gloucester Road was operated by a fleet of 65 forward-entrance Routemasters. These had 175bhp AEC 11.3-litre AV690 engines compared with 115bhp 9.6-litre AV590s in most other AEC-powered Routemasters. In 1973 a Spanish holiday could be had for just £33. Thirteen of these vehicles ran briefly with London Transport in Romford in 1975-76.** Stewart J Brown

Below **London Country inherited an old fleet from London Transport, which included 484 RTs out of a total fleet of 1,267 vehicles. The registration letters on this RT in Croydon seem particularly apt.** Stewart J Brown

Coaches were also hired to work certain bus routes with their owners providing the drivers and LT the conductors, but union opposition also thwarted these plans. The shortage of serviceable buses saw LT cutting service levels on around 100 routes.

London Country Bus Services was NBC's biggest subsidiary, with a fleet of just over 1,200 buses and coaches. It had been formed in January 1970 to take over LT's green country bus operation at the time when ownership of LT and its red bus fleet was being transferred from the London Transport Board to the Greater London Council. It started life with 1,267 vehicles, many of them elderly RTs and RFs. Over two-thirds of the initial LCBS fleet – 924 buses and coaches – was over 15 years old. And LCBS also had an unusually-shaped operating area, circling London and described at the time as being like a Polo mint.

Of the initial fleet, 484 were RTs of which the youngest would have been described as being well past their sell-by date had such a term been in use in 1970. There were also 413 equally ancient RF class Regal IVs. The only rear-engined double-deckers in the original fleet were eight Daimler Fleetlines and three Atlanteans – some of the 1966 trial vehicles. Other types included Routemasters (209), AEC Reliances (14) and AEC Merlins (109). LT influence continued to be felt during 1970-71 with the delivery of 138 LT-style AEC Swifts.

The ancient LCBS fleet had to be modernised and NBC was quick to invest in new buses for its biggest subsidiary. First there was an urgent need for more new double-deckers which would be suitable for omo. An order was placed for 90 Leyland Atlanteans with Park Royal bodies and these were delivered in 1972. This became the LCBS standard and further batches were delivered in the later part of the 1970s, ultimately building the company's Atlantean fleet up to 293 by the early 1980s. The final vehicles were bodied by Roe, but to the same basic Park Royal design. Also delivered in 1972 were 30 Atlanteans with Metro-Cammell bodies, diverted from part of a Midland Red order. All 120 of the 1972 Atlanteans were in a livery described as light National green, with canary yellow lower deck window surrounds – although the green was in fact considerably darker than the leaf green which was adopted later that year as the corporate NBC colour and which by 1975 was being applied to Atlanteans as they became due for a repaint.

The Atlanteans were the first LCBS order, but the first new double-deckers were in fact 11 Leyland-engined Daimler Fleetlines. These entered service in green and yellow at the start of 1972. Based in Godstone, they were the first new omo double-deckers in the LCBS fleet. The Fleetlines had two-door Northern Counties bodies and were diverted from Western Welsh. The only other double-deck type bought by LCBS in the 1970s was the Bristol VRT. Fifteen would be delivered in 1977 and allocated to Grays. They had Leyland engines and ECW bodies of the relatively rare (on a VRT) full-height design.

Single-deckers played a significant part in the LCBS operation. The RF fleet included some which had been modernised in the late 1960s with twin headlights, a curved windscreen, new body side mouldings and improved interiors. These were intended for Green Line operation, but the few survivors were largely being used on normal bus services by the middle of the decade. Their original two-tone green livery was still in evidence, although some were in green with a yellow waistband. Only a few RFs received NBC leaf green. The last were taken out of regular service in 1978.

LT had in 1965 bought 14 Willowbrook-bodied Reliances for Green Line service. These were still in the LCBS fleet 10 years later, although by then demoted to bus work at Hertford. NBC's solution to the problem of updating the Green Line fleet, which was largely being operated by Routemaster coaches and refurbished RFs, was to order 90 AEC Reliances. The choice of chassis was not particularly surprising, but the body order went to bus builder Park Royal, rather than to a coach manufacturer. These bus-like vehicles did have 45 coach seats and forced-air ventilation, and they entered service in two-tone green. They were quite quickly repainted into NBC's local coach livery – green for the lower half, white for the top. The Reliances set in motion the conversion of Green Line routes from crew-operation to one-man. The Park Royal bodies used the same windscreens as on the Atlanteans which were being delivered around the same time.

Other types were added to the Green Line fleet. Among the more attractive were 21 AEC Swifts with Alexander W-type bodies. The W-type was essentially a bus body, but for LCBS 45 coach seats were fitted and, unusually, a rear destination display. The Alexander-bodied Swifts had been delivered in the same two-tone green livery as their Park Royal-bodied contemporaries, but they too were being repainted into NBC's local coach livery in the middle of the decade. They had been diverted from a South Wales Transport order and were used on the 725 orbital service linking Windsor and Gravesend.

There was another SWT/LCBS link, in the shape of 15 AEC Swift buses which had joined the LCBS fleet from SWT in 1971. The first three were two years old and had dual-door Willowbrook bodies; they operated in Crawley. The remaining 12 were just six months old when they joined LCBS at St Albans and had single-door Marshall bodies of standard BET design.

Top **London Country had 109 AEC Merlins which were the modern part of its London Transport inheritance. All but one had dual-door bodywork by Metro-Cammell. They could carry 60 passengers with either 33 or 45 seated, depending on the body layout. All were still in use in the mid-1970s. NBC could not afford to discard buses as easily as could London Transport. One is seen in Hemel Hempstead in 1973.** Capital Transport

Above left **The Leyland Atlantean became the London Country standard double-decker in the 1970s. Most had Park Royal bodywork of the style seen here on one of the 90 buses delivered in 1972. This photograph was taken in Stevenage in 1978 and the bus was still in its original livery, albeit with the addition of the NBC logo below the windscreen.** S J Butler

Above right **The eight XF-class Daimler Fleetlines which had been bought by London Transport in 1965 were allocated to country area routes and passed to London Country in 1970. They had Park Royal bodies. For most of the 1970s they were based in East Grinstead, the location of this 1977 photograph.** S J Butler

The various batches of new and nearly-new Swifts continued the long-established link between AEC and LCBS and its green country bus predecessors but they were to be the company's last AEC buses. The bus of the future was the Leyland National and NBC ordered 70 for LCBS, delivery of which started in 1972. Although designed as urban buses, many Nationals were painted in local coach livery and allocated to the Green Line network. They retained standard bus seats, although on some later batches they were trimmed with moquette rather than pvc, to convey the impression of some added luxury. Nationals were to play a growing part in the LCBS fleet as the 1970s progressed. Ultimately there would be 540, giving the company the world's biggest fleet of the type. (The fleet numbers would reach 543, but three early Nationals were diverted first to Nottingham City Transport, on loan, and then to Hants & Dorset.)

The Nationals ousted many older types – RFs, RTs and Routemasters. Where smaller buses were needed for RF replacement the choice was the Bristol LH with ECW body. Most were 7ft 6in wide. The first were delivered in 1973, with further batches following until 1977.

Bus route and network branding was still fairly rare in the 1970s. One early attempt was the Stevenage Superbus network, launched by LCBS in 1971 using a bright blue and yellow livery which survived the imposition of NBC's corporate colours and in fact lasted until the late 1970s. The vehicles used on Superbus services included standard LT-style Metro-Cammell-bodied AEC Swifts, some early Nationals, and seven Metro-Scanias. Four had been bought new in 1971-72 – the only examples of the type delivered new to an NBC subsidiary – while the other three came from Hants & Dorset in 1973, following the takeover by H&D of Winchester-based King Alfred Motor Services, the buses' original owner. The three Nationals mentioned above went to H&D in exchange.

Another unusual – and short-lived – opera-

Top left **The first real upgrade of Green Line services in the 1970s came in 1971-72 with the delivery of 90 AEC Reliances with Park Royal coach bodies which helped reinforce the received wisdom that bus builders could not build convincing coaches. This coach in Sevenoaks in 1974 is in the original two-tone green livery.** Stewart J Brown

Centre left **NBC's only Metro-Scanias were operated by London Country and were allocated to Superbus services in Stevenage – an early example of modern bus industry marketing. They were withdrawn in 1978.** S J Butler

Left **Continental Pioneer was probably the only British operator to specify a registration to match the number of its only route, the 235 from Richmond Station to Richmond Hill. The bus was a Willowbrook-bodied Ford.** Stewart J Brown

Right **Golden Miller ran Plaxton-bodied buses in Staines and Feltham. This is a Bedford YRQ at Shepperton Station in 1976.** Stewart J Brown

Below left **Aldershot & District's traditional livery was still to be seen in the mid-1970s. Here it is carried on a Dennis Loline III with Alexander body, seen in Guildford where Dennis chassis were (and still are) built. It carries an NBC-style Alder Valley fleetname.** Stewart J Brown

Below right **Before NBC adopted its corporate livery, Alder Valley introduced a new red scheme, seen here in Guildford bus station on a 1965 Loline with 68-seat Weymann body. These had been Aldershot & District's last Dennises.** Stewart J Brown

tion was a dial-a-ride service in Harlow, launched in 1974 as the Pick-me-up service using five Ford Transits with 16-seat Dormobile bodies. The service ran for two years with outside funding by a number of organisations. It then ran for a short while longer as a conventional service.

Some added colour was provided in LCBS operations in the mid-1970s as vehicle shortages forced the company to hire buses in from other operators. It began in 1974 with London Transport Merlins, and gathered pace in 1975 with Maidstone Borough Transport PD2As at Dartford, Bournemouth Transport Fleetlines and Roadliners at Leatherhead and Staines, and Western National Bristol MW coaches in NBC's overall white livery at Dunton Green. Most of these returned to their owners in 1976. Later hires included Eastbourne Regent Vs at Swanley in 1976, Southend PD3s at Harlow in 1976-77 and Maidstone Borough Atlanteans at Chelsham in 1977.

There were few small operators in the area served by LT and LCBS. In Richmond a local service to the top of Richmond Hill, the 235, was provided by Continental Pioneer, generally using an Willowbrook-bodied Ford R1014 which was unusual in having a registration – PGX235L – to match the route number. This had been purchased in 1973 to replace an ex-Thames Valley Bristol LL5G. Elsewhere in Surrey Banstead Coaches operated a Coulsdon local service with a Willowbrook-bodied Bedford YRQ. Orpington & District ran from Croydon to Forestdale with a variety of second-hand types which included ex-Western Welsh Tiger Cubs, an ex-Yorkshire Woollen Reliance and a Leyland Atlantean which had been new to Maidstone & District.

In Staines and Feltham Golden Miller ran local services using a 1969 Bristol LH and three 1974 Bedford YRQs. These had all been bought new and had Plaxton bus bodies. Golden Miller was primarily a coach operator and the company's name came from a winning racehorse. NBC, through its Tillings Travel subsidiary, for a time ran a minibus between Victoria railway station and Victoria Coach Station. The bus was a Ford Transit in full National white coach livery.

To the north of London Rover Bus Service ran between Chesham and Hemel Hempstead, using Ford R-series buses. One of the more unusual routes in LCBS country was operated by Thames Weald which provided a link between Romford and Sevenoaks via the Dartford Tunnel using Mercedes-Benz minibuses.

To the west of London the NBC subsidiary providing local services was the Thames Valley and Aldershot Omnibus Co, trading as Alder Valley. This was an NBC creation, having been formed in January 1972 by merging Thames Valley, which had been a Tilling company based in Reading, with Aldershot & District, a BET subsidiary with its headquarters in Aldershot. Thames Valley's buses had been Tilling red; Aldershot & District's a distinctive two-tone green. Thames Valley's fleet had been made up mainly of Bristols. Aldershot & District had for a number of years run Dennises and AECs, but had more recently been buying Bristol REs. Thus Alder Valley started life with a mixed fleet. Its livery was initially a deep red, but after less than 12 months this was replaced by corporate poppy red and by 1975 had virtually disappeared.

Double-deckers were mainly FLF Lodekkas (Thames Valley had been an early convert to forward entrances) and Dennis Lolines. The newest Lolines were 1965 buses with Weymann bodies, but there were a number of earlier Alexander-bodied buses. Newer double-deckers were the NBC 1970s standard, the ECW-bodied VRT. These included some 1968 buses – which pre-dated the formation of NBC – and 14 ex-SBG vehicles which had been part of the 1973 vehicle exchange.

There was considerably more variety in the single-deck fleet, although that was rapidly changing as growing numbers of Nationals were taken into stock – 150 between 1973 and 1976 alone helped put paid to many ex-Aldershot & District Reliances and ex-Thames Valley mid-engined Bristol MWs and SUs. However Aldershot & District had been buying Reliances right up to 1969 – 30 G-registered buses with Marshall bodies – and these as well as earlier Metro-Cammell and Willowbrook bodied buses would still be running in the second half of the decade.

Aldershot & District's G-registered Reliances had been followed by H-registered Bristol REs, also bodied by Marshall, which added variety to Alder Valley's RE fleet, most of which was bodied by ECW. For rural operations Alder Valley took delivery in 1974 of the unusual combination of Ford R-series chassis with ECW bodywork. There were 25 R1014s; a further 10 with Plaxton bodies were to follow in 1976. After that the ECW-bodied LH was specified for use on less busy services. A weight restriction on a bridge over the Thames on the Marlow to Maidenhead route was the reason for operating three 1974 Leyland EA minibuses with 19-seat bodies built in Ireland by Asco. The company's territory extended roughly from Windsor to High Wycombe, and south to Hindhead and Alton. Major towns served included Bracknell, Guildford, Maidenhead, Newbury, Reading and Slough.

In Reading local services were run by Reading Transport, which until 1968 had had a significant trolleybus system. Reading had been among the first British urban operators to show serious interest in omo, and from 1957 many of its new buses were two-door standee single-deckers. The 1957 Reliances, with 34 seat (plus

Top left **An AEC Reliance with Metro-Cammell body in Alder Valley service in 1973. The chassis dated from 1954; the body, despite its appearance, was actually built in 1967. When new this AEC had had a Strachans coach body. It was one of 15 to be rebodied. The deep white panel below the windscreen had been designed to accommodate Aldershot & District's impressive fleet name.** Stewart J Brown

Centre left **Reading Transport favoured standee single-deckers long before they became popular (or unpopular) in other parts of the country. The last were Bristol REs with Pennine bodies of a design unique to Reading. New in 1968, their general appearance was intended to echo the original Burlingham-bodied Reliances of 1957. The winged emblem below the windscreen is a poor imitation of a device used with greater panache by Burlingham.** S J Butler

Left **In 1976 Reading switched from Bristol VRTs – of which it had 50 – to MCW Metropolitans. This one is seen outside Reading Station, in the company of a Chiltern Queens AEC Reliance. The arrow-like symbol above the driving compartment is a stylised form of the letters RT for Reading Transport.** David Brown

26 standee) Burlingham bodies, were still in service in 1975, as were later batches of Reliances bought up until 1965, and some broadly similar Bristol REs, delivered in 1967-68. These, too, were 34 seaters but with their extra length could squeeze in a maximum of 35 standing passengers. Bodywork was by a variety of builders – Duple (Northern) which was the successor to Burlingham, plus Neepsend and Strachans – and all were styled to have a passing resemblance to the original vehicles.

The legalisation of double-deck omo saw a switch in 1971 to long-wheelbase Bristol VRTs with angular two-door Northern Counties bodies. Fifty entered service between 1971 and 1976 when Reading switched allegiance to MCW, ordering Metro-Scanias. There were earlier generations of double-decker still in service including a handful of exposed-radiator AEC Regents, and a few East Lancs-bodied Dennis Lolines.

There were a few small operators in Alder Valley country. In Windsor, Imperial ran a town service using Bedfords which included an unusual SB5 with Strachans body, a combination more commonly associated with government departments. It had been bought new in 1965. In the Guildford area Safeguard provided local routes using Willowbrook-bodied Reliances, which were followed by Leyland Leopards and a Bedford YRQ with Duple Dominant bus bodies. The Tillingbourne Bus Company ran from Guildford to Peaslake using Plaxton and Willowbrook-bodied YRQs, which ousted unusual second-hand Bristol SUs. Tillingbourne – the name of a tributary of the River Wey – also ran ex-London RFs and two ex-Pennine Tiger Cubs with Duple Donnington bodies. Blue Saloon introduced a Guildford local service in 1973 using former London Transport RF-class AEC Regal IVs. These remained in use, but were joined in 1975 by a new Bristol LH with ECW body – an unusual vehicle for an independent operator – and by a Plaxton-bodied LH coach.

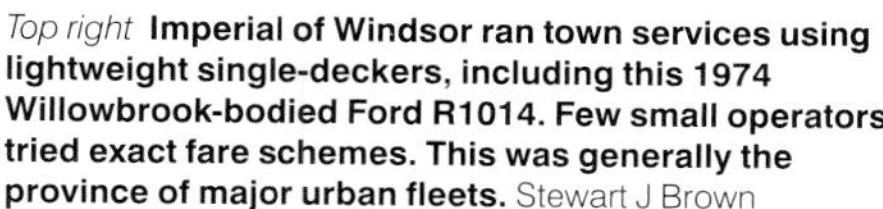

Top right **Imperial of Windsor ran town services using lightweight single-deckers, including this 1974 Willowbrook-bodied Ford R1014. Few small operators tried exact fare schemes. This was generally the province of major urban fleets.** Stewart J Brown

Centre right **Safeguard of Guildford ran mainly Leyland Leopards and Y-series Bedfords. This Bedford has Duple bodywork.** D J Little

Right **Blue Saloon operated Guildford local services using Bristol LHs and this ex-London Country AEC Regal IV, new in 1953 as part of London Transport's RF-class.** Stewart J Brown

Above **At the start of the 1970s City of Oxford was running a sizeable fleet of AEC Renowns. This one retains the company's final pre-NBC livery, albeit with NBC-style Oxford South Midland fleetname. It has Park Royal bodywork.** D J Little

Below **In the early part of the 1970s most of City of Oxford's double-deckers were Daimler Fleetlines. Northern Counties bodywork is fitted to this 1969 bus, one of the last deliveries to incorporate maroon in the livery.** Iain MacGregor

The area to the north of Alder Valley was served by City of Oxford Motor Services, an ex-BET company. It had in 1971 taken over the South Midland express coach operations previously under the control of Thames Valley. These included routes to London, and this part of the company's inheritance was acknowledged on its buses by the use of the South Midland name underneath the main Oxford fleetname. The bulk of the company's operations were in and around the university city and its Oxfordshire hinterland, in an area which stretched out to Aylesbury, Bicester and Faringdon.

City of Oxford had been a big user of AECs and these were still around in reasonable numbers, including 27 Renowns built in the mid 1960s, 18 Swifts with BET-style bodies by Marshall and Willowbrook, and 29 Reliances. The oldest Reliances, dating back to 1963-64, were the company's oldest buses. The cessation of double-deck production by AEC saw a switch to Daimler from 1968, and 60 Fleetlines were bought in the period up to 1972. Most had Northern Counties bodies, but there were 20 with lowheight Alexander bodies, unique in being of two-door layout, and there was also one single-decker, with Alexander W-type body. The Fleetlines were the last buses to be delivered in City of Oxford's distinctive maroon and duck egg green livery. Also in the fleet were a dozen Atlanteans acquired from South Wales Transport to extend one-man-operation. Some Oxford Regents went to SWT as part of the deal. From 1973 the VRT was the standard double-decker, and with it came NBC poppy red, albeit in local coach livery on the first examples. The use of NBC's half red, half white livery was rare on double-deckers.

Other 'deckers included a trio of early VRTs, dating from 1970, four ex-North Western Fleetlines and three 1967 Nottingham-style Northern Counties-bodied Atlanteans which had been transferred from Stratford Blue when that business was absorbed by Midland Red in 1971. There were also three ex-Midland Red Fleetlines with Alexander bodies. In fact City of Oxford seemed to have become something of a repository for unwanted Midland Red buses and in 1975 it received a few lightweight Fords and Bedfords which Midland Red had acquired from some of the small operators which it had taken over.

City of Oxford carefully avoided the Leyland National and when it received its first new single-deckers under NBC ownership in 1973 these were 25 Willowbrook-bodied Ford R1014s.

A service to Oxford was provided by another AEC operator, Charlton-on-Otmoor Services, generally using ex-South Wales Regent Vs or second-hand Reliance coaches. Also running AECs in City of Oxford territory was Chiltern Queens of Woodcote, with services in the Wallingford area and running south to Reading. Its fleet was made up primarily of Reliances – it had two dozen – which included three bought new in 1955 which had Duple (Midland) bus bodies. Its newest Reliance was a 1972 model with Plaxton bus body, while its newest bus was a 1974 Plaxton-bodied Leopard. Chiltern Queens also had second-hand Reliances, both buses and coaches. Worth's of Enstone ran bus-grant coaches on a service to Oxford, as did Heyfordian of Upper Heyford.

On the other side of City of Oxford's territory, Red Rover of Aylesbury ran services both locally in the town and out to Bicester and Buckingham. This was yet another AEC fleet which included two Bridgemasters and one

Renown bought new (the company's last new double-decker), a pair of Willowbrook-bodied Swifts, and assorted Reliances, most of which had Plaxton bus or coach bodies and had also been bought new.

To the south of London and LCBS the main operator was Southdown Motor Services, a company with a long and honourable history. It had come into the NBC fold by way of BET and this was reflected in a fleet which still included a large number of Leyland Titans and Leopards. Southdown ran over 800 buses, including those in the former Tilling-owned Brighton Hove & District operation, which had been put under Southdown control in 1969. Southdown's routes stretched along the south coast with depots from Portsmouth in the west to Eastbourne in the east and inland in towns such as Haywards Heath, Lewes and Petersfield. Services in Portsmouth were co-ordinated with those of Portsmouth City Transport, while those in Brighton were part of the Brighton Area Transport Services operated jointly with Brighton Borough Transport and BH&D. Indeed prior to the formation of NBC the buses of BH&D and Brighton Corporation shared a common red and cream livery.

Under NBC control the BH&D livery was abandoned and Southdown's green and cream was used, with Southdown-BH&D fleetnames. But with the advent of NBC corporate green even that distinction vanished and by 1975 most of the fleet was in corporate colours although a few vehicles survived in traditional Southdown green.

The oldest vehicles in regular service were the company's distinctive PD3s with fully-fronted Northern Counties bodies. Southdown bought 285 PD3s and around half of them were still running in 1975. The forward-entrance body was an adaptation of Northern Counties' standard structure, lengthened to fit the PD3 by the insertion of a short bay in mid-wheelbase (an idea also used by Park Royal for the 30ft long RML-type Routemasters) and with the full-width front to add a touch of modernity. Southdown stuck with its reliable and simple Titans, eschewing the more complex Atlantean. Indeed after taking delivery of its last PD3s in 1967 it switched to single-deckers – Marshall-bodied Bristol REs in 1968 and 1969 – before taking its first rear-engined double-deckers in 1970. These were not Atlanteans, as might have

Top left **The first Bristol VRTs for City of Oxford arrived in 1970 and had ECW bodies and a simplified version of the company's livery. There were three; subsequent VRTs were delivered in corporate NBC colours.** Iain MacGregor

Top right **Before taking advantage of new bus grant to buy new vehicles, Worth's of Enstone ran second-hand double-deckers. These included a 1958 Park Royal-bodied Regent V which had been new to City of Oxford, seen at Oxford bus station.** Iain MacGregor

Below **Red Rover was one of the few independent operators to buy a new AEC Renown. Delivered in 1964, like most Renowns it had Park Royal bodywork. It is seen in Aylesbury.** Iain MacGregor

been expected, but Fleetlines with Northern Counties bodies. ECW-bodied Fleetlines followed in 1972 and were the last buses to be delivered in the company's old livery. A few still wore it in 1975. Also delivered before NBC leaf green was forced on the company were its first Bristol VRTs. These had ECW bodies. There were 41, including 15 two-door vehicles for Brighton area local services.

More VRTs followed, but Southdown was among the few NBC subsidiaries which was able to take delivery of other types of double-deckers – Bristol and ECW couldn't satisfy all of NBC's new vehicle needs – and 47 Park Royal and Roe-bodied Atlanteans were taken into stock in 1974-75. More followed, along with the VRTs, later in the decade.

There were Lodekkas in the Southdown fleet too, a result of its takeover of BH&D. Most were rear-entrance FS-series models, but the newest were forward-entrance FLFs, delivered in 1966-67. Also part of the BH&D business were 25 Fleetlines with two-door Northern Counties bodies, the first of which entered service in red and cream, although they were delivered after Southdown had taken control of BH&D. The only other ex-BH&D buses running in 1975 were 13 ECW-bodied REs, which had in 1969 been the fleet's first omo vehicles.

Southdown's most common single-decker at the start of the 1970s was the 11m-long Leyland Leopard with BET-style bus bodywork by three different builders, Marshall, Weymann and Willowbrook. The final batch of Leopards for the stage service fleet were 30 delivered in 1969 which had unusual Northern Counties bodywork with 49 dual-purpose seats. These could double as coaches and were generally used on longer distance services; they received local coach livery when repainted in NBC corporate style. From 1973 all new single-deck buses were Leyland Nationals. There were 26 in operation by 1975, with more to follow.

Top left **NBC's corporate livery style did nothing for the appearance of Southdown's full-fronted Northern Counties-bodied Leyland Titan PD3s. This one was new in 1965 and is seen in 1977 with the improved double-N logo in red and blue on a white background, which had been adopted in 1976 in place of the original plain white logo.** David Brown

Centre left **Brighton Hove & District was put under the control of Southdown in 1969. As a former THC subsidiary most of its buses were Bristols. Ten were RESL6Gs with 37-seat two door ECW bodies, new in 1968.** D J Little

Left **A few ex BH&D buses were painted in traditional Southdown colours, as illustrated by this smart Bristol Lodekka FS6B. New in 1960, it was a convertible open-topper.** David Brown

The 64-vehicle Brighton Borough Transport fleet had also abandoned the red and cream which it had shared with BH&D. By the mid 1970s all of its buses were blue and white. Just over half the buses in Brighton Borough service were Leyland Titans with forward-entrance bodywork by Weymann and Metro-Cammell. The only single-deckers were seven Leyland Panther Cubs which were to have short lives. They had been new in 1968, and were withdrawn in 1976, giving much older – but more reliable – Titans a further lease of life. From 1973 Brighton had standardised on Atlanteans and by 1975 there were 20 in the fleet with bodywork divided equally between East Lancs and Willowbrook. More from both builders would follow in the second half of the decade. With the demise of the Panther Cubs the fleet was 100 per cent double-decked. It was also 100 per cent Leyland.

In Eastbourne there were three basic generations of municipal bus – rear-entrance double-deckers, followed by rear-engined single-deckers and finally rear-engined double-deckers. The older generation comprised just under 30 AEC Regent Vs and Leyland Titan PD2As with East Lancs bodies. The last of these – Titans – had been delivered in 1967 and had been the last buses in the undertaking's dark blue livery, which disappeared in 1974. From 1967 to 1971 Eastbourne had bought two-door single-deckers, designed for one-man-operation. There were three Roadliners and 13 Panthers, all bodied by East Lancs, plus a former demonstration Panther Cub with Strachans body. The Panthers had respectably long lives with Eastbourne. An unusual single-decker was a solitary Seddon Pennine midibus. Double-deckers had made a return in 1972 and by 1975 there were 15 East Lancs-bodied Atlanteans in operation. All post-1967 deliveries had worn a predominantly cream livery from new. Eastbourne laid claim to having been the country's first municipal bus operator, in 1903.

To the east of Southdown there were two major NBC operators covering Kent. Both were ex-BET companies. The larger of the two, with almost 700 vehicles, was Maidstone & District.

Above **The Southdown bus station at Haywards Heath in 1978 with two ex BH&D Bristol REs and a 1968 Willowbrook-bodied Leyland Leopard. Southdown was a major user of Leopard buses and coaches. In the mid-1970s it was running almost 250.** A Moyes

Below left **Brighton Corporation's red livery – similar to that used by BH&D – on a 1959 Weymann-bodied PD2 Titan. This four-bay variant on the MCW Orion design was relatively uncommon.** David Brown

Below right **From 1971 Brighton Corporation standardised on Atlanteans, first with Willowbrook bodies and later with bodywork by East Lancs. Ten East Lancs-bodied Atlanteans were delivered in 1975, one of which is seen here at Old Steine in 1977.** Stewart J Brown

Although based in Maidstone, its operations stretched down to the south coast, where it had depots at Hastings, Rye and Bexhill. It also served Tunbridge Wells, and its routes met up with those of London Country in places like Sevenoaks and Gravesend.

Maidstone & District had had a fairly adventurous buying policy in BET days, and this legacy lived on through the 1970s. It had in 1959 been among the first BET fleets to order Leyland's radical new Atlantean, showing great faith in the concept with an initial tranche of 50, including 14 lowbridge examples, some of which were still in use in 1975. Further batches totalling 107 were added and then M&D tried another new type, the Daimler Fleetline, taking 35 in 1963, with another 40 soon following. Many of the Atlanteans and all of the Fleetlines were to run until the late 1970s.

Another part of the BET legacy was a fleet of Leyland Panthers. Ninety had been purchased in the mid to late 1960s, with bodies by Willowbrook and – an odd choice for a BET company – Strachans. Some were withdrawn in the early 1970s, being transferred to Hants & Dorset, but most were still in operation in the middle of the decade. Not that the company's inheritance from BET was all avant-garde buses, far from it. The fleet also included AEC Reliances and Leyland Leopards with bodies by Marshall, Weymann and Willowbrook. A few Harrington-bodied Reliances survived too, although these would be withdrawn before the 1970s ended.

Under NBC control standard types – VRTs and Nationals – soon started to replace older vehicles. But there were some interesting non-standard types, including acquisitions from other NBC group companies. Indeed some of the first vehicles to be delivered after the formation of NBC were 30 Fleetline single-deckers, although most of these were soon dispersed to other companies. These were, of course, part of a BET rather than an NBC order. Five Bristol MWs from United Auto re-introduced that marque to the fleet in 1972. M&D had been a Bristol customer prior to Bristol's nationalisation and the last of an earlier generation of

Top left **Eastbourne's last half-cab buses were AEC Regents and Leyland Titans with East Lancs bodies. A 1961 Regent V loads at the pier for the town tour in 1974. The dayglo promotional lettering on the waistband seems just a shade out of character in genteel Eastbourne.** Malcolm Keeley

Centre left **Most of Eastbourne's omo single-deckers were Leyland Panthers, but there were three Roadliners. They had East Lancs bodies.** Stewart J Brown

Left **Maidstone & District had been an early convert to rear-engined double-deckers and its last new half-cabs were AEC Regents in 1956. Its first 50 Atlanteans were delivered in 1959 and included this Metro-Cammell-bodied bus seen in Maidstone in 1974. Like most early Atlanteans it was a maximum-capacity 78-seater.** Stewart J Brown

Bristols had been withdrawn not that many years before.

From Northern General came a dozen Fleetline double-deckers with Alexander bodies. New in 1969, they had joined M&D in 1972. At the same time 20 Metro-Cammell-bodied Atlanteans were received, diverted from a Midland Red order for 50; the other 30 had gone to London & Country. Further variety appeared in 1975 when M&D was selected as one of the companies to test new types of double-decker for NBC. Five Alexander-bodied Ailsas and five MCW Metropolitans were put into service in Hastings to run alongside full-height VRTs. They later moved to the Medway Towns. M&D's fleet included unusual open-top single-deckers which ran in Hastings. These were two AEC Regals and a Reliance.

In 1974 M&D took over the operations of Dengate of Rye, run by eight modern single-deck buses, mainly Willowbrook-bodied Leopards and Fords, which were added to the M&D fleet.

The other NBC subsidiary serving Kent was the East Kent Road Car Co, a company which in BET days had followed a fairly individualistic vehicle policy. It did, for example, buy large numbers of Guy Arab double-deckers – until 1957 – and then it switched to 30ft-long AEC Regent Vs with forward-entrance Park Royal bodies. The first had full-width fronts which were perhaps rather more attractive than the fully-fronted PD3s operated by neighbouring Southdown. The retention of the AEC grille gave them a less severe appearance. However later half-cab Regents – the last entered service in 1967 – were rather less attractive and many of these were to survive until the end of the 1970s.

East Kent's headquarters were in Canterbury, although rationalisation by NBC saw the company being managed from Maidstone for a period, under the aegis of Maidstone & District. It had depots in, among other places, Ashford, Ramsgate, Dover and Folkestone. One thing which set East Kent apart from other NBC companies was the fact that it did not use fleet numbers. In the period before registration numbers became a marketable

Top right **This 1958 AEC Reliance had a Harrington coach body which was later rebuilt for bus use by grafting on a completely new front end with power-operated doors and a destination display. Maidstone & District was a major customer for Harrington bodywork, produced in Hove.** Stewart J Brown

Centre right **An unusual body choice for a BET company was Strachans, which supplied 30 bodies on Leyland Panther chassis to Maidstone & District in 1968. The end result was not unattractive.** Stewart J Brown

Right **Maidstone & District operated a couple of veterans in Hastings. These were 1946 AEC Regals with Beadle bodies which had been converted to open top for use on local tours. In 1976 they retained traditional M&D colours and fleetnames, and the town tour cost 25p.** Malcolm Keeley

commodity, East Kent booked numbers for its new vehicles in a way which avoided any duplication. Its fleet totalled around 550 vehicles in the mid-1970s.

AECs figured prominently in the single-deck fleet, mainly Reliance coaches including batches with Park Royal bodies which helped confirm the perceived wisdom that bus body builders were not very good at designing coaches. East Kent's Park Royal-bodied Reliances looked distinctly bus-like. Perhaps in recognition of this, a batch of 20 dating from 1962 were rebodied by Plaxton in 1972-73. There were Reliance buses too, with Marshall bodies, and three batches of AEC Swifts, two bodied by Marshall and the third by Alexander. The K-registered Alexander-bodied Swifts were to be East Kent's last AEC buses – although a few more Reliance coaches were purchased – the last in 1975.

The double-deck fleet in the mid-1970s still contained over 100 Regent Vs plus one batch of 20 Park Royal-bodied Daimler Fleetlines delivered in 1969. These were the last double-deckers ordered under the auspices of BET and it was to be 1976 before the next batch of new 'deckers was delivered – 15 ECW-bodied Atlanteans. Here, as in many other parts of NBC, the Leyland National quickly made an impression – there were just over 70 in operation by the end of 1975. Parts of East Kent's territory are relatively sparsely populated – by the standards of the South East at any rate – and the company usually had in its fleet some lightweight buses for rural services. Eleven Plaxton-bodied Ford R1014s fulfilled this role from 1975-76, running alongside a small number of Bristol LHSs.

Kent had one municipal operator, Maidstone Borough Transport with a fleet of 46 double-deckers – although that was about to change. All were Leylands and all had bodies built in Wigan either by Massey or by Northern Counties. There were 28 Atlanteans delivered between 1965 and 1972. Twenty had Massey bodywork, not all that common on rear-engined double-deckers, which made Maidstone the biggest operator of Massey-bodied Atlanteans. The remaining 18 buses were rear-entrance Massey-bodied PD2s.

But in 1975 that started to change, as the fleet switched from Leyland double-deckers to Bedford single-deckers. Ten entered service in 1975, with bodies by Willowbrook and Duple. More would follow in 1976, along with the first of 14 Duple-bodied Leyland Leopards which were less than two years old and came from Nottingham City Transport. They operated in the lilac livery in which they arrived. These replaced all the PD2s, while further Duple-bodied Bedfords would see the withdrawal of the last Atlanteans when they were just six years old. In just five years the Maidstone fleet was to change beyond all recognition. Its livery would change too, reverting from the blue and cream adopted with the first Atlanteans in 1965, to the previous brown and cream. A dial-a-ride service

Above left **East Kent's standard double-decker from 1958 to 1967 was the 30ft-long AEC Regent V with Park Royal bodywork. The early examples had attractive full-fronted bodies, but from 1963 rather more utilitarian-looking half-cab bodywork was specified. This is a 1964 bus, showing how NBC poppy red could look bright and attractive when clean and well varnished.** David Brown

Above right **East Kent's first rear-engined double-deckers were 20 Park Royal-bodied Fleetlines, which entered service in 1969. They were the last 'deckers to be delivered in maroon and cream. By the time new double-deckers were next bought by East Kent – ECW-bodied Atlanteans in 1976 – poppy red would be the order of the day.** D A Lawrence

Left **For services from Kent into London East Kent operated 36ft-long AEC Reliances with 49-seat Park Royal coach bodies. The body was not dissimilar to the BET standard of the time, apart from the front end. A 1965 Reliance heads out of Victoria for Dover in the summer of 1970.** Iain MacGregor

Above left **Maidstone Corporation's last half-cabs were four Massey-bodied Leyland Titans, bought in 1963. They were relatively short-lived, being replaced by Bedford single-deckers when little more than 12 years old. This one is seen in 1973.** Stewart J Brown

Above right **Massey Bros of Wigan were taken over by Northern Counties in 1967, which meant that the company built relatively few bodies on rear-engined chassis. The biggest fleet of Massey-bodied Atlanteans was to be found running for Maidstone Corporation, which took 20 in the mid-1960s. This was the last, one of two G-registered buses which entered service in 1968.** Stewart J Brown

was operated by Streamline Taxis with two Ford Transits. The service and the buses were taken over by Maidstone Borough Transport in 1976.

So much for operators to the east of Southdown. To the west the City of Portsmouth Passenger Transport Department – to give it its full title – was not quite 100 per cent Leyland, but 157 out of 169 wasn't a bad score. And the odd 12 came from sister manufacturer AEC. Portsmouth's was a fleet in the modern idiom. The undertaking had embraced the Leyland Atlantean with some enthusiasm from as early as 1962 and had stuck with it, despite the trials and tribulations associated with early rear-engined buses. Between 1962 and 1966 it bought 54 PDR1s with Metro-Cammell bodies. There then followed a single-deck interlude, before a return to double-deckers in 1972. Between 1972 and 1975 no fewer than 65 Alexander-bodied AN68s joined the fleet, the high volume being boosted by the availability of new bus grant. The choice of Alexander bodywork by an operator on the south coast was unusual at this time. The only other double-deckers in the fleet were six Leyland Titan PD2 open-toppers for summer sea front services.

Portsmouth had switched to single-deckers in 1967 to start a programme of large scale omo conversions. Like Brighton, it opted initially for the Leyland Panther Cub, and its fleet of 26 delivered in 1967 with bodies by Marshall and Metro-Cammell survived intact in the middle of the 1970s. The Panther Cubs were followed in 1969 by 12 Marshall-bodied Swifts, but in 1971 Portsmouth gave up on horizontal rear-engined single-deckers and instead ordered 12 long-wheelbase Atlanteans which were fitted with 40-seat Pennine bodies. The only other operators to have Atlanteans bodied from new as single-deckers were Great Yarmouth and Birkenhead.

Below left **Portsmouth Corporation's Leyland Titans were phased out in the early part of the 1970s. A Metro-Cammell-bodied PD2/40, one of 15 delivered in 1957, passes the station.** Iain MacGregor

Below right **There were a number of single-deck types in the Portsmouth fleet, but the most unusual were 12 Leyland Atlanteans with Pennine bodies. New in 1971, they were 40-seaters. The main body structure was similar to that fitted to the Seddon RU, but with a much lower driving position and with a quite different rear end to accommodate the Atlantean's vertical engine.** D J Little

Just across the harbour at Portsmouth was one of NBC's smaller subsidiaries, the Gosport & Fareham Omnibus Co, which traded as Provincial. Provincial had a colourful history as an independent prior to its purchase by NBC in January 1970 and in fact had originally been a tramway operator way back in 1882. When NBC took over the fleet was a varied one, with some remarkable vehicles still in service including 1943 Guy Arabs with postwar full-front Reading bodies and Deutz air-cooled engines. The last of these Guy rebuilds had been completed as late as 1967 and carried an E-suffix registration. These, and various postwar Arabs, were fairly quickly withdrawn by NBC. In 1968-69 Provincial had gone modern, buying front-engined Seddon Pennine IVs with dual-door bodies by Strachans and Pennine. There were 15 in all, but these were withdrawn in the mid-1970s.

To replace this odd collection NBC transferred buses in from other fleets as a stop-gap measure, starting with Regent Vs from City of

Top left **After years of running rebuilt and rebodied Guys and AECs, Provincial changed direction in 1968 with the delivery of nine front-engined Seddon Pennine IVs with 40-seat two-door Strachans bodies. Another six Pennine IVs, but with Seddon's own bodywork, followed in 1969.** Iain MacGregor

Top right **After being bought by NBC older types were quickly weeded out of the Provincial fleet and replaced by younger buses transferred from other NBC subsidiaries. These included a number of Bristol LS6Gs, two of which were 1955 buses from Midland General.** Iain MacGregor

Centre left **The Park Royal bodies supplied to Southampton Corporation in the early 1960s were far from being one of the high points of that company's designs. They clearly owed something to the ungainly Bridgemaster. This is a 1961 PD2/27, photographed in 1973.** Stewart J Brown

Left **In sharp contrast to the square-rigged Park Royal bodies on Southampton's Titans, East Lancs supplied nicely-proportioned bodies on AEC Regent Vs in the mid-1960s. A 1965 bus heads towards the city centre on its way to the docks.** Stewart J Brown

Oxford. These were the company's last double-deckers. New buses soon started arriving, beginning with a dozen Bristol REs in 1971-72, with 21 Leyland Nationals following by 1975. More Nationals came later in the 1970s and the Provincial variety was soon replaced by NBC uniformity. By 1975 the fleet was made up entirely of two-door single-deckers – REs, Nationals and a few surviving Seddons which by this time were in NBC leaf green. They were the only Pennine IVs to wear NBC corporate colours.

East of Portsmouth, Southern Motorways of Emsworth operated services around Emsworth and Petersfield using seven Plaxton-bodied Ford R1114 coaches which were bought in 1975 and replaced the company's existing fleet apart from an ex-London Transport GS-class Guy and a Leyland Tiger Cub.

To the west, Southampton City Transport operated a 186-strong fleet which since 1968 had standardised on East Lancs-bodied Leyland Atlanteans. There were 101 in operation and they had introduced a brighter livery layout – although this was not applied retrospectively to older buses in the fleet. Earlier types were mainly AEC Regent Vs and Leyland Titan PD2As. The Titans and a few of the oldest Regents had Park Royal bodywork which was derived from the Bridgemaster design. It featured an upright front and was of distinctly unprepossessing appearance. The later Regents, in sharp contrast, had shapely bodywork by East Lancs or its associate Neepsend company. The newest were 10 F-registered buses.

Single-deckers played a very small part in Southampton's operations. There were 10 late 1960s AEC Swifts, six of which had Strachans bodies bearing a strong resemblance to those built for London Transport. The other four were bodied by East Lancs. The only other single-deckers were five Seddon Pennine RUs, new in 1972.

Across the Solent, the Isle of Wight was the preserve of Southern Vectis. Ever wondered why there was no Northern (or Eastern or Western) Vectis? The company had quite simply been called Vectis – the Roman name for the island – until Southern was added to the title following the acquisition of a significant share in the company in 1929 by the Southern Railway.

The standard Southampton bus in the 1970s was the Leyland Atlantean with East Lancs bodywork. There were 101 in the fleet in 1975 and over 160 by the end of the decade. John Jones

Southern Vectis services covered the island, using a fleet of 189 buses and coaches. Before the formation of NBC, Southern Vectis had been part of the THC organisation, and this was reflected in its predominantly Bristol fleet. The double-deckers ranged from 1955 LD-series Lodekkas through to new VRTs. There were also three secondhand VRTs, acquired in 1973 from Central SMT and Scottish Omnibuses in exchange for FLF Lodekkas. A veteran Bristol K open-topper provided a summer season service for visitors. Who in 1975 would have forecast that this bus, then 36 years old, would still be going strong 20 years later? There were half-a-dozen open-top Lodekkas too.

The single-deck bus fleet was just as standardised – there were Bristol MWs, REs and LHs. The last-named included eight short LHSs, four of which had Marshall bodies. The first of the inevitable Leyland Nationals – 10 in number – had arrived on the island in 1973. In fact the real interest in the Southern Vectis fleet lay not in its buses, but in its coaches. Because most of its tours were on the island, mileages were fairly low. The Isle of Wight was not famed for its motorway network, so there was no need for relatively high-powered Leopards or REs in the coach fleet. Consequently Southern Vectis ran Bedford SBs and VALs (it had 14 of the latter, the biggest number in an NBC fleet), as well as the more mundane Y-series. It did in fact have two RE coaches too, one of which was an unusual 10m RESH model with 41-seat Duple Northern bodywork.

There was one independent operator running a local bus service on the Isle of Wight, Seaview Services, linking Seaview with Ryde. At one stage this route had been run by double-deckers, but in the mid 1970s it was normally run by a 1964 Bedford VAL with 54-seat Willowbrook bus body, or by a YRQ with Plaxton bus body.

Right **In 1973 Southern Vectis received three Bristol VRTs from Scottish Bus Group companies, bringing to 24 the number of VRTs on the Isle of Wight. They took the fleet numbers previously occupied by the company's three newest Lodekkas, which went north to Scotland.** Tony Wilson

Far right **Between 1954 and 1959 Southern Vectis added 65 LD-series Lodekkas to its fleet. Withdrawal of the type started in 1970, but most were still in stock in the middle of the decade. This is a 1959 bus.** Tony Wilson

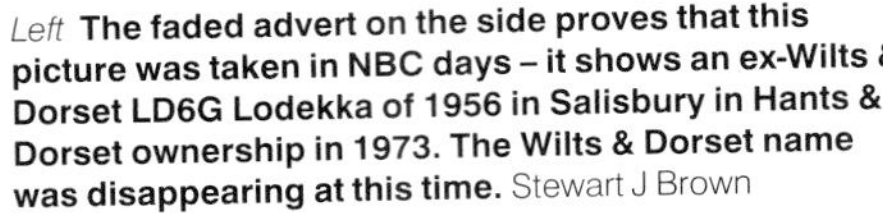

Left **The faded advert on the side proves that this picture was taken in NBC days – it shows an ex-Wilts & Dorset LD6G Lodekka of 1956 in Salisbury in Hants & Dorset ownership in 1973. The Wilts & Dorset name was disappearing at this time.** Stewart J Brown

Centre left **Hants & Dorset's fleet in the early 1970s included some quite elderly buses. This ECW-bodied Bristol KSW6G was 21 years old when photographed in Southampton in the summer of 1973. There's a certain irony in such an ancient bus carrying corporate NBC advertising. The LRU registration sequence embraced Hants & Dorset's last Ks and first Lodekkas.** Stewart J Brown

Bottom left **Early production Lodekkas had a full-depth polished surround to the grille, shaped in the style of the traditional Bristol radiator. This is a 1955 LD6G, whose ECW body is fitted with platform doors. It is in Hants & Dorset's pre-NBC Tilling green livery, which was replaced by poppy red.** Mike Greenwood

In the Southampton area out of town services were operated by Hants & Dorset. This NBC subsidiary had its head office in Bournemouth, but its routes covered a large part of central southern England, from Winchester, Basingstoke and Salisbury, down to Southampton and across to Poole. Its fleet incorporated Wilts & Dorset – before 1972 a separate company which, like Hants & Dorset, had been part of the Tilling empire.

In pre-NBC days Wilts & Dorset buses had been red while those of Hants & Dorset were green. When the two companies were united they adopted the Hants & Dorset name and the Wilts & Dorset colour – by this time NBC poppy red. By 1975 red ruled and all traces of green had virtually disappeared. The fleet was made up primarily of Bristols, as might be expected from a company with a THC background. The double-deckers were Lodekkas, including some rare Leyland-engined FLF6Ls, built in 1967 after the share exchange between Leyland and Bristol. There were also unusual 30ft-long rear-entrance FL models dating from 1961-62; most 30ft Lodekkas of this era were forward-entrance FLFs. Double-deckers added under NBC auspices included standard Bristol VRTs, but of more interest were six Roe-bodied Daimler Fleetlines which had been ordered by Provincial. They entered service in 1971 and were in fact the company's first rear-engined double-deckers.

The single-deck fleet included a few Bristol MWs, along with REs and a large fleet of LHs – no fewer than 127 in 1975. The oldest, built in 1969, were unusual in having 39-seat dual-door ECW bodywork – a specification unique to the Hants & Dorset and Wilts & Dorset companies. The LHs were not the only lightweights – there were 25 Ford R1014s with 45-seat ECW bodies which were delivered in 1974; Plaxton-bodied Fords were to follow in 1976.

Right **Unusual vehicles to find in a THC fleet were the half-dozen 1968 Bedford VAM70s with 40-seat two-door Willowbrook bodies which were operated by Hants & Dorset. This example is seen in the company's new poppy red livery in the summer of 1973. The Bedfords were withdrawn in the middle of the decade.** Stewart J Brown

Below right **An ex-King Alfred Leyland, still operating in Winchester but now in Hants & Dorset ownership. New in 1967 it was one of four Roe-bodied Atlanteans which passed from King Alfred to Hants & Dorset in 1973. They had been the most modern 'deckers in the King Alfred fleet.** Mike Greenwood

1975: Major bus fleets – South East England

Operator	*Fleet size*
London Transport	6,342
London Country	1,233
Hants & Dorset	825
Maidstone & District	688
Southdown	662
Alder Valley	614
East Kent	555
City of Oxford	268
Southern Vectis	189
Southampton	186
Portsmouth	169
Brighton Hove & District	157
Reading	136
Brighton	64
Eastbourne	59
Provincial	48
Maidstone	46

An earlier generation of Bedford VAMs with two-door Willowbrook bodies lasted into the early 1970s but had gone by 1975. It goes without saying that from 1973 any requirement for full-size single-deck buses was met by the Leyland National, but single-deck variety was provided by 17 Willowbrook-bodied Leyland Panthers which were transferred from Maidstone & District in 1971-72 when they were around six years old. The coach fleet included Duple-bodied Bedford VALs, not a common type in NBC service.

The company had in April 1973 reluctantly taken over the business of King Alfred of Winchester, strengthening its position in and around the town. This move reportedly followed discreet pressure from the traffic commissioner, concerned that the independent was struggling to keep going and came at a time when Hants & Dorset itself was not in the strongest of financial positions. King Alfred ran 38 vehicles, some of which were quickly disposed of, including three Metro-Scanias which went to London Country in exchange for three Leyland Nationals. But a number of non-standard types remained, including Roe-bodied Atlanteans, Plaxton-bodied Panther buses and Park Royal-bodied AEC Renowns, all repainted in poppy red.

A new operator of rural services in the 1970s was the Post Office. Beginning at Canterbury in 1972, by 1976 it was running 16 routes in the South East. All were one-bus operations, using Commer or Dodge PB2000 minibuses. They could be found in a diverse range of places including Newbury, Henley, Tunbridge Wells and the Isle of Wight.

South West England

THE Bristol Omnibus Co was one of NBC's biggest subsidiaries. It ran just under 1,200 vehicles and ranked as number three, after Midland Red and London Country, both of which had fleets just a bit over the 1,200 mark. It was however rather less interesting than its two bigger counterparts – which largely reflected its straightforward THC/NBC heritage and, of course, its strong affinity to the products of Bristol Commercial Vehicles which in the mid-1970s was turning out chassis at the rate of 13 a week – mostly for NBC subsidiaries.

The highly standardised fleet contained only three types of double-decker in regular service – all Bristols, naturally enough. In the majority were Lodekkas, around 250 of them and all forward-entrance FLF models, many powered by Bristol engines including some of the newest, E-registered buses. There were also a few earlier LD models and the last surviving KSWs, which ran until 1976. Open-top LDs were retained for use on summer sea-front services in Weston-super-Mare and a Bristol city tour. And there was a venerable K5G open-topper, built in 1941 which had rejoined the fleet in 1969, coming from Thomas of Port Talbot.

The more modern double-deckers were VRTs, and the vast majority were of dual-door layout for use on one-man-operated services in and around Bristol. The early deliveries had ECW's original style of flat-fronted body, while later vehicles featured the double curvature BET screen. The first batch of VRTs, delivered in 1972, carried an attractive bright livery with cream for the main body side panels and green relief restricted to window surrounds, skirt and roof – but the might of the NBC corporate identity machine had soon put paid to that and by the middle of the decade leaf green with a narrow white relief band was the order of the day.

The Bristol city service network was in fact operated jointly with Bristol City Council, an arrangement which dated back to 1937. In recognition of this the buses which operated on city routes carried the council crest and retained the Bristol scroll fleetname, rather than NBC's block lettering. This arrangement continued until 1978 when NBC bought out the city's minority interest – and the scroll and the crest soon disappeared.

There was just a bit more variety in the single-deck fleet, including the first examples of one of the models which was to play a part in bringing to an end bus-building in the city: the Leyland National. Most of the company's single-deckers were Bristol REs. There were almost 400 in the fleet, all but 14 Leyland-engined, and all bodied by ECW although to a variety of specifications. Many were of two-door layout, which typically meant the loss of six seats – 44 instead of 50 – but was seen as an integral part of a smoothly-run omo service. However the newest urban single-deckers were the shape of things to

Facing page **The introduction of urban one-man-operation saw Bristol Omnibus break away from the rather dull uniformity of THC's single-deck livery, adopting the layout shown on this 1965 Bristol MW6G. The standard THC layout limited the cream relief to the waistband.** Stewart J Brown

Above **Bristol's buses latterly carried an attractive scroll fleetname, as shown on a 1966 FLF Lodekka in Swindon in the autumn of 1973.** Stewart J Brown

Below **The Bristol RE had been the standard Bristol Omnibus single-decker until the appearance of the Leyland National. The REs had ECW bodies of different styles – bus, coach and as on this 1970 RELH6L, dual-purpose. The polished wheel trims were a nice touch – but whether it was the ideal coach for a trip to London, the location of this view, is open to question.** Stewart J Brown

come. From 1972 Leyland Nationals had been arriving – in smaller numbers than the REs being delivered at the same time, it's true; but the last REs arrived in 1974 and the Nationals would keep on coming. At this stage most were of two-door layout and many were on Bristol city services.

The oldest single-deckers in use were a few mid-1950s Bristol LSs which had been rebuilt and modernised in the 1960s, and there were also around 150 of the later MW model. There were LHs too, but of more interest were two survivors of an earlier generation of light Bristol, the Albion-engined SU. All of these earlier generation single-deckers had ECW bus bodies and were generally used on country routes. The SUs were used in the Stroud area, where steep hills and narrow roads made life difficult for drivers of full-size buses.

At this time Bristol Omnibus covered quite a lot of country. Outside Bristol, where the city services took up almost one-third of the fleet, the company's territory extended south to Bridgwater, east to Swindon, and north to Cheltenham. In Cheltenham, where services were run by the associated 36-vehicle Cheltenham District Traction business, the livery was poppy red – although that changed in 1975 to leaf green as used for the remainder of the fleet. Cheltenham's buses carried the town's coat of arms – even though unlike the situation in Bristol there was no municipal involvement. This practice was continued when the fleet acquired its first, poppy red, NBC repaint, but the crests were quietly dropped on the second, green, NBC repaint. Buses running in Cheltenham included most of the types to be seen elsewhere – Lodekkas, REs, Nationals and, from 1975, VRTs. Before the advent of NBC's corporate colours the Cheltenham District Traction fleet had been dark red and cream. In nearby Gloucester, city buses carried Gloucester fleetnames and crests, although this practice too was eventually to cease.

Top left **When NBC adopted its corporate identity in 1972 the Cheltenham District fleet was initially painted in poppy red, as demonstrated by this 1955 Bristol KSW. From 1975 Cheltenham's buses switched to leaf green.** Paul Caudell

Centre left **The majority of the VRTs in the Bristol Omnibus fleet had dual-door ECW bodies. When VRT production came to an end, Bristol Omnibus would be running over 150 two-door VRTs. This one carries recruitment advertising, a reminder that staff shortages were fairly common in the bus industry for much of the 1970s.** Stewart J Brown

Left **Swindon's last rear-entrance 'deckers were five Leyland Titans with 65-seat Weymann bodies, purchased in 1962. The only other Leylands in the predominantly Daimler fleet being operated by Thamesdown Transport in the mid-1970s were three 1967 Leopards.** Stewart J Brown

Non-standard types in Bristol service were limited to two small buses. A Ford Transit was added to the Bath fleet in 1970 for use on a central area tourist route running between the Assembly Rooms and the Pump Room. With 16 seats it was the company's smallest bus. Only one seat bigger was a Leyland 440EA with Ascough bodywork. This operated on a city centre service in Gloucester, with a flat fare of 3p.

There was one municipal bus operation in Bristol Omnibus territory: Thamesdown Transport. The name was a new one for what had been Swindon Corporation Transport and the change was one of the results of local government reorganisation in April 1974. The Swindon fleet was made up largely of Daimler double-deckers. The oldest were CVG6s with bodywork by Park Royal, Weymann and Roe, which dated from the 1957-61 period. The newest were Fleetlines with bodies by Northern Counties and Metro-Cammell. Thamesdown would stick with the Gardner-engined Fleetline for the rest of the decade, but from 1976 all deliveries had ECW bodywork. The Fleetline/ECW combination was relatively unusual outside the Scottish Bus Group. Between the CVG6s and the Fleetlines there was a batch of three 30ft-long CVG6/30s which entered service in 1967 and had the distinction of being the town's last half-cab double-deckers and the only ones with forward entrances.

Running alongside the Daimlers were five 1962 Leyland Titans with Weymann bodies and 13 single-deckers – five Reliances, three Leopards (with unusual Pennine bodies) and five new ECW-bodied Bristol REs. Single-deckers had long featured in the Swindon fleet because of the extensive railway workshops in the town and the number of low overbridges which these inflicted on roads to the north of the town centre.

Small operators in Bristol Omnibus territory in Gloucestershire ran services to the county's two principal towns – Gloucester and Cheltenham. Running double-deckers into Gloucester from the Forest of Dean was Cottrell's of Mitcheldean. These were a Northern Counties-bodied Fleetline, bought new in 1972 to replace a Regent V, and a Roe-bodied Atlantean which had been supplied in 1972 to Halls of Hounslow for operation on TWA contracts at Heathrow Airport. Cottrell's had been operating to Gloucester since the late 1920s. In contrast, the company named after the partnership of Mr Brook and Mr Swan – Swanbrook – had only moved into regular bus operation in the summer of 1974 with the takeover of a service from Gloucester to Tewkesbury which had previously been

Above left **The first Fleetlines for Swindon were five with lowheight Northern Counties bodies in 1968. From that point the Fleetline became the standard chassis for both Swindon Corporation and Thamesdown Transport, but with bodywork by Metro-Cammell and ECW on most later deliveries.** Stewart J Brown

Above right **Cottrell's of Mitcheldean bought small numbers of new double-deckers for a service to Gloucester. A 1972 Daimler Fleetline was joined by a Leyland-built bus later in the decade. Both had Northern Counties bodies. This is the newer of the two, a 33ft-long model, which entered service in 1979.** D J Little

Right **Castleways was one of Britain's smartest bus fleets, as this gleaming Daimler Fleetline in Cheltenham in 1977 shows. It has a Northern Counties body and was new to Nottingham City Transport in 1964.** John Jones

Above **Hutchings & Cornelius was the first independent to buy a Bristol VRT. New in 1973 it had a standard NBC-style lowheight body by ECW. The only other independents to buy new VRTs were Mayne of Manchester and Stevensons of Uttoxeter.** D J Little

Below **The VRT for Hutchings spelt the end for this East Lancs-bodied Dennis Loline, bought new by H&C in 1958 and seen here in March 1973.** John Jones

operated by Cathedral Coaches. For this the company bought a new Bedford YRT with Willowbrook Expressway, body. By the end of the decade Swanbrook would also be running south of Gloucester to Arlingham, taking that service over from Ladvale of Dursley and running Bedford coaches on it.

From the spa town of Cheltenham, Pulham's of Bourton-on-the-Water ran to Moreton-in-the-Marsh. Services were covered by modern Leyland Leopards and Bedford YRQs with Plaxton coach bodies. Castleways of Broadway had in 1971 taken over the service to Cheltenham operated by Gilletts of Winchcombe, to which town the Castleways business was moved. The route was run jointly with Bristol Omnibus until 1976. Plaxton-bodied Leopards coaches were used. Kearsey's Coaches of Cheltenham also operated on the Winchcombe service until 1976 and had a route to Alderton too. These were covered by AEC Reliance coaches with Plaxton bodies. Kearsey's had since 1968 been a subsidiary of Marchant's Coaches.

To the south-west of Bristol Omnibus was another of NBC's big subsidiaries. Western National, based in Exeter, had since 1971 controlled the former BET Devon General business and this gave it a fleet nudging the 1,100 mark. Its territory was huge, stretching from a line drawn roughly through Bridgwater, Yeovil and Weymouth, right down to the tip of England at Land's End. Yeovil and Land's End are not far short of 150 miles apart.

Yeovil was of note as being served by an independent whose newest buses had a strong NBC flavour about them. Hutchings & Cornelius of South Petherton operated to Taunton and to Yeovil, and between Yeovil and Crewkerne. For this it had an interesting bus fleet which included a 1973 ECW-bodied VRT, at that time the only VRT to have been bought new by an independent operator. It had two ECW-bodied LHs too, one of which had in 1972 been the first to be supplied to an independent. Older single-deckers were AEC Reliances with Willowbrook bodies, most of which were not that old at all, having been bought in 1969.

Another significant Somerset independent was Safeway of South Petherton, also running to Yeovil. Safeway's front-line buses were two 1973 Leopards with Willowbrook bodies. Its oldest bus was a 1956 Burlingham-bodied Reliance which had been purchased from Safeguard of Guildford in 1962. A Yeovil to Shepton Mallet service was run by Wakes of Sparkford using Bedford YRTs with Willowbrook bus bodies.

Although now part of Western National, Devon General retained its own identity. Its buses were red, where Western National's were green. And, of course, much of its fleet bore witness to the company's BET heritage compared with Western National's Tilling group history. Devon General's operations were concentrated in south Devon – the company's head office had been in Torquay. The company's position in Exeter had been strengthened in April 1970 when Exeter Corporation decided to sell its 65-strong bus operation to NBC. Initially Exeter's green and cream livery continued unchanged, but after 12 months a start was made in repainting Exeter's buses in Devon

Not all rural routes used lightweight buses. Many of the company's older single-deckers, standard THC MWs and even a few surviving LSs, were used on country services. The newest of the MWs were built in 1966. There were even some second-hand examples, transferred in 1973-74 from Bristol Omnibus and Mansfield District, although with ECW's standardised body production only the registration marks gave a clue to these vehicles' origins. Modern single-deckers in the Western National fleet followed the typical THC/NBC pattern – Bristol REs succeeded by Leyland Nationals.

There was variety in the double-deck fleet too. The old order was marked by Lodekkas, 60-seat FSFs and longer 70-seat FLFs with a mixture of Bristol and Gardner engines. The new order was, of course, the Bristol VRT, of which there were but 30-odd. The real interest lay in double-deckers acquired from elsewhere in NBC to allow the quick extension of omo and the replacement of high-cost crew-operated Lodekkas.

Thus in 1975 Western National was adding 15-year-old PDR1 Atlanteans to its fleet as part of a cost-reduction programme. These had BET-style square bodywork by Metro-Cammell, Roe

Top **Western National was the biggest user of the Bristol SU. In 1960 16 of the short SUS4A model joined the Western and Southern National fleets. Most were sold after 12 years use but this one, after a period with Greenslades Tours, was in service with Western National until 1979. It is seen in Falmouth shortly before withdrawal.** D J Little

Centre right **Devon's narrow lanes helped the survival of some odd vehicles, such as this 7ft 6in-wide AEC Reliance with bodywork by Willowbrook. New in 1959 to Devon General it joined the Western National fleet in 1970 after a short spell in the Greenslades fleet. It survived until 1980.** Royston Morgan

Right **Western National's last LD-series Bristol Lodekkas were 17 delivered in 1959 which ran until 1976, the year this one was photographed in Paignton. From 1960 most of Western National's Lodekkas would be FLFs.** Malcolm Keeley

and Weymann and came from Maidstone & District and Trent. A touch of modernity was added by five lowheight PDR1/3 models which had been new in 1971 to Western Welsh and had moved south the following year. They had Alexander bodywork.

Western National's operations surrounded Britain's most southerly municipal bus fleet in Plymouth. This was a highly standardised fleet. It had two types of bus: Leyland Atlanteans and Leyland Nationals – and a solitary PD2 open-topper. Plymouth had been among the first municipal fleets to embrace the perceived benefits of the integral National and it bought 60 between 1972 and 1974, in doing so replacing well over one quarter of its fleet. The Atlanteans ranged from 1962 PDR1s to 1971 long-wheelbase PDR2s, with the first of the updated AN68 models just entering service in 1975. The AN68 would be the fleet standard for the rest of the decade. Bodywork on pre-1967 buses was by Metro-Cammell. All of the later Atlanteans had Park Royal bodywork. Plymouth's operations, like those of virtually every other municipal fleet in the country, were confined largely to the city area.

Top **The rugged Bristol LS with ECW body was a standard Tilling group single-deck bus in the mid-1950s, and some gave 20 years service. Western National used LS5Gs for bus work, but specified the more powerful LS6G for its coach fleet. This 1954 bus was one of the last LS types in Western National service when it was withdrawn in 1977.** Tony Wilson

Centre left **The early 1970s saw some unusual vehicle movements within NBC, partly to extend one-man-operation in those areas where it was most urgently needed to cut costs, or where it could be most easily introduced. In the spring of 1972 Western National received five Leyland Atlantean PDR1/3s with lowheight Alexander bodies, which had been new to Western Welsh less than 12 months previously.** Geoff Rixon

Left **Most of Plymouth City Transport's buses were Atlanteans. This is a long-wheelbase PDR2 with 77-seat Park Royal body. It was new in 1970. A similar 1968 bus follows.** Royston Morgan

Right **Plymouth became the biggest municipal user of Leyland Nationals, with a fleet of 60 entering service between 1972 and 1974. All were two-door 46-seat 11.3m versions. In 1975 Plymouth went back to buying Atlanteans.** Royston Morgan

Centre right **Unusual buses operated by Bournemouth were two petrol-engined Bedford VAS3s with 27-seat Strachans bodies of the short-lived SC design which had been developed primarily for export. They were new in 1973.** Stewart J Brown collection

Bottom **In the early 1960s Weymann built a copy of Alexander's successful Glasgow-style double-deck body. Two, on 1964 Atlantean chassis, are seen in the Bournemouth Transport fleet, flanking a Daimler Fleetline with bodywork by MH Cars of Belfast.** Mike Greenwood

The other municipal operator in the South West was Bournemouth Transport. The residents of genteel Bournemouth were generally transported in rear-engined double-deckers, both Atlanteans and Fleetlines. The oldest Fleetlines were two 1964 buses, unique in Britain in having bodywork by MH Cars of Belfast, whose only other double-deck customer was Belfast Corporation. The oldest Atlanteans had Weymann bodies. From 1969 all new double-deckers had Alexander bodywork and by 1975 there were 58 Atlanteans and 20 CRL6 Fleetlines with Scottish-built bodywork. The undertaking's general manager was a Scot, which may or may not have been an influencing factor. Front-engined 'deckers – Leyland Titans – were phased out in the early 1970s.

The small single-deck fleet included a few oddities. There were 11 Daimler Roadliners with Willowbrook bodies, four Ford Transit minibuses, and two Bedford VAS3s with Strachans SC bodies, bought in 1973 for a town centre service. The use of petrol-engined VAS3s (rather than diesel-engined VAS5s) as buses or coaches was indeed rare and was done to minimise the disturbance to the town's gentility

Left **New in 1965 to MacBrayne, this Bedford VAS1 with Duple (Midland) bodywork had reached the other end of the country by the late 1970s, running for Tally Ho! of Kingsbridge in Devon.** D J Little

Below **Willowbrook-bodied Bedfords featured increasingly in the Grenville Motors fleet as the 1970s wore on. This 1969 VAM70 was a second-hand acquisition in the latter part of the decade.** D J Little

by noisy clattering diesels. Bournemouth was going through a subtle livery change. The base primrose colour was being retained, but with a flash of blue relief in place of maroon bands. Out-of-town services were run by NBC's Hants & Dorset company.

In rural Dorset Bere Regis & District Motor Services, based in Dorchester, operated a substantial fleet of coaches covering local services and school contracts. Many of the services were infrequent, often running only on market days. The company had 80 vehicles, the majority of which were Bedford SBs with bodywork by Duple and Plaxton. There were Fords too, and a few Bedford YRQs, Leyland Leopards

Top right **Marshall-bodied Bristol LHSs were relatively rare, although there were a few in the West Country. Western National had a dozen, and Harvey of Mousehole had this one.** Royston Morgan

Below right **In 1975 Deeble of Upton Cross was using this smart lowbridge Leyland Atlantean on service. It had been new to Silver Star, the Wiltshire independent which had been taken over by Wilts & Dorset in 1963.** Malcolm Keeley

and AEC Reliances. A Shaftesbury to Bruton service was operated by Brutonian using second-hand Reliances.

Devon hosted the only operator in this book with an exclamation mark in the fleetname – Tally Ho! of Kingsbridge. In 1971 Tally Ho! had taken over a number of Kingsbridge area routes which Western National had found unprofitable and its fleet included a rare Strachans-bodied Bedford SB5, running alongside the more common Plaxton- and Duple-bodied Fords and Bedford coaches which formed the bulk of the fleet.

The biggest independent in Cornwall was Grenville Motors of Camborne, serving Redruth, Troon, Falmouth, Heston and Penzance. Grenville ran just under 30 vehicles including five modern Y-series Bedfords with bus bodies by Willowbrook and Duple. But the bulk of the fleet was made up of 1960s Bedford coaches, including half a dozen acquired in 1973 with the business of the Penryn & Falmouth Motor Co. Jennings of Bude was another operator to expand as Western National cut back and in fact took over the old Western National garage in the town as its base. Services ran to Plymouth and to Exeter, the latter as a result of the closure of the Okehampton to Exeter rail link in 1972. The fleet comprised Y-series Bedfords with Plaxton and Duple coach bodies. Deeble of Upton Cross, near Liskeard operated to Looe and Polperro. The quaintly-named village of Mousehole, near Penzance, was served by Harvey. At the start of the 1970s an Albion Nimbus was used; this was replaced by a Marshall-bodied Bristol LHS later in the decade.

1975: Major bus fleets – South West England

Operator	*Fleet size*
Bristol Omnibus	1,196
Western National	1,089
Plymouth	214
Bournemouth	160
Thamesdown	70
Cheltenham District	36

BLAEN-Y-MAES
84
WOODFORD ROAD
CAEREITHIN
GLENGETTIE SUCH GOOD TEA
SOUTH WALES
508
RCY 350
SKINNER
Boots

THE biggest bus company serving Wales was in fact based in England. Crosville Motor Services was one of NBC's biggest subsidiaries running 1,200 buses and coaches in an area which stretched from Cheshire, through Merseyside and across North Wales. Its headquarters were in Chester, and it had depots as far apart as Macclesfield and Newcastle Emlyn.

The company's name came from its two founders – Messrs Crosland-Taylor and Ville – who started running buses in 1910. It had been a THC subsidiary which meant that its vehicles were largely ECW-bodied Bristols – there were just over 900 in operation in 1975. The double-deckers included most varieties of Lodekkas. Until 1966 Crosville had bought large numbers of both forward-entrance FLFs and rear-entrance FSs. The last Lodekkas were FLFs in 1968, after which there were no new double-deckers until 1975 and the arrival of the company's first 12 VRTs – a number which would grow dramatically by the end of the decade.

These were not Crosville's first rear-engined double-deckers. In January 1972 it had taken over North Western's Cheshire operations when the bulk of the North Western business was sold to the SELNEC PTE. This added 124 buses to the Crosville fleet, including Park Royal-bodied AEC Renowns, and Alexander-bodied Dennis Lolines and Daimler Fleetlines. Examples of all three types survived until the late 1970s.

Bristols dominated the single-deck fleet – MWs, REs and LHs. There had been LSs and SCs at the start of the 1970s, but all had gone by 1976. Variety had been injected here by the North Western take-over, including REs with Marshall bodies and nine ECW-bodied buses with a special low roof profile for operation through the Dunham Massey canal bridge. Other ex-North Western types were AEC

Facing page **A classic South Wales Transport AEC Regent V in Swansea at the start of the 1970s. It was one of 26 delivered in 1958 which were the company's first forward-entrance Regents. The bodywork was by Weymann. These buses were withdrawn in 1971-72.** A Moyes

Top right **For a time NBC decreed that the band of white relief would be omitted from single-deck repaints. The rule was not applied to double-deckers, but a number of Crosville Lodekkas appeared in unrelieved green, as witnessed by this 1962 FLF6B in Liverpool.** Stewart J Brown

Centre right **In 1963 Crosville took delivery of 26 Bristol MWs with 39-seat coach bodies by ECW. In the late 1960s the windows in the cove were replaced by solid panels, and in the early 1970s most were demoted to bus work. The polished mouldings and wheel trims provide some relief for the all-over green livery.** John Robinson

Right **Crosville inherited from North Western a unique batch of Bristol REs with low height ECW bodies, designed to allow passage under the Bridgewater Canal at Dunham Massey. There were nine such buses; one is seen in Warrington.** Michael Fowler

Left **In 1971-72 Crosville bought 100 Seddon Pennine RUs, the biggest order placed for the model. The first 50 were single-door 47-seat dual-purpose vehicles, as seen here at Northwich in original Tilling green and cream livery. The balance were 45-seat two-door buses.** John Robinson

Centre left **Crosville acquired 11 Leyland Tiger Cubs from Western Welsh in a redrawing of the two companies' operating boundaries in 1972. The newest of these was a 1966 PSUC1/12 model with 41-seat dual-purpose body by Marshall.** John Jones

Reliances and Leyland Tiger Cubs and Leopards. A smaller expansion in the spring of 1972 was the acquisition of Western Welsh's operations around Newcastle Emlyn and New Quay, along with 11 Leyland Tiger Cubs, most of which survived until 1976.

Crosville was in the unusual position in being an NBC subsidiary and of being the biggest operator of Seddons, with a fleet of 100 Pennine RUs delivered in 1971-72 to speed fleet renewal. The RU used the same horizontal Gardner engine as powered most of the fleet's Bristol REs. An odd-man-out was the only mid-engined Pennine VII in NBC ownership. This was a 1974 example with Seddon body which had been a demonstrator. It operated in Chester. Crosville was an early recipient of the Leyland National. Its first was K-registered – not that common on Nationals – and by 1975 there were 178 in service.

An unusual alpha-numeric fleet numbering system was used by Crosville with a three-letter prefix indicating vehicle type, chassis make and engine make. Thus for example DFB was a Double-deck, F-series Lodekka, with Bristol engine, while SRG was a Single-deck, RE-series Bristol, with Gardner engine. Much of Crosville's operations lay in England, and the company's buses could be seen in Liverpool, Manchester and Warrington. It was the main operator in Runcorn New Town, with services running on the innovative segregated busway.

There were two small local authority fleets in North Wales, at Colwyn Bay and Llandudno.

Below **Llandudno Urban District Council operated normal-control Guy Wolf buses until 1975. This was one of a pair which dated from 1949 and had 21-seat Barnard bodywork. Both were sold for preservation.** John Robinson

Below right **Purple Motors operated a number of second-hand single-deckers including an ex-Trent Leyland Tiger Cub with Willowbrook body. It is seen in Bangor in 1977. Note the boarding passenger's flared trousers, then the height of fashion.** D J Little

Right **Aberconwy Borough Council, the successor to Llandudno UDC, bought the biggest buses in the operation's history in 1976 – two Bedford SB5s with 41-seat Willowbrook bodies. One is seen on the road to St Tudno's Church.** Stewart J Brown

Centre right **Clynnog & Trevor ran second-hand single-deckers, as shown by this Weymann-bodied AEC Reliance which had been new to Maidstone & District in 1956. It is loading in Caernarvon for Pwlhelli in the summer of 1973. The front grille is not original.** Iain MacGregor

Bottom right **Caernarvon Square was the terminus for out of town services run by a variety of operators. On the left in this 1977 shot is an ECW-bodied Bristol SC4LK and on the right a Duple-bodied BedfordOB. The Bristol belonged to Silver Star and had been new in 1957 to Eastern National. The OB, one of the last in regular service, was owned by Whiteways.** John Jones

Colwyn – 'Bay' was dropped from the title in 1974 – ran just two buses and was easily Britain's smallest municipal bus operator. In the mid-1970s its buses were two Plaxton-bodied Bedford J2s. Colwyn's service ran along the sea front.

Along the coast in Llandudno the local authority had changed its title in 1974 to Aberconwy. Here there were nine buses. The oldest were three small Guys, a marque with which Llandudno had long been associated. Two were 1954 Otters with Roe bodies, the third a 1948 normal-control Wolf with Barnard body – the last bonneted bus in British municipal service. More modern vehicles were a pair of Dennis Pax V goods chassis, built in 1968 and fitted with the last bus bodies built by Dennis. Then came a couple of second-hand Bedford VAS5 coaches. The newest buses in the fleet, and the biggest in the undertaking's history, were two SB5s with 41-seat Willowbrook bodies which were the operation's front-line service buses. Both Colwyn Bay and Llandudno were served by Crosville.

In Bangor, the next major town along the coast, two small operators ran rural services. Purple Motors had a route from Bethesda on which could be found a varied selection of second-hand buses such as an ex-Yorkshire Woollen Reliance with Park Royal bus body, an ex-Trent Willowbrook-bodied Tiger Cub or a Bedford SB5 with Duple (Midland) bus body. Deiniolen Motors ran from the village of that name and had two second-hand Tiger Cubs, from Ribble and Trent, and a 1973 Willowbrook-bodied Bedford YRQ.

In Caernarfon Crosville was the main operator, but there was also a strong independent presence. Clynnog and Trevor operated to Pwlhelli, serving on route the two villages which made up the company's title. Second-hand single-deckers were used on service. Most were AEC Reliances, including examples from Maidstone & District and City of Oxford. There was one new coach in the 12-vehicle fleet, a 1973 Bedford YRT with bus-grant Plaxton body. Whiteways ran a service from Waenfawr to

Caernarfon using what was probably the oldest double-decker still in regular year-round service in Britain, a 1946 Leyland Titan PD1 which had been acquired in 1963 when it had been pensioned off by its original owner, Warrington Corporation. This was the company's only double-decker. The remainder of the fleet was made up of Bedford coaches ranging from a 1951 OB to a 1973 YRQ.

Silver Star of Upper Llandwrog ran from Caernarfon to Cesarea using in the main second-hand Bristols, including a former United Auto MW and a Bristol SC which had started life with Eastern National. There were rather more mundane Duple-bodied Bedford coaches too. Caelloi Motors ran rural services in the Pwlhelli area with second-hand Reliances although there were also two Lodekkas, ex-Red & White, in the fleet.

There were a few small operators in Powys, serving the relatively sparsely populated country between Aberystwyth and the English border. In the Newtown and Welshpool areas Mid-Wales Motorways ran a number of services. There were 25 Bedfords in the fleet including an OB, assorted VASs and SBs, a few VAMs, a solitary VAL, and three Y-series. Most were second-hand and all had coach bodies, by Duple, Plaxton and Yeates. Brown of Builth Wells ran a network of generally infrequent rural services using assorted Bedford coaches, as did Cross Gates Motors of Llandrindod Wells.

Further north in Clwyd, Wrexham attracted a number of small operators. Williams of Ponciau ran from Wrexham to Rhosllanerchrugog with a Willowbrook-bodied Bedford SB and new R-series Fords bodied by Willowbrook and Plaxton. Also running to Rhosllanerchrugog was Phillips of Rhosyllen, with Willowbrook-bodied Fords. A new Bedford YRQ with Plaxton coach body joined the fleet of Edwards of Wrexham in 1975, for use on the service to Llanarmon-yn-lal. Chaloner of Wrexham ran just one bus, a Duple (Midland)-bodied Bedford SB on a service to Moss. Elderly SBs, including some with petrol engines, were used by Evans on Wrexham locals. A Pennine-bodied Seddon Pennine IV was operated by Wright of Penycae on a route to Wrexham.

Top left **Thirty-year-old double-deckers in regular year-round service have never been common. Whiteways ran this ex-Warrington PD1 until the mid 1970s by which time it was nudging the 30 year mark, having been built in 1946. It had a Leyland-style body built by Alexander.** Iain MacGregor

Centre left **Chaloner of Moss ran into Wrexham. When this Willowbrook-bodied SB was delivered in 1976 it was already becoming an increasingly uncommon type. By the time it was withdrawn – in 1990 – it was a rare survivor indeed.** A Moyes

Left **A Willowbrook-bodied Ford of Phillips of Rhosyllen in Wrexham bus station in the summer of 1975. The early 1970s were boom years for the Loughborough-based body builder as small operators bought buses like this in large numbers.** John Jones

Right **Cardiff's traditional livery on a traditional bus, a 1965 Guy Arab V with Gardner 6LW engine and 65-seat rear-entrance Neepsend body. There were 17 buses in the batch. This one is seen approaching the city's bus station in 1975.** John Jones

Below left **The first rear-engined buses for Cardiff were 32 Daimler Fleetlines – 16 with Metro-Cammell bodies which were delivered in 1967, followed by 16 Park Royal-bodied buses in 1968. A Metro-Cammell-bodied Fleetline loads in Cardiff bus station in 1973.** Stewart J Brown

Below right **Cardiff's post-1972 orange livery was applied to a variety of half-cab types, including this AEC Regent V with bodywork by East Lancs. The batch of a dozen Regents delivered in 1963-64 were Cardiff's last AEC double-deckers. This one is seen in 1977, nearing the end of its life.** John Jones

The biggest bus company serving Wales may have been in the north, but the bulk of the country's buses were to be found in the densely-populated industrial south. Here there were seven local authority fleets (down from nine prior to 1974's local government reorganisation) and four NBC fleets.

Local services in the capital were the preserve of City of Cardiff Transport, which with 218 buses was quite easily the biggest Welsh municipal fleet. A new orange livery had been adopted in 1972, to replace the undertaking's traditional maroon and cream. With the new livery came the first use by a major operator of fleetnames in two languages – City of Cardiff on the nearside and Dinas Caerdydd on the offside. Both old and new liveries could still be seen in 1975, but the last of the maroon buses were repainted by the end of the year.

Cardiff's operation was a busy double-decked one. The last Leyland Titans, East Lancs-bodied PD3As were withdrawn in 1975, but there were still a dozen 1963 AEC Regents with East Lancs bodies, and 54 Guy Arab Vs dating from the 1964-66 period. The final 37 of these had the last rear-entrance bodies to be produced by Alexander.

From 1967 to 1972 Cardiff had bought Fleetlines and had 92 with bodies by Metro-Cammell, Park Royal and Willowbrook. Willowbrook supplied 25 in 1969-70, one of its biggest double-deck orders of that period and also its only contract for low-height two-door bodies. In 1973 the fleet's new double-deckers were 20 Bristol VRTs with lowheight ECW bodies. These NBC-style buses were ironically

Left **The last AECs for Cardiff were 20 Swifts with two-door Alexander W-type bodies. The W-type usually had an attractively-styled front end with curved glass windscreens, but those for Cardiff featured less expensive flat glass. In the early 1970s they were Cardiff's only single-deckers. New in 1968, they were withdrawn in the mid 1970s. This is a 1975 view.** John Jones

Centre left **Alexander-bodied Atlanteans were the standard Newport bus from 1966, when this one was delivered, until 1971.** Stewart J Brown

Bottom left **After the Atlanteans Newport switched to Metro-Scanias. A fleet of 44 took to the town's streets in 1972, replacing all of the surviving half-cabs and giving Newport the country's most modern municipal fleet with no buses over six years old.** Stewart J Brown

running in an area where none of the NBC companies had as yet received any VRTs. Delivery of more VRTs to Cardiff was scheduled, but these would have bodies by Willowbrook and, later in the decade, Alexander. Cardiff's single-deckers were 21 Leyland Nationals and a few surviving Alexander-bodied AEC Swifts. There were also three Seddon Pennine midis, bought in 1974 for use on shoppers' services.

A joint service was operated by Cardiff and Newport Transport between the two towns. Newport had a fleet of just over 100 modern vehicles, none of which was over 10 years old. The last half-cab 'deckers – Leyland Titans with Longwell Green bodies – had gone in the early 1970s, leaving 1966 Atlanteans as the oldest buses in service. There were 43 Atlanteans, the newest being J-registered 1971 examples, and all with Alexander bodywork. In 1971 Newport had gone for omo single-deckers and over two years took delivery of 44 dual-door Metro-Scanias, giving it the biggest fleet of this relatively short-lived model. Later in the decade Newport would add some redundant ex-London Transport Metro-Scanias to its operations. The Scania-MCW combination clearly impressed, and when 10 new double-deckers were delivered in 1975 they were not yet more Atlanteans, but were instead MCW Metropolitans. Other types in the Newport fleet were eight ECW-bodied Bristol REs, bought in 1967, and two Bedford YRQs taken over in 1974 with the business of Smith of Newport, who had briefly operated a local service in the town.

The other South Wales municipal fleets were based in the valleys. Blackwood, north-east of Newport, was the headquarters of Islwyn Borough Transport, which had until 1974 been the West Monmouthshire Omnibus Board. All of Islwyn's buses were Leylands, and most were Leopard single-deckers with Willowbrook bodies. There were also four Tiger Cubs. The seven double-deckers were PD2 Titans with 55-seat lowbridge Massey bodies. The last of these had entered service in 1966. There were no rear-engined buses in the fleet.

South down the Rhymney Valley lay Caerphilly, the main centre of operation of Rhymney Valley District Council, created in 1974. It had taken over three fleets – Caerphilly, Gelligaer and Bedwas & Machen. A new and distinctive brown, yellow and cream livery was being applied to the fleet, replacing Caerphilly's green and cream, Bedwas & Machen's dark blue and cream, and Gelligaer's red, white and green.

Above **Typifying the fleet operated by the West Monmouthshire Omnibus Board and its successor, Islwyn, is this 1970 Leyland Leopard with 47-seat Willowbrook body, seen in Pontypridd in 1974.** Stewart J Brown

Below **A more typical Caerphilly Titan, seen in Cardiff in 1974. It is a 1965 PD3 with 68-seat lowbridge Massey bodywork. Caerphilly was by this time one of very few operators still buying side-gangway lowbridge buses.** A Moyes

Above **Rhymney Valley's distinctive livery, worn by a 1967 PD2 with Massey body. It was one of a pair which had been new to Caerphilly and had been that undertaking's last Titans. They were also the only Caerphilly Titans with highbridge bodywork and with forward entrances. The location is Cardiff.** Geoff Rixon

Below **After buying three Bristol VRTs in 1971, Gelligaer added three REs in 1972. These were 10m RESL6Gs with 47-seat ECW bodies.** John Jones

Above **Gelligaer was the first Welsh operator of Bristol VRTs, taking three with Northern Counties bodies in 1971. These were the fleet's first new double-deckers since a 1960 Titan, and its first Bristols. They had 77-seat bodies by Northern Counties. One is seen outside the depot on the eve of the formation of the Rhymney Valley operation. Behind are a 1968 Austin minibus, a 1963 Reliance and a 1973 Bedford YRQ coach.** Stewart J Brown

Caerphilly and Gelligaer had each operated 31 buses, while Bedwas & Machen had just eight.

The Rhymney Valley fleet was varied, reflecting the buying policies of its constituents. From Caerphilly had come Leylands. Most were Leopards, including four with unusual Northern Counties bodies, but there were also PD2s and PD3s, most with lowbridge Massey bodies, and three East Lancs-bodied Atlanteans. Gelligaer operated AECs and Bristols. The former were mainly Reliances, but included three Swifts, one an ex-demonstrator. The latter were ECW-bodied REs, plus three 1971 VRTs with low-height Northern Counties bodies – an unusual combination. The ex-Bedwas & Machen buses were Leyland Leopards and lowbridge Massey-bodied double-deckers one of which, a 1968 F-registered PD3, was the last bus built with a side-gangway lowbridge body. The other Bedwas & Machen double-deckers were AEC Regents. New additions to the Rhymney Valley fleet in 1975 were more REs, Atlanteans and Leopards. The REs had ECW bodies, while the

Below **Bedwas & Machen was the smallest of the South Wales municipal operations with a fleet strength typically in the region of seven buses. At the start of the 1970s four of these were AEC Regent Vs with lowbridge Massey bodies. This, the last one, was new in 1964.** John Jones

Below **Longwell Green bodywork was bought by a few South Wales operators. In 1963 Pontypridd took two Reliances which were bodied by Longwell Green. One unloads in the town centre in 1973.** Paul Caudell

Leylands were bodied by East Lancs. Leopards would become the fleet standard. The bulk of Rhymney Valley's services were short local routes, but it did have lengthy trunk services linking Newport and Rhymney Bridge, shared with Red & White and Western Welsh, and a Cardiff to Tredegar service, run jointly with Cardiff and Islwyn.

In Pontypridd the local authority had from 1974 been known as Taff-Ely. The fleet livery was light blue and cream, having been changed in 1971 from a rather more sombre dark blue and cream. AEC was the dominant manufacturer in this operation, accounting for 26 out of 42 buses. These were Reliances and Regent Vs, the latter including two G-registered 1969 examples with forward-entrance Willowbrook bodies. These were among the last Regents to enter service in Britain, and were the last new half-cab double-deckers supplied to a Welsh bus operator. An earlier pair of Regents supplied in 1966 had the last bodies built by Longwell Green, which were also the small Bristol-based manufacturer's only forward-entrance double-deck bodies. Older 'deckers were Roe-bodied Guy Arabs, including a pair with Johannesburg-style bonnets.

Pontypridd's last AECs were three Willowbrook-bodied Reliances in 1972. Unusually for such a small operation, Pontypridd had embraced new-generation integral single-deckers with enthusiasm and in 1975 Taff-Ely was running three Metro-Scanias and six Leyland Nationals. More Nationals would follow.

To the north, Merthyr Tydfil's buses began a Cardiff-style livery change in 1974 from dark red and cream to orange and white. This was an operation which was moving away from double-deckers to single-deckers. All of the double-deckers were East Lancs-bodied PD3s, the newest being 1966 buses with forward-entrance bodies. These had been followed by East Lancs-bodied Leopards – 42 were added to the fleet between 1964 and 1972. In 1973 Merthyr Tydfil had switched to low-floor rear-

Top right **The post-1971 lighter blue livery used by Pontypridd was retained by Taff-Ely. Two Arab IVs delivered in 1962 brought to 11 the number of Arab 'deckers in the Pontypridd fleet, all of which were still in use when Taff-Ely took over in 1974.** John Jones

Centre right **The only double-deckers in the Merthyr Tydfil fleet in the 1970s were Leyland Titans. The newest were 12 PD3s with exposed radiators and forward-entrance East Lancs bodies, delivered in the period 1964-66. The last were withdrawn in 1978.** Stewart J Brown

Right **Merthyr Tydfil adopted a bright new orange and white livery in 1974, as seen on a 1972 East Lancs-bodied Leyland Leopard in the town's bus station. Merthyr Tydfil ran both 10m PSU4s and 11m PSU3s with single-door and two-door bodywork. The 1972 buses were single-door 51-seat PSU3s.** Stewart J Brown

Above **Double-deckers were on their way out in Aberdare in the 1970s. The last were five Guy Arab IVs with 64-seat Longwell Green bodies, which had entered service in 1958. The last one is seen leaving the depot in 1974.** Stewart J Brown

Below **Cynon Valley ran 13 Bristol REs, all 10m RESL6Ls with Leyland engines and 44-seat ECW bodies. This was one of seven which had been new to Aberdare in 1972.** A Moyes

engined models, taking two Metro-Scanias and four ECW-bodied Bristol REs, which were followed in 1974-75 by seven Leyland Nationals and four East Lancs-bodied REs. The 1975 REs would be the last, but more Nationals – and Leopards – would join the fleet later in the decade.

Nearby Aberdare had been another local authority fleet to have a change of title in 1974, to Cynon Valley. Aberdare's livery was an uninspiring all-over maroon – cheap to apply but hard on the eye. At the start of the 1970s there were still double-deckers in service. Aberdare had last bought this type in 1958 – five Guy Arabs with Longwell Green bodies. Its next new buses, in 1962, had been AEC Reliances with two-door bodies, a layout adopted on all subsequent Reliances. In 1975 there were 19 Reliances and six Swifts in service. The surviving Reliances included three 1965 Strachans-bodied buses; all the other AECs had Willowbrook bodies. New buses in the first half of the 1970s had been the Swifts, ECW-bodied Bristol REs, of which there were 13, and three Leyland Nationals. By the end of the decade the Reliances would have gone and the National fleet would stand at 19. An odd little bus in the Cynon Valley fleet was a 1972 Commer with 15-seat Rootes body.

In the south and south-east of Wales the main NBC operator was Red & White. This was a former THC business and its fleet was made up almost entirely of Bristols – MWs, rear-entrance Lodekkas, and REs. There were no rear-engined double-deckers in the fleet; from 1964 all of its new buses had been single-deckers. Leyland Nationals had started to appear in 1974. Its headquarters were in Chepstow and its operations extended west to Swansea, north to Brecon, south to Newport and Cardiff, and across the English border to Gloucester, Hereford and, via the Severn Bridge, to Bristol.

Red & White would from the mid-1970s become more closely aligned with Western Welsh, a former BET subsidiary. This would lead ultimately to the creation of a new National Welsh company in 1978. Both fleets were poppy red, but in 1975 Western Welsh had a rather more varied collection of buses and coaches than could be found in its ex-THC partner. The oldest were standard BET-style Atlanteans of the early 1960s with lowbridge Weymann bodies. These had been followed by forward-entrance Titans, Regents and Renowns during the mid-1960s, and all of these types remained in regular service. The fleet's newest 'deckers were Atlanteans delivered in 1968-69 and 1971, with bodies by Northern Counties and Alexander. It would be 1977 before the first Bristol VRTs would be delivered.

Western Welsh's single-deckers were mainly Tiger Cubs and Leopards with Marshall or Weymann bodies. The company had continued to buy Tiger Cubs long after most major operators had switched to the heavier Leopard and its newest dated from 1968. In consequence most of the Leopards were post-1969 models.

BET had a separate subsidiary based in Porth, the Rhondda Transport Co, and an early move by NBC was to amalgamate this with Western Welsh. The fleet was not dissimilar, and included Regent Vs, Tiger Cubs, Atlanteans and a few Leopards. The Rhondda name continued in use although the NBC poppy red livery was of

Above **Red & White never operated any forward-entrance Lodekkas, staying instead with the rear-entrance FS and FL models until it stopped buying double-deckers in 1964. This is a 1962 FS6G in Pontypridd in 1974. It would be 1977 before new double-deckers would make another appearance in Red & White's orders.** Stewart J Brown

Above right **A 1966 Bristol MW6G with 45-seat ECW body in Aberdare is typical of the buses being bought by Red & White in the early 1960s. These were the company's last MWs and most were still in use when National Welsh was formed at the start of 1978.** Stewart J Brown

Right **High-backed seats for 47 passengers were fitted to 13 ECW-bodied RELH6Gs delivered to Red & White in 1972, which justified repainting them in NBC local coach livery, rather than as buses. This one was clearly fresh out of the paintshop when photographed in Merthyr Tydfil in 1974.** Stewart J Brown

Below **The last buses for Western Welsh in the company's pre-NBC livery were 24 Marshall-bodied Leyland Leopards, delivered in 1972. This one is seen in Merthyr Tydfil towards the end of that year, by which time Western Welsh was proclaiming itself proud to be part of NBC.** John Jones

course the same as that used by Western Welsh and Red & White. This gave Western Welsh an area which extended broadly from Cwmbran in the east to Bridgend in the west – which in fact was not that far west considering the company's title. However at the start of the 1970s Western Welsh had had depots in Haverfordwest and Neath (transferred to South Wales Transport in 1972) and in Cardiganshire, taken over by Crosville in the same year.

The unusual aspect of NBC's operations in South Wales was the Jones fleet, based in Aberbeeg. This had been an independent company until 1969 when it sold out to NBC. At that time it ran 43 buses and coaches in a cream and blue livery. This survived – as blue and white – in NBC days and by 1975 was the only NBC bus operation not to be using either poppy red or leaf green. The Jones operation was entirely single-decked and to the surviving ex-

Top left **In January 1971 Western Welsh took over the 160-strong Rhondda operation, based in Porth. Among the buses which were acquired were five Leyland Tiger Cubs with Park Royal bus bodies. This one is seen in Cardiff after the fleet had been renumbered in 1974 using a year code system similar to that used by Red & White.** John Jones

Above **NBC took over Jones of Aberbeeg in 1969. An early transfer was this 1966 Red & White ECW-bodied Bristol MW6G which moved to the Jones fleet in the summer of 1972 and was repainted in the livery which the company had been using while still independent. It is seen in Aberbeeg in 1974.** A Moyes

Left **Jones became the only NBC subsidiary to use a blue livery, which looked refreshingly different in the days of poppy red and leaf green, as shown on a 1969 Willowbrook-bodied Tiger Cub.** Malcolm King

Jones Tiger Cub and Leopard buses, most with Willowbrook bodies, NBC had added three ECW-bodied REs and four Leyland Nationals. The blue Jones livery would survive into the early 1980s.

All of these fleets – Red & White, Western Welsh (including Rhondda) and Jones – used a complex fleet numbering system inherited from Red & White. Each year buses were numbered from 1, followed by the last two digits of the year and preceded by a type code. Confused? An example makes it all clear. In 1974 a total of 26 new vehicles joined the fleet, numbered from 174 to 2674. They were of three different types – Nationals (N), Leopards (UC for Underfloor-engined Coach), and Bristol REs (RC for Rear-engined Coach). Thus armed with fleet number N1274 you could identify a 1974 Leyland National, which was the 12th bus added to the fleet that year. It worked better than it sounds. Second-hand buses were numbered by the year of manufacture, not the year of acquisition.

With almost 500 buses South Wales Transport was the biggest bus company in the southern part of Wales. This had come about at the start of 1971 following rationalisation by NBC of its operations in the area which involved SWT taking over United Welsh, Thomas Bros and Neath & Cardiff. United Welsh had been a THC subsidiary while SWT and the two other, smaller, companies had been owned by BET. Further expansion came in 1972 with the take-over of operations in West Wales which had been run by Western Welsh and Crosville. This gave the company an operating area stretching from Cardiff to the south-west tip of Wales and embracing Swansea, Llanelli, Ammanford, Carmarthen and Haverfordwest.

South Wales had been an AEC operator, buying Regent Vs until 1967 and Reliance buses until 1971. Most of those AECs running in the mid-1970s had Willowbrook bodies. There were also Reliances and Renowns which had been taken over with Western Welsh services, as well as ex-Western Welsh Leylands in the shape of Atlanteans and Tiger Cubs. The absorption of the Thomas Bros fleet added a variety of single-deck types. These included Tiger Cubs with bodies by Park Royal, Alexander and Marshall and a number of Reliances, the newest of which were 1971 Willowbrook-bodied buses ordered by Thomas Bros but delivered new to South Wales. The most unusual buses taken over from Thomas Bros were three 1966 Panther Cubs with Strachans bodies, an unlikely purchase for a small BET fleet. The ex-United Welsh buses in the South Wales fleet were an assortment of ECW-bodied Bristols – MWs, REs and Lodekkas. There were also Marshall-bodied REs which had come from Western Welsh.

The last remnants of a much earlier South Wales take-over – of James of Ammanford in 1962 – were three 1963 Leopards with Marshall bodies which had been ordered by James, an all-

Above **All of the buses which SWT acquired from United Welsh in 1971 were Bristols. A 1959 LD6G Lodekka – United Welsh's last LD – is seen in SWT ownership in Merthyr Tydfil in 1975. The last SWT LD was withdrawn in 1977.** John Jones

Below **SWT took over a variety of types from Western Welsh. These included 15 AEC Reliances with dual-purpose bodywork by Marshall.** Stewart J Brown

Left **Y-series Bedfords with Willowbrook Expressway bodies were an unusual buy for an NBC subsidiary. In 1973 South Wales Transport received 10. They were followed in 1974 by 35 Willowbrook-bodied Ford R1014s. A Bedford YRQ is seen in Cardiff. The absence of a route number blind is compensated by stickers in the windscreen.** Stewart J Brown

Centre left **Minibuses were a rarity in NBC fleets in the 1970s. South Wales Transport ran two Strachans-bodied Ford Transits from 1977. These had come from City of Oxford – which had been running dial-a-ride operations in Abingdon and in Witney – although this bus had originally been operated in London by National Travel (South East) on a service linking Victoria Coach Station with Victoria railway station.** Royston Morgan

Bottom **Henley's of Abertillery ran AEC Reliance buses on local services. The newest was a 1973 model with Plaxton Derwent bodywork. This was destined to be a long-lived bus and was still in service 20 years later.** John Jones

Leyland operation, but delivered new to South Wales, then running mainly AECs. Other AECs in the mid-1970s fleet were Reliance coaches taken over from Neath & Cardiff, which had used them on Cardiff to Swansea express services.

South Wales was unusual among NBC fleets in the early 1970s in receiving both Bedford and Ford buses. Nine YRQs and 35 R1014s, all with Willowbrook bodies, joined the fleet in 1973-74. The Bedfords were Expressway dual-purpose 45-seaters; the Fords were straightforward buses. More Fords, but with Duple Dominant bodies, would follow. There were, of course, growing numbers of Leyland Nationals – but no VRTs until 1976. Until then the only rear-engined double-deckers were four H-registered Atlanteans taken over from Western Welsh.

There were a large number of old-established independent operators in South Wales and even more so in West Wales.

At Abertillery, Henley's ran two local services. The newest bus in the fleet was a 1973

Right **Until 1976 two local services in Merthyr Tydfil were run by Davies of Tredegar. The Davies fleet included this ex-East Kent Guy Arab IV with Park Royal body.** John Jones

Below right **Brewer bought new AEC Reliances in the 1960s and 1970s. Willowbrook bodywork is fitted to this 1965 bus, seen at the company's depot in 1975 .** John Jones

AEC Reliance with Plaxton Derwent bus body. A similar bus was used by Edmunds on a service from Rassau to Ebbw Vale. Several services in the Pontypool area were run by Peake using R-series Fords with Willowbrook bodies, as well as older second-hand Leyland and Bristol single-deckers. Tredegar was the home of Hill's, one of the best-known coach businesses in South Wales. Hill's ran 60 vehicles, most of them Leyland Leopards and Y-series Bedfords with Plaxton coach bodies, some to bus grant specification. Purpose-built buses comprised two Tiger Cubs and six Leopards. The Tiger Cubs were of widely differing ages. One had been bought new in 1955 as a Burlingham Seagull coach and then rebodied as a bus by Willowbrook in 1963; the other was new in 1969. Most of the newer buses had Plaxton Derwent bodies. The bulk of Hill's bus operations were works services, but Tredegar local routes were operated too. Another Tredegar coach operator, Davies, ran two services from Merthyr Tydfil with a fleet which included Willowbrook-bodied Fords. One was jointly operated with Merthyr Tydfil Borough Transport, which took over both routes in 1976. At the same time Hill's took over the rest of the Davies business. Bebb of Llantwit Fardre ran a long-established service from Pontypridd to Beddau but in 1975 expanded with a service from Cardiff to Hensol Castle, on which were used three Bristol LHSs with Plaxton Supreme Express bodies. A service from Cardiff to Barry Island was run by Thomas of Barry with a Willowbrook-bodied Leopard.

At Maesteg, north of Bridgend, which housed the westernmost Western Welsh depot, Brewer of Caerau operated local services using buses bought new. These included early 1960s Reliances with Weymann bodies and more modern Willowbrook-bodied Reliances. There were two Leylands in the fleet, a 1963 Marshall-bodied Leopard and a 1969 Willowbrook-bodied

Tiger Cub. Second-hand buses appeared in 1975 with the arrival of four seven-year-old Alexander-bodied Swifts from Cardiff. From Maesteg to Port Talbot a service was provided by Llynfi Motor Services. In the summer period this was run jointly with South Wales Transport and extended to Aberavon Beach. Double-deckers were often used on this and included a Massey-bodied Leyland Titan bought new in 1958, plus ex-South Wales Regents and, from 1976, ex-Glasgow Atlanteans. The single-deck fleet had a Willowbrook-bodied Leopard, bought new in 1971, running alongside second-hand Leopards from Portsmouth and Trimdon Motor Services, and two Bristol LHs with Plaxton Derwent bodies. Another small operator in this area was Coity Motors, whose fleet included an unusual Bristol LHL with Plaxton Derwent body. Coity ran routes in the Bridgend area.

On the coast local services were run by the Porthcawl Omnibus Co, an associate of Kenfig Motors which operated contract services. Changes of ownership in 1977 would see Porthcawl Omnibus being taken over by John Williams Coaches, while Kenfig Motors would go to Mansel David of Pontycymmer. Both operators had taken advantage of new bus grant to update their fleets and the front-line vehicle in the Porthcawl Omnibus operation was a Bedford YRT with Willowbrook Expressway body.

Neath, a few miles inland from Swansea, was served by Cream Line of Tonmawr using three ex-Trimdon Leopards with Plaxton Derwent bodies, running alongside a Willowbrook-bodied Bedford YRQ bought new in 1970, and assorted second-hand Tiger Cubs. Double-deckers, which included Leyland Titans from Edinburgh, Blackpool and Southdown and an ex-Crosville Lodekka, were also used on service. West Wales was a geographically inexact title for a company based a few miles inland from Swansea, at Tycroes, near Ammanford. West Wales had run double-deckers and in 1964 had been the last Welsh independent to buy a new one – an AEC Renown. However conversion to one-man-operation meant that by the mid-1970s

Top left **Most of Llynfi Motor Services' buses were single-deckers. This Willowbrook-bodied Leyland Leopard L1 had been bought from Jones of Aberbeeg in 1967.** John Jones

Left **By the mid-1970s early rear-engined double-deckers were appearing in growing numbers on the second-hand market, prompting small operators to give the type a try. Cream Line briefly ran two one-time Newcastle Corporation Atlanteans with Alexander bodies. They had been new in 1961 and reached Cream Line in 1974 by way of Tyneside PTE and Rennie of Dunfermline.** D J Little

the 20-strong fleet was made up exclusively of single-deck Leylands, most of which were Leopards with Plaxton Derwent bodies. There was a Willowbrook-bodied Tiger Cub and a similarly bodied Leopard, both bought new in 1969. Also based in Tycroes was Rees & Williams, running Leopards with Willowbrook and Plaxton bus bodies on services from Llandeilo to Swansea and Llanelli. The Swansea service was operated jointly with West Wales and South Wales Transport.

West of Swansea, Eynon of Trimsaran ran from Llanelli to Carmarthen. A 1971 Willowbrook-bodied Leopard was used on the service, alongside other second-hand Leopards and Leyland Titans. The Titans had been new to

Right **In the 1970s West Wales operated Leyland single-deckers and little else. These were bought both new and second-hand, and included a 1966 Massey-bodied Leyland Tiger Cub which had started life with Fishwick of Leyland.** D J Little

Below **Willowbrook was a major supplier to small fleets in the 1970s which included Rees & Williams, with this dual purpose body on an 11m Leopard chassis. It is seen in Tycroes in 1973.** John Jones

Left **The oldest bus in the fleet of Davies Bros of Pencader in the mid-1970s was this 1960 Leyland Leopard with 43-seat Willowbrook body. It would see service into the early 1980s.** John Jones

Below left **Jones of Carmarthen operated this former Stratford Blue Leyland Leopard with a Willowbrook bus body. The Jones business was taken over by Davies Bros in 1978.** John Jones

Ribble, Bolton and Plymouth and were for use primarily on school contracts. Carmarthen was served by two other established independents, Davies Bros and Jones. Davies Bros was based in Pencader and ran an interesting fleet made up mainly of buses and coaches bought new. The oldest bus was a 1956 Tiger Cub with Willowbrook body, the newest a pair of 1975 Bristol LHs, one bodied by ECW, the other by Duple. There were also three Willowbrook-bodied Bedfords, two VAS5s and a VAM70. The Jones fleet also had ECW-bodied LHs – three in service, with a fourth on order. Here too there were Willowbrook-bodied Bedfords and an ex-Trimdon Plaxton Derwent-bodied Leopard. The Jones business, whose main service was to Llandeilo, would be taken over by Davies Bros in 1978.

Smaller businesses with services to Carmarthen included Ffoshelig of Newchurch with second-hand Tiger Cubs from Trent and Western Welsh, plus new Bedford YRQs with Duple bus and coach bodies. An ex-Western Welsh Tiger Cub could also be seen on the service operated by Jones of Login, while Thomas Bros of Llangadog ran a Llandeilo to Carmarthen service (among others) with a fleet which included a Bedford VAS with Willowbrook bus body, a YRQ coach, and Leyland Leopards and Tiger Cubs. One of the most varied fleets was that run by Pioneer of Laugharne with assorted second-hand single-deckers including a Massey-bodied Royal Tiger from Caerphilly UDC, Tiger Cubs from Yorkshire Traction and Western Welsh and an ex-City of Oxford Reliance. Pioneer ran from Carmarthen to Pendine, famed for its sands.

The area around Pembroke and Tenby was served by one of the biggest independents in Wales, the Silcox Motor Coach Co with some 65 vehicles. Bristols had long featured in the Silcox fleet and were prominent in the mid-1970s with ex-NBC LSs and Lodekkas running alongside modern Plaxton- and Duple-bodied LHs. There was a new Leopard bus, with 65-seat Duple body, while the fleet's oldest buses were a pair of Bristol KSWs with highbridge ECW body, a rare type in an independent fleet. From Haverfordwest a service to St Davids was operated by Marchwood Motorways, a Southampton-based operator which had taken the route over in 1973 from Collins of Roch. Buses in the Welsh-based Marchwood fleet were Tiger Cubs and an Olympian acquired with the Collins business and two new Duple-bodied YRQs added to the operation in 1975. Marchwood's connection with the Haverfordwest area had originally been through the provision of contract services for the oil terminal at Milford Haven – a type of work which it had previously carried out at Fawley, near Southampton. A substantial network of bus services had been built up by Richards Bros of Moylgrove in Haverfordwest, Fishguard, Newport (the Pembrokeshire one) and Cardigan. Much of the company's growth in the early 1970s came about as a result of retrenchment by Western Welsh and then by Crosville. The fleet was made up almost entirely of Bedfords, including bus-bodied SBs, VAMs, a VAS and a YLQ, as well as a range of coaches. The Richards Bros operation expanded at the start of 1976 with the takeover of Roberts of Newport with a 12-strong fleet, in which the newest bus was a 1972 Bedford SB5 with Willowbrook body.

Above **Silcox ran mainly Bristols and Leylands. The latter were mostly 11m-long PSU3 Leopards, such as this bus with 65-seat Duple Dominant body. The high capacity was achieved by using three-plus-two-seating.** John Jones

Below **Bedfords were the dominant make in the fleet of Richards Bros of Moylgrove. Added to the fleet in 1975 was this 1969 VAM70 with Willowbrook body. It was one of a pair bought from Diamond of Stanley.** Iain MacGregor

1975: Major bus fleets – Wales

Operator	*Fleet size*
Crosville	1,200
South Wales Transport	497
Western Welsh	468
Red & White	357
Cardiff	218
Newport	102
Merthyr Tydfil	78
Rhymney Valley	74
Jones Omnibus Services	43
Taff-Ely	42
Cynon Valley	36
Islwyn	30

End of a decade, end of an era

THE final years of the 1970s saw further rationalisation amongst Britain's bus companies.

The South Yorkshire PTE pursued a policy of acquiring small operators in its area and by 1979 had swallowed up most of the Doncaster independents. Booth & Fisher of Halfway was acquired early in 1976, followed a few months later by Felix of Hatfield. Blue Ensign was taken over in 1978, and Morgan, Severn and Store sold out to the PTE in 1979. This left Leon, Harold Wilson (Premier) and Rossie Motors.

The West Yorkshire PTE had taken over Baddeley Bros of Holmfirth in 1976 and followed this in April 1977 with Bingley of Kinsley. Bingley had only weeks before bought out the three vehicle operation of Cooper of South Kirkby. Cooper and Bingley were partners in United Services. Bingley retained its own identity as a PTE subsidiary. The West Yorkshire PTE's Hanson and Baddeley coaching businesses were for sale in 1979. The former was sold to Abbeyways of Halifax in April; the latter to Hirst of Holmfirth in January 1980.

Elsewhere a few small operators sold out to NBC and SBG. Eastern Counties took over Burwell & District in 1979, but kept none of its vehicles. Similarly when Eastern Counties had taken over Waveney District Council's bus operation in 1977 all of the vehicles were sold rather than being taken into the fleet. Yorkshire Traction took over the Thurnscoe to Barnsley service operated by Larrett Pepper in 1978. A rare example of municipal expansion saw Leicester City Transport take over the operations of Gibson Bros of Barlestone in 1979, and retain both the Gibson name and the Barlestone operating base. Old-established Somerset operator Hutchings & Cornelius decided to give up in 1979, with the business being sold to Safeway. Both companies were based in South Petherton.

Two of the Paisley independents called it a day in 1979 and Western SMT took over the operations of Paton and Cunningham's. Most of the acquired vehicles were quickly sold, other than a few ex-Paton Leopards, most of which soon found themselves being used to start up Western SMT operations on Islay where an independent had given up.

Unlike NBC, SBG had steered clear of a corporate identity. All of its subsidiaries ran throughout the 1970s in their traditional colours, even if the application varied from time to time. The only sign of corporate thinking at SBG came in 1978 with the introduction of standardised fleetnames using the company name followed by a stylised Scottish flag and the word Scottish. It has to be said that it was more subtle than NBC's approach.

SBG's buying policy continued to support a number of manufacturers. Leyland supplied

Left **All of the PTEs ordered Leyland Titans. However, production problems and the closure of the Park Royal factory, which was building Leyland's new flagship double-decker, meant that only 32 Titans were delivered to UK operators outside London. Greater Manchester got 15, with a mixture of Gardner and Leyland engines. They carried a non-standard version of GMT's livery.** Stewart J Brown

Above right **By the end of the 1970s the South Yorkshire PTE had taken over most of the small independent operators running within its area. This 1971 Roe-bodied Daimler Fleetline came with the business of Felix of Hatfield, purchased by the PTE in 1976.** Stewart J Brown

Right **Fifteen Leyland Fleetlines delivered in 1978-79 were the first new double-deckers for Highland Omnibuses. They had ECW bodies and a revised livery which incorporated grey relief.** Stewart J Brown

Leopards, Fleetlines and, from 1978, Nationals. Seddon supplied its Pennine VII, which was used for both bus and coach duties – including a few 12m motorway coaches with Alexander M-type bodies. Ailsa continued to supply small numbers of double-deckers. Most of SBG's bodies came from Alexander and included a minority of T-type coaches, a design also supplied to a few NBC fleets. ECW built some double-deck bodies on Fleetlines for SBG, as did Northern Counties. Unusual second-hand purchases by Eastern Scottish in 1977 were a dozen ex-Lothian PD2s with highbridge Alexander bodies.

There was some further rationalisation among NBC subsidiaries. In April 1978 a new National Welsh company took over the operations of Red & White, Western Welsh and Jones of Aberbeeg. The last-named continued as a separate trading name and in non-standard blue livery. In the South West, Western National had retained the Devon General name since absorbing that company in 1971, and had used poppy red for its Devon General fleet. At the end of the decade a number of Devon General buses started to appear in leaf green (Western National's colours) but still with Devon General fleetnames.

NBC's new buses were primarily Leyland Nationals and ECW-bodied Bristol VRTs. Variety was injected into the VRT fleet in 1976 with the delivery of Willowbrook-bodied examples to East Kent and Northern General. Similar buses were built by Willowbrook for the municipal fleet in Cardiff. For services needing something smaller than the National, most NBC fleets received ECW-bodied Bristol LHs, but there were also small numbers of lightweights – Bedfords and Fords. Later in the decade the emphasis would move to durability, and the simplified B-series National would be ordered where a less expensive single-decker was needed. The biggest B-series operators were London Country and Crosville. Another approach to mid-range single-deck operation was adopted by Midland Red in 1978, with the shortening of a few of its five-year-old Plaxton-bodied Fords, reducing their capacity from 45 to 27 seats. Minibuses were bought by NBC in very small numbers for specific operations. Unusual examples were four British Leyland EAs with Asco bodies for National Welsh in 1978-79. Similar buses were run by Alder Valley.

Evaluation of new types by NBC was carried out primarily by Maidstone & District. This had started in 1975 with five Ailsas and five MCW Metropolitans. In 1979 M&D had on order five MCW Metrobuses and six Dennis Dominators. NBC's first Dominator, with Alexander bodywork, entered trial service with PMT in 1978. PMT also had NBC's only Foden-NC.

Above **The B-series Leyland National, built to a simpler specification and offered only in the shorter 10.3m length, was developed as a lower-cost option to the standard model. It was immediately identifiable by the absence of the roof-mounted heating pod. London Country took 100 in 1978-79 and was the biggest user of the type.** Stewart J Brown

Left **The Leyland EA light truck chassis was occasionally bodied as a bus or coach. Most EA passenger vehicles were bodied in Ireland by Asco and were bought by independents, but a few found their way into major fleets, including NBC subsidiaries Alder Valley and Western Welsh. The latter took four in 1977 for services in the Cowbridge area, where this pair are seen after the creation of the new National Welsh company in 1978.** Stewart J Brown

A new approach to route planning was being explored by NBC in the middle of the decade. It started off as the Viable Network Project in 1976 – with its implications of routes which were unviable not being part of the network – and then became the rather less threatening Market Analysis Project. MAP saw whole route networks being examined and recast from 1977 onwards, often with local marketing names such as Reddibus in Redditch. MAP would later be adopted – as ScotMAP – by SBG.

Two PTEs had minor changes of identity towards the end of the decade. West Yorkshire abandoned its four district names from 1977 and traded simply as MetroBus. The livery remained Verona Green and Buttermilk, but was applied in a different style. In 1979 Greater Glasgow dropped its GG logo, replacing it with the fleetname Trans-Clyde. The livery remained unchanged. The West Yorkshire PTE and NBC had in 1978 jointly set up the West Yorkshire Metro-National Transport Company to improve service planning and co-ordination.

London Transport had embraced overall advertising with some enthusiasm at the start of the decade and had then become disenchanted with the concept, with the last overall advertising buses reverting to fleet livery in 1976. Variations on this theme appeared towards the end of the decade. First, in 1977, 25 Routemasters were repainted silver for the 25th anniversary of the coronation of Queen Elizabeth. Each was sponsored by a different advertiser and the buses were even given temporary SRM fleet numbers which presumably helped to ensure that the garage operations departments allocated them to the correct routes. The success of this led to a similar exercise in 1979 to mark the 150th anniversary of London's first bus service, with 12 Routemasters being repainted in Shillibeer livery – George Shillibeer having been the man who started it all back in 1829. The last Fleetline, DM2646, was also painted in this livery. It was sponsored by Leyland Vehicles who did not want their name on an obsolete Routemaster. That the Fleetlines were earmarked for relatively early withdrawal was presumably an irony which Leyland could live with.

A smart red and yellow livery was adopted for a fleet of 15 Routemasters allocated to a West End Shoplinker service, which for a time displayed 30p as its route number – this was in fact the rather high flat fare. The service ran in the summer of 1979.

Unusual additions to the London Transport fleet in 1978 were seven ex-Bournemouth Fleetlines with convertible open-top Weymann bodies. These replaced Obsolete Fleet's open-top BMMO D9s on the Round London Sightseeing Tour.

Above **Silver buses appeared in most British cities in 1977, to mark the Queen's Silver Jubilee. London Transport ran 25 silver-liveried Routemasters, each sponsored by an advertiser. A Woolworth-supported Routemaster is seen in Trafalgar Square in April 1977, soon after entering service in its promotional livery.** Stewart J Brown

Right **The Shoplinker was a short-lived service operated by London Transport and aimed at visitors wanting to travel round the main West End shopping area. It was run by a fleet of attractively-liveried Routemasters.** Stewart J Brown

Above **By the end of the 1970s a few Metrobuses had been delivered to operators outside London. Each of the PTEs ordered trial batches, including Merseyside which took five.** Stewart J Brown

Below **The Dennis Dominator was launched in 1977 and the vast majority of Dominators would be bodied as double-deckers. However in the early years of Dominator production there was some interest in it as a single-decker among municipal fleets. These included Darlington which had 18 with dual-door Marshall Camair 80 bodywork.** Stewart J Brown

New bus models had been appearing as the decade progressed. The Ailsa and the MCW Metropolitan had been launched in 1973. The Metropolitan only lasted until 1978 – high fuel consumption didn't endear it to many fleets, and the onset of severe body corrosion saw most Metropolitans being withdrawn after just seven years in service – seven years marking the expiry of the initial Certificate of Fitness, a time when major overhaul work was scheduled for most bus types. The Ailsa had been designed to meet the needs of the Scottish Bus Group, and it was in Scotland that it proved most popular, selling not just to SBG but to Tayside and Strathclyde too. It was still in production when the 1970s drew to a close.

MCW's Metropolitan replacement, the Metrobus, was announced in 1978. By the end of 1979 there were small numbers of Metrobuses in service with Greater Glasgow, Greater Manchester, London Transport, Merseyside, Midland Scottish, Tyne & Wear and West Midlands. The three Metrobuses operated by Midland Scottish had Alexander bodies of a unique design.

As the first Metrobuses entered service in London in 1978, so, too did the last of the 2,646 DMS-type Fleetlines, making LT the world's biggest Daimler operator. Withdrawal of the DMSs started in 1979 – the same year as the last RTs were taken out of service. The DMSs were eight years old; the RTs were 25. In an industry where a 15 year vehicle life was the norm both of LT's extremes point to an organisation that was not wholly in touch with reality.

The longest-lived of the new 1970s models was the Dennis Dominator, launched in 1977. The first went to the South Yorkshire PTE, which was to standardise on the type. Another early user was Leicester City Transport. At the end of 1979 there were also Dominators in service with A1 of Ardrossan, Blackburn, Cardiff, Central Scottish, East Staffordshire, Hyndburn, PMT, and, in single-deck guise, with Barrow, Darlington, Hartlepool and Merthyr Tydfil. Most 1970s Dominators had East Lancs bodies (a connection which helped Dennis win Lancashire municipal orders from under Leyland's nose) but two of Leicester's early Dominators had the first double-deck bodies to be built by Marshall. Alexander built five-bay bodies on one Dominator each for Central Scottish and PMT; when series production began of Alexander-bodied Dominators in 1980 they would have the all-new four-bay R-type body. The Dominator featured a Gardner engine and a Voith gearbox which was an untried combination. To put this drivetrain to the test, Dennis installed it in a 1959 Roe-bodied Daimler CVG6LX/30 purchased from the West Yorkshire PTE. It was demonstrated to a number of major operators in 1976-77.

Having replaced all of its home-market rear-engined single-deckers with the National, Leyland planned to do the same trick with its

Above **Production of the Fleetline, now badged as a Leyland, was being wound down at the end of the 1970s. Between 1976 and 1980 Thamesdown Transport bought 35 Fleetlines, all with Gardner engines and full-height ECW bodies.** Stewart J Brown

Below **There was a brief flurry of interest in articulated buses towards the end of the 1970s. One operator, the South Yorkshire PTE, took the plunge and ordered ten – five each from MAN and Leyland. The German-built MANs were the first to arrive in 1978-79 and, as well as running in Sheffield, were demonstrated to a number of other operators. This, the first one, is working a car park shuttle service at the new National Exhibition Centre in Birmingham in the autumn of 1978.** Royston Morgan

Willowbrook's importance as a double-deck builder was on the wane. Its last big contracts for operation in Britain came from NBC in the late 1970s, with angular bodies on Bristol VRTs for East Kent and, as seen here in Sunderland, Northern General. Double-deck body manufacture by Willowbrook petered out in the early 1980s. Stewart J Brown

double-deck range which comprised the Leyland Atlantean, Daimler Fleetline and Bristol VRT. A prototype of an advanced new integral double-decker to be built by Park Royal, the B15, was in trial service with London Transport from 1976. The B15 was not the bus the market wanted to buy (nor as it transpired the one that the workers at Leyland's Park Royal factory wanted to build) and it found few buyers. In 1979 there were Titans running for Greater Manchester, London Transport, Reading Transport and West Midlands. Orders had been placed by other operators, but were not to be fulfilled. The real replacement for the old Leyland double-deck models would have to wait until 1980 and the appearance of the Olympian. An updated National, the National 2, was announced in 1979 and featured a Leyland 680 engine in place of the unpopular 500. It also had a front-mounted radiator which increased the overall length by 0.3m to 10.6m or 11.6m. One prototype National 2 had been built with a 680 engine and a rear-mounted radiator – and was thus virtually indistinguishable from the original model. It found a home with Ribble.

Foden linked up with Northern Counties to produce the Foden-NC, but few were sold. Another flop was the rear-engined Bedford JJL minibus – a great concept, but too expensive and ahead of its time. Only prototypes were built, styled by General Motors (Bedford's parent) and bodied by Marshall. AEC disappeared in 1979, with the closure of its Southall factory bringing an end to Reliance production. Seddon was hanging on with its Pennine VII, but had only one high-volume customer, SBG. Scania, no longer tied to MCW in the Metropolitan, decided to begin selling its rear-engined N-series underframe as the basis of a double-deck bus. This would not appear until 1982.

The South Yorkshire PTE took an interest in articulated buses. A left-hand-drive Danish-built Leyland-DAB was tried in service in Sheffield in 1977 and produced an order for 10 artics – five from German manufacturer MAN and five from Leyland-DAB. The Leylands were bodied in Workington, using extensively modified National structures. The first of the artics arrived in 1979 and were put to use on a Sheffield city centre service. At the other end of the scale, there were still few minibuses around and most of these were van conversions. Alexander had launched its S-type integral, which used Ford A-series running units, but it found few customers. Reeve Burgess offered the stylish coachbuilt Reebur 17 on Ford Transit and Bedford CF chassis. Most of these were sold as coaches rather than buses.

The market for new buses and coaches had been boosted in the 1970s by the government's new bus grant. It peaked in 1979 when a total of 5,591 new psvs were registered in the UK. The top-selling heavy-duty models in 1979, based on registration figures published by the Society of Motor Manufacturers and Traders, were:

Leyland National	855
Leyland Leopard	756
Leyland Atlantean	607
Bristol VRT	421
Leyland Fleetline	318
MCW Metrobus	226

In addition Bedford sold 870 chassis (mainly Y-series) and Ford sold 592 R-series. These were primarily for coach use as, indeed, were the Leyland Leopards. No other model achieved over 200 sales.

In May 1979 there was a change of government. Possibly the most significant change since the war. The Conservatives, led by Margaret Thatcher, were now in power. The bus industry – both operators and manufacturers – were heading for greater change in the 1980s than any of them could possibly have realised.

For the British bus industry 1979 didn't just mark the end of a decade. It was the end of an era.